Library of Congress Catalog Card Number 60-14970

Second Printing 1962

HISTORY OF LIFE SCIENCE

Outlines and References

ELDON J. GARDNER

Utah State University
Logan, Utah

BURGESS PUBLISHING COMPANY
426 South 6th Street, Minneapolis 15, Minn.

PREFACE

Biology students are expected to "pick up" a background in the history of biology and to read the classics in the literature, but they are often left without much help or direction. These outlines are intended to present in a logical sequence the main landmarks and themes in the history of biology to orient and direct the student in his reading. They are not intended to stand alone or to serve as a text, but rather as a guide and stimulus to further reading. Some "classical materials" not readily available for library reading are summarized in some detail, but for the most part the outlines are brief and designed to establish continuity. General references covering the entire subject are given in the front of the outlines, and those for more restricted topics are given at the end of the appropriate chapter.

History is oversimplified when only key figures are chosen to represent periods or movements in which many contributors have participated. Much space would be required to review the history of biology in complete detail, and it is better for each original author to tell his own story. The outlines are intended to provide only the pillars and superstructure. Students are encouraged to read extensively and fill in the framework.

Chronological order is followed from the early period to the Renaissance (Chapters 1-5). Developments of special tools and biological concepts are considered in the center section (Chapters 6-10), and the final chapters (11-17) are devoted to the development of the main themes or areas of modern biology.

I am deeply indebted to my colleagues and students for their assistance and suggestions as this project has progressed. Professor S. George Ellsworth of our history department has read several chapters and suggested improvements. For his encouragement, as well as for his assistance, I am deeply grateful. My colleague, D. M. Hammond, has helped in many ways. B. Austin Haws and D. W. Davis have reviewed the chapter on entomology. Mrs. Gladys Harrison edited the manuscript. Portraits of biologists were drawn by Everett Thorpe, whereas maps and diagrams were prepared by Carol Byington. Several people assisted with the typing of the original manuscript and the revisions. Many students have made valuable comments as we have discussed various aspects of the outlines. In thanking students and colleagues, I should like to request that they continue to suggest improvements.

Eldon J. Gardner

CONTENTS

General References on
History and Philosophy of Science

Arber, A. *The Mind and the Eye.* Cambridge: The Univ. Press, 1954.

Beveridge, W. I. B. *The Art of Scientific Investigation.* New York:
W. W. Norton, Inc., 1950.

Boynton, H. ed. *Beginnings of Modern Science.* New York: Classics Club, 1948.

Brown, G. B. *Science, Its Method and Its Philosophy.* London: George Allen and
Unwin, Ltd, 1950.

Butterfield, H. *The Origins of Modern Science.* London: G. Bell, 1957.

Conant, J. B. *On Understanding Science.* New Haven: Yale Univ. Press, 1947.

Conant, J. B. *Science and Common Sense.* New Haven: Yale Univ. Press, 1951.

Dampier, W. C. *A History of Science.* New York: The Macmillan Co., 1944.

Feigl, H. and M. Brodbeck, eds. *Readings in the Philosophy of Science.* New York:
Appleton, Century, Crofts, Inc., 1953.

Forbes, R. J. *Man the Maker.* New York: Henry Schuman, 1950.

Frank, P. *Philosophy of Science.* Englewood Cliffs, N. J.: Prentice Hall, Inc.,
1957.

Hall, A. R. *The Scientific Revolution.* London: Beacon Books, 1956.

Hildebrand, J. H. *Science in the Making.* New York: Columbia Univ. Press, 1957.

Ingle, D. W. *Principles of Research in Biology and Medicine.* Philadelphia:
J. B. Lippincott, 1958.

Koyré, A. *From the Closed World to the Infinite Universe.* Baltimore: Johns
Hopkins Press, 1957.

Libby, W. *Introduction to the History of Science.* Boston: Houghton Mifflin Co.,
1917.

Mees, C. E. K. and J. R. Baker. *The Path of Science.* New York: John Wiley and
Sons, 1946.

Moulton, F. R. and J. J. Schifferes, eds. *The Autobiography of Science.*
Garden City, N. Y.: Doubleday, Doran and Co., 1945.

Needham, J. *Background to Modern Science.* New York: The Macmillan Co., 1938.

Oppenheimer, J. R. *Science and the Common Undertaking.* New York:
Simon and Schuster, 1954.

Pledge, H. T. *Science Since 1500.* New York: Philosophical Library, 1939.

Sarton, G. *A Guide to the History of Science.* Waltham, Mass.: Chronica Botanica Co., 1952.

Sarton, G. *An Introduction to the History of Science.* 5 Vol. Baltimore: Williams and Wilkins, 1927-48.

Sarton, G. *History of Science and the New Humanism.* Cambridge: Harvard Univ. Press, 1937

Singer, C. *A Short History of Science in the Nineteenth Century.* Oxford: Clarendon Press, 1941.

Singer, C., E. J. Holmyard and A. R. Hall, eds. *A History of Technology.* 5 Vol. Oxford: Clarendon Press, 1954-58.

Smith, V. E. *The General Science of Nature.* Milwaukee: The Bruce Publ. Co., 1958.

Taylor, F. S. *A Short History of Science and Scientific Thought.* New York: W. W. Norton and Co., 1949.

Thomas, D. L. and H. Thomas. *Living Biographies of Great Scientists.* New York: Garden City Books, 1959.

Whetham, W. C. *Cambridge Readings in the Literature of Science.* Cambridge: The Univ. Press, 1924.

Wiener, P. P. and A. Noland. *Roots of Scientific Thought.* New York: Basic Books, 1957.

Wightman, W. P. D. *The Growth of Scientific Ideas.* New Haven: Yale Univ. Press, 1953.

Wilson, G. *Great Men of Science.* Garden City, N. Y.: Garden City Publ. Co., 1937.

Wolf, A. *A History of Science, Technology and Philosophy in the 16th, 17th and 18th Centuries.* 2 Vol. New York: The Macmillan Co., 1935-1939.

Woodruff, L. L. *The Development of the Sciences.* New Haven: Yale Univ. Press, 1923.

General References on History of Biology

Andrews, R. C. *Under a Lucky Star.* New York: The Viking Press, 1943.

Barbour, T. *Naturalist at Large.* Boston: Little, Brown and Co., 1943.

Beebe, C. W. *The Book of Naturalists.* New York: A. A. Knopf, 1945.

Dawes, B. *A Hundred Years of Biology* London: Gerald Duckworth and Co., 1953.

Ditmars, R. L. *The Making of a Scientist.* New York: The Macmillan Co., 1937.

Drachman, J. M. *Studies in the Literature of Natural Science.* New York: The Macmillan Co., 1930.

Gabriel, M. L. and S. Fogel. *Great Experiments in Biology.* Englewood Cliffs, N. J.: Prentice-Hall, Inc., 1955.

Locy, W. A. *The Main Currents of Zoology.* New York: Henry Holt and Co., 1918.

Locy, W. A. *Biology and Its Makers.* New York: Henry Holt and Co., 1910.

Meisel, M. *Bibliography of American Natural History.* Brookland, N. Y.: Premier Publ. Co., 1924-29.

Miall, L. C. *The Early Naturalists.* London: Macmillan and Co., Ltd., 1912.

Needham, J. *A History of Embryology.* Cambridge: The Univ. Press, 1934.

Nordenskiöld, E. *The History of Biology, A Survey.* New York: A. A. Knopf, 1928.

Peattie, D. C. *Green Laurels, the Lives of the Great Naturalists.* New York: Simon and Schuster, 1936.

Peattie, D. C. *The Road of a Naturalist.* Boston: Houghton Mifflin Co., 1941.

Raven, C. E. *English Naturalists from Neckham to Ray.* Cambridge: The Univ. Press, 1947.

Singer, C. *A History of Biology.* New York: Abelard-Schuman, 1959.

Snyder, E. E. *Biology in the Making.* New York: McGraw-Hill, 1940.

Suner, A. P. *Classics of Biology.* New York: Philosophical Library, 1955.

Wood, L. N. *Raymond L. Ditmars.* New York: J. Messner, Inc., 1944.

Woodruff, L. L. *The Development of Biology in "The Development of the Sciences".* New Haven: Yale Univ. Press, 1923.

References on the History of Medicine

Ackernecht, E. H. *A Short History of Medicine*. New York: The Ronald Press, 1955.

Baker, R. *Dr. Morton, Pioneer in the Use of Ether*. New York: Julian Messner, Inc., 1946.

Bettmann, O. L. *A Pictorial History of Medicine*. Springfield, Ill.: Charles C. Thomas Publ., 1956.

Calder, R. *Medicine and Man*. New York: Mentor Books, 1958.

Castiglioni, A. *A History of Medicine*. 2nd Ed. New York: A. A. Knopf, 1947.

Clendening, L. *Source Book of Medical History*. New York: Paul B. Hoeber, Inc., 1942.

Cumston, C. *Introduction to the History of Medicine*. New York: A. A. Knopf, 1926.

Elgood, C. *A Medical History of Persia*. Cambridge: The Univ. Press, 1951.

Garland, J. *The Story of Medicine*. Boston: Houghton Mifflin Co., 1949.

Garrison, F. H. *An Introduction to the History of Medicine*. Philadelphia: W. B. Saunders Co., 1929.

Gordon, B. L. *The Romance of Medicine*. Philadelphia: F. A. Davis Co., 1945.

Graham, H. *The Story of Surgery*. New York: Doubleday, Doran and Co., 1939.

Guthrie, D. *A History of Medicine*. London: J. B. Lippincott Co., 1946.

Haggard, H. W. *Devils, Drugs, and Doctors*. New York: Harper and Brothers, 1929.

Haggard, H. W. *The Doctor in History*. New Haven: Yale Univ. Press, 1934.

Hillier, L. *Surgery Through the Ages*. New York: Books, Inc., 1944.

Keys, T. *The History of Surgical Anesthesia*. New York: Henry Schuman, 1945.

Robinson, V. *The Story of Medicine*. New York: Tudor Publ. Co., 1931.

Selwyn-Brown, A. *The Physician Throughout the Ages*. New York: Capehart-Brown Co., 1928.

Sigerest, H. E. *A History of Medicine*. New York: Oxford Univ. Press, 1951.

Wilder, A. *History of Medicine*. New Sharon, Maine: New England Electric Publ. Co., 1936.

New York Academy of Medicine. *Landmarks in Medicine*. New York: Appleton Century, 1939.

It is difficult to obtain an understanding of biological principles held among people who lived in the remote past, nevertheless, we will begin with the earliest possible period. Because of the difficulty of obtaining facts and formulating realistic interpretations, our ideas of early man's accomplishments are usually meager and uncertain. Some biological understanding was prevalent, however, and significant advancements were made before man's account of what had already happened was made in writing.

Early man had appreciation and respect for the laws of nature. Through trial and error and good management, he was able to apply some of these laws for his own advantage. Early man learned to use fire, to make tools from stone and later from bronze, to improvise eating and cooking utensils and pottery for his own needs. Of greater interest to the biologist, he learned to domesticate virtually all of the animals and plants that have proved capable of domestication.

During long periods of time, early man was interested in retaining good health and prolonging his life. This interest led him to a practice of medicine which sometimes was simple and realistic but often became complex and mystical. Medicine, founded on empirical knowledge and experience, was the central theme of early biology. It has always been important because men and animals even before the beginnings of written history have had parasites and disease. Causes of life and death were mysteries, and to a large extent they remain mysterious at the present time.

Sources of information for early biology are: mummies, art work, and present-day primitive peoples who are presumed to have much in common with ancient primitive peoples. The evidence suggests that early man felt the necessity of being friendly with the destructive powers of nature. He became familiar with some plants and animals because they were food and others because of their physiological and medical importance. Plant lore thus became an important aspect of medicine and biology and many plants became known for their "virtues." Some remedies were found through trial and error to be worthless, others were found to have values and were retained, some even until the present time.

In spite of the limitations of the medicine man, he must have been quite

successful. He had a few effective drugs, made use of physical therapy, that is, massage, heating and bathing, and employed psychological factors. The ailments with which the medicine men had to deal were different from those of a modern practitioner. Epidemic diseases, such as smallpox, typhoid, cholera, measles, syphilis, and diphtheria were not common until mankind began to live in groups and to develop a complex community life. Contagious diseases were known before the time of Christ and received widespread attention in the 15th century. Degenerative diseases such as cancer and heart disease were rare because life expectancy was low. Most people who reached maturity died from

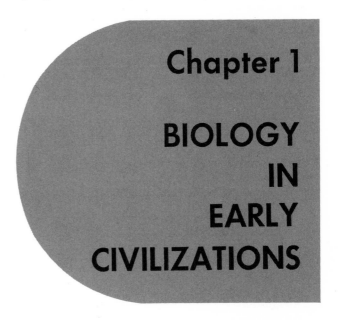

Chapter 1
BIOLOGY IN EARLY CIVILIZATIONS

other causes such as accidents and warfare before they reached the "heart disease age" or the "cancer age." High infant mortality contributed to making the average age of the population low. Early medicine men were mainly concerned with digestive disturbances, respiratory diseases, rheumatic disease, skin diseases, and irregularities at child birth. They were equipped to deal with most of these diseases and conditions.

The more rational and realistic people were always attempting to find natural causes and treatments for disease and they ran into the difficulty of confusing a sequence of events with cause and effect. One point missed by some primitive peoples and only recently fully appreciated was the fact that people usually tend to get well even without any special treatment. If there were no doctors, nurses, hospitals, or drugs, perhaps 4 out of 5 of all the ill people would eventually recover from their illnesses. Although the healing processes may be slow, nature tends toward health rather than illness. When it happened that some treatment was applied during nature's course of improvements in health it was natural for primitive people, not understanding cause and effect, to attribute cures to wrong causes or to ineffective treatments. Many weird practices that were believed to have health-giving values became established and some persist at the present time.

Reproduction has always stimulated interest. The oldest recorded idea of procreation was spontaneous generation, that is, plants and animals were believed to arise from mud in the bottom of a pool or from various other materials rather than from reproduction of parent organisms. Demonstrations could easily be made to show that worms and flies developed in manure piles and other favorable places, frogs and insects became prevalent at certain times of the year for no known reason except that conditions were favorable and mice accumulated in places where dirty rags and food materials were available. An easy explanation was spontaneous generation. It was a remarkable achievement for early man to apply cause and effect to human birth. Among primitive peoples sex was understood and usually surrounded with beauty, the menstrual cycle was likened to the cycle of the moon and rituals at puberty showed logic and honesty of thinking. Festivals with some biological significance were conducted to celebrate important events such as the rebirth of spring. The most famous of the pagan festivals was taken over by the Christians as Easter.

Biology Known and Applied by Early Chinese

A high civilization was developed both in Eastern and Western Asia in an early period of history. In Eastern Asia, independent developments of biology occurred among the Chinese and Hindus. These were not related to those of the Babylonians, Egyptians, and later the Greeks in the West, and they made little contribution to present day biology. In contrast, the developments in Western Asia made valuable beginnings in western culture.

Early developments in China that bear biological implications were sporadic and utilitarian and for the most part have little in common with the modern science of biology. There were, however, some applications of biological principles which are worthy of note. Medical literature developed early and was extensive. As early as 3000 B. C., medicinal values were ascribed to several different plants. Beginnings in medicine were attributed to three legendary emperors: Fu-Hsi (2900 B. C.), Shen-Nung (2700 B. C.), and Huang-Ti (2600 B. C.). Medicinal values of such plants as rhubarb, ginseng, opium, and pomegranate root were recognized and as time went on the pharmacopodia became extensive including several hundred drugs.

Agar-agar, the vegetable solidifying matter derived from marine algae, was used by the Chinese for food and medicine and has since become a laboratory substance of considerable importance in microbiology. The narcotic, marihuana, from the hemp plant Cannabis indica, was used by the Chinese as an anesthetic. Acupuncture, accomplished by inserting a needle into the flesh near a sprain or dislocation to relieve pressure and pain, was practiced by the early Chinese. The treatment may have had value in some cases where fluid had accumulated near the injury and could be removed by the puncture. Early Chinese had no knowledge of the structure of the human body, mainly because of their horror of death and dead things. To them the bones of the body represented a perfect number; no one knew how many there were and no one cared.

Among the lasting contributions, the Chinese used ashes of sponges to relieve goiter and opium from poppy juice to relieve pain. Ephedrine was used for treating asthma, a fact recorded in the Book of Herbs, attributed to the Emperor Shen-Nung about 2700 B. C. The plant called ma huang (Ephedra vulgaris) by the Chinese was listed for its properties as a diaphoretic and circulatory stimulant. In 1887 A. D., Nagai isolated the alkaloid ephedrine from this plant and the particular therapeutic value attributed to the plant by the Chinese was recognized in 1923 when Chen found that an extract from the ma huang plant increases blood pressure, producing an effect similar to that of adrenalin.

Another unique practice among Chinese medical men was a burning process on an inflamed or injured part of the skin. A tuft of dried leaves, called a moxa, composed from the plant <u>Artemisia</u> <u>vulgaris</u>, a relative to common sagebrush, was placed on the skin of the injured person and ignited. Heat from this particular kind of fire was supposed to have healing power for sprains, bruises, rheumatism, and other local conditions which required medical attention.

Much of what is known of the biological and medical knowledge available to the Chinese was included in the treatise <u>Neiching</u>, attributed to the Royal Huang Ti or Shen-Nung. One of these men supposedly wrote the treatise some 4500 years ago on strips of bamboo. Some medical procedures described have survived to the present day with little or no alteration. In the descriptive part of this treatise the seat of thought was located in the spleen while the center for will power was placed in the kidneys.

Another development of biological interest and of great economic significance in China was the silk industry. Because of the ability of the caterpillar of <u>Bombyx</u> <u>mori</u> to produce silk, it is the most important beneficial insect in history. The origin of silk for man's use is unknown, but the Chinese Empress, See Ling, was using silk in the year 2697 B. C. Paintings, wood work, and embroidery dating back to early periods of Chinese history show that these people have had a great appreciation for insects and particularly the silkworm. This worm cannot live without man at the present time. It must have been developed purposely by the early Chinese for its product, silk that replaced grass and leaves as a material for clothing.

For centuries the silk industry was a highly prized monopoly in China. The death penalty could be exacted for giving worms or information about their care to outsiders. Silkworms made their first appearance in the Mediterranean region in about 300 B. C. In about 200 A. D. silkworms were smuggled into Japan. By 400 A. D., when transportation by ships was well established, Ceylon became the center of silk distribution in the world. Silk was important in the Roman Empire particularly for women's and church-men's clothing. At this time silk was literally worth its weight in gold.

Other biological applications in ancient China were associated with food getting. Wild plants and animals native to China were taken for food and some were domesticated and made to serve man on a more permanent basis. The saliva of

birds became a delicacy. Nests of the Asian swift which were made of mud cemented with saliva were boiled and made into a choice dish. Sea foods such as fish, snails, crabs, cuttlefish, and sea cucumbers were obtained from China's long sea shore and used abundantly. The Chinese made good use of the soil and began early their intensive cultivation of tea, oranges, soybeans, rice, barley, and bamboo, for practical purposes. Ornamental gardens where the morning glory, chrysanthemum, and rose were grown and improved became closely associated with botanical gardens in which plants with medicinal values were raised.

Hindus Practiced Surgery

The Hindus in India developed the physical sciences and mathematics and accomplished little in biology except in the fields of anatomy and surgery. At the time of Christ and perhaps long before the Hindus were practicing plastic surgery. Unlike the Chinese they developed little plant lore but in the field of surgery, the Hindus attained a skill far ahead of their time.

Mesopotamians' Contribution to Biology

Two cultures developed in western Asia during an early period of history.

Fig. 1-1. Map of Mesopotamia between the Tigris and Euphrates rivers

One was located in the valley of the Nile River and gave rise to the Egyptian civilization and the other was between the Tigris and Euphrates river systems (Fig. 1-1), and became known as the Mesopotamian culture because of its location (between two rivers). The Egyptian and Mesopotamian civilizations were parallel in many ways, but the Mesopotamian developed to a high level at an earlier period than the Egyptian. Both left some evidence of biological knowledge and interest in biological subjects. In Mesopotamia an extensive knowledge of zoology was developed. This was especially true of one highly civilized group, the Babylonians, who occupied the Euphrates valley. They gained experience in anatomy by preparing sacrifices to the Babylonian gods. The liver was examined carefully and substantial knowledge concerning other aspects of internal anatomy was also obtained. Observations gained in preparing sacrifices carried over to medicine and are recorded in medical texts from the Babylonian period which are now available for examination and comparison.

Babylonians made contributions in the physical sciences as well as in the biological. They observed the heavenly bodies and developed their lore around the movements of those bodies. Dates for planting crops were interpreted from the stars and mystical explanations were derived to account for the relations between the movements of the stars and seasons of the year. The seven days of the week were named after the seven planets that were observed to change positions regularly. Some of the names, such as Sunday, Monday, (moon day), Saturday (Saturn's day), still persist. The Babylonians also developed practical methods of irrigation some of which gave rise to modern practices. Babylonians had little plant lore. They used plants for food but did not attempt to learn much about them.

A complex civilization was reflected by an involved code of laws relating to the practice of a physician. "An eye for an eye" principle was the basis for the code. If a physician injured a patient in the course of his treatment, the physician was punished by having the same injury inflicted upon him. If, for example, a patient should lose his eyesight, while under treatment, the physician should have his eyes removed as a punishment. Modern laws and precedents concerning the legal aspects of malpractice may be traced back to the Babylonians, but they

are usually tempered by a better understanding of the physician's problem.

Sewer systems and drains were built by the Babylonians. These people also developed water storage facilities and practical methods of sanitation, which enabled them to make good progress in community hygiene.

Their method of writing, as well as other aspects of their civilization, was extremely complex. Some contributions carried over to the Greeks, but most of the intricacies of the Babylonian culture remain to be unraveled at the present time.

Egyptians' Development in Medicine

In the early Egyptian civilization (Fig. 1-2) many things were accomplished in biology, particularly in the field of medicine. Evidence concerning Egyptian culture is fragmentary. Many questions have been left to be speculated upon by members of later generations. Early Egyptians learned to write; they took moist earth from the Nile river, dried it in the sun, and made bricks; they fashioned pottery, learned to bake bread, and brew beer; they made glass, prepared leather, and domesticated plants and animals. Early dwellers in the Nile valley developed agriculture and in the process made use of slave labor.

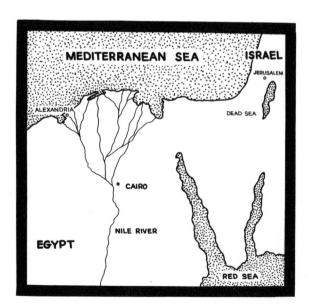

Fig. 1-2. Map of the Nile River Valley, the seat of the early Egyptian civilization

Records of these accomplishments have been difficult to piece together. When Herodotus the Greek historian explored the Nile River, the evidence of the earlier civilization had already been destroyed or carried to the sea. Even the documents which were cast in bronze do not tell much of the story, but they give evidence of an important development in the refining and use of metal. This was a major step forward because much may be done with bronze that is impossible with flint or limestone. In early Egypt as well as in Mesopotamia the Age of Stone was followed by the Age of Bronze.

By the time the Egyptians began to write about medicine, the art was so old that the writers did not attempt to describe the beginnings but attributed its origin to the gods. The separation between medicine and magic was impossible, for all the physicians were priests, and gods were ever present. Early history of medicine is centered around one personage, Imhotep. Presumably, Imhotep lived in the period about 3000 B. C. and was a physician to one of the pharaohs. Although there is much tangible information about him, it is difficult to be sure whether he was an actual man or a myth. Whatever the beginning might have been, he has since become glorified and finally deified. Legends about Imhotep have persisted and are reflected throughout the medical history of Egypt.

During the period from 3000 to 1000 B. C. Imhotep was given divine powers and invoked in prayers for the sick. By 1000 B. C. he had become a god; temples were erected to him and people came from great distances to be cured from their illnesses and protected from their fears. Imhotep and his emissaries were supposed to appear to people in temples to give cures for illness. Ill people were said to have gone to sleep in a temple and awakened well and free from their symptoms. The influence of Imhotep persisted for many centuries. During a period of widespread disease in Rome as late as 273 B. C. a special emissary was sent to the temple of Imhotep to invoke assistance for the stricken Romans.

Civilization among the Egyptians was complex and it continued at a high level from about 3000 to about 1000 B. C., a period of some 2000 years. Earliest tangible records came from the pyramids and were dated about 2600 B. C. Most of the biological and medical information now available concerning the early Egyptians has come from a single source, the Ebers papyrus, entitled the Therapeutic Papyrus of Thebes. This is the oldest and most important biological document of ancient Egypt now known. It was written in hieroglyphics on a strip of papyrus about a foot wide and 65 feet long with a total of 2289 lines. An Arab was said to have found it in a tomb in the Nile River Valley some time before 1873. It came into the hands of George Ebers, an Egyptologist, in 1873 and is now preserved in a library at Leipzig, Germany. Ebers himself translated most of the document, but it was not until 1937 that some of the more obscure symbols were finally deciphered by scholars who followed Ebers. Even now there are some parts that have not been satisfactorily translated. This document was probably written about 1550 B. C. and was apparently a copy of an older manuscript prepared about a thousand years earlier.

Emphasis is on supernatural aspects of medicine, but there are descriptions of diseases and treatments which reflect critical observation. Diseases of the viscera and organs of special sense were given particular attention. Sections on tumors and obstructions, and those on diseases of the ear and eye, from which the Egyptians suffered extensively, were given considerable space. Many ailments, from pains in the head to sore toes, were discussed; one chapter was devoted to diseases of children; another to diseases of women. Chapter twenty contains "remedies for burns and suppurative sores, gangrene, and wallops from flogging." More than seventy cosmetic prescriptions were included for: sunburn, freckles, wrinkles, and other facial blemishes. Perfumes for women were recommended so their clothing and breath would be pleasant. For men, there were remedies for the care and preservation of the hair. Methods for overcoming baldness and for preventing the hair from turning gray were included. There were also directions for inducing hair to grow on scars on the scalp.

One passage compares the pulsation of blood circulation with the inundations of the Nile, that were known to come and go. An early Egyptian conception of the pulse is expressed in the following quotation: "There is in the heart a vessel leading to every member of the body. If the physician places his finger on the head, neck, arms, feet, or body, everywhere he will find the heart, for the heart leads to every member, and speaks in the vessels of every member."

Some seven hundred remedies were included in the Therapeutic Papyrus including opium, castor oil, copper salts, squill, acacia, calamus, saffron, gentian, pomegranate, and olive oil. Although the Egyptians used these drugs effectively, they did not know their specific values. Other agents such as fly-specks scraped from a wall and moisture from a pig's ear were sometimes recommended as highly as those which have gained a place in modern medicine. Common present-day parasites were evidently prevalent in ancient Egypt. The large intestinal worm, Ascaris, received detailed consideration. Egyptians included in their materia medica many miscellaneous remedies, whether they had any special use or not. A few of the drugs which they apparently stumbled onto have lasted as long as the pyramids.

Another document, more recently added to the body of information about the Egyptians, has been called the Edwin Smith papyrus or Surgical Papyrus. Cases, mostly surgical, were enumerated in the papyrus, some in great detail and some with a workable checklist of questions such as: "Can he lift his arm?" "Does he shiver?" "Does he bleed from the nose?" "Can he open his mouth?" "How strong is his pulse?" Injuries to the different parts of the body were discussed separately. The eyebrow, nose, cheek, ear, jaw, temple, and forehead were included under the general headings of head and skull. Directions for bandaging wounds, restoring fractures, and burning out tumors were carefully enumerated. Although these writings have given way in many places to magic and superstition, they contain much applied human biology.

The Surgical Papyrus as now known is more than fifteen feet long but originally it must have been considerably longer. Most of the writing is in black ink with important words and subsections written in red (i. e. rubrics). In one column the scribe omitted a phrase, and inserted the missing words in the upper margin, marking the place in the text with a little red cross. In some papyri, a cross was placed not only where the missing words occurred, but by the words themselves (i. e. an asterisk). The first part of the Surgical Papyrus describes forty-eight cases including: ten cases of wounds of the head; seven, nose; ten, ear, lips, and jaw; six, neck and throat; five, collar bone and shoulders; nine, chest and breast; and one incomplete case of a spinal ailment. It is apparent that the papyrus was meant to be a complete Book on Surgery and External Medicine, beginning with injuries of the head and concluding with the feet. It ends, however, abruptly, at the bottom of the seventeenth column in the middle of a line.

Each case discussion begins with the name of the ailment, followed by the symptoms, diagnosis, prognosis, and treatment. In knife-cuts, sword-slashes, and battle-axe blows of the skull, the surgeon is instructed to probe the wound. The prognosis is favorable in contusion, doubtful in a penetrating gash, and unfavorable in fracture. Feeble pulse and fever are noted among the symptoms of severe cranial injuries. In fracture of the skull under the skin, the practitioner must elevate the depression outward. A cut in the forehead is treated by a linen bandage prepared by the embalmer and known as the "physicians' skin." Nasal secretions are to be cleared away by swabs consisting of two rolls of linen dipped in ointment and inserted in the nostrils. Fracture of the temporal bone produces deafness. In dislocations of the jaw the attendant is instructed to force the bones into place. According to the text, temperature develops from a knife wound of the gullet. If the patient with such a wound drinks water, it turns aside, issuing from the wound. Associated with dislocations of the vertebrae and the neck, there is loss of control of arms, legs, and excretory organs, and the physician can do nothing.

Egypt became the medical center of the ancient world. The Biblical statement, "And Moses was learned in all the wisdom of the Egyptians," indicates that the Egyptians influenced the origin of the Mosaic laws of health. The comment of Jeremiah, "Go up into Gilead and take balm, O virgin daughter of Egypt; in vain dost thou use many medicines; there is no healing for thee," shows that Egypt was noted for numerous remedies. Homer spoke of "Egypt teeming with drugs, the land where each is a physician skillful beyond all men." Herodotus described Egypt as the home of specialists: "Medicine is practiced among them on a plan of separation; each physician treats a single disorder, and no more; thus the country swarms with medical practitioners, some undertaking to cure diseases of the eye, others of the head, others again of the teeth, others of the intestines, and some those which are not local." Diodorus Siculus explained: "The whole manner of life in Egypt was so evenly ordered that it would appear as though it had been arranged according to the rules of health by a learned physician, rather than by a lawgiver. Cyrus of Persia sent for an Egyptian oculist to take care of his sick mother, and the body physician of Darius likewise came from the Nile.

The dependence of the early Egyptians on the weather and the floods of the Nile River greatly influenced their attitude toward science and life in general. Supernaturalism was associated with this dependence. There was little or no speculation such as that found among the Greeks in a later period. This may be due in part to the cumbersome language dependent on hieroglyphics or exact pictures to represent objects. The Egyptians made some attempt to figure out the reason for things. They had great fear of death and dead things and, although they were forced to do some dissection in preparation of mummies, they did no more than necessary. In spite of themselves they gained some knowledge of the viscera and other internal structures. Studies of mummies show evidence of diseases similar to those now present. Cancer and other common diseases were prevalent among the ancient Egyptians.

Hebrews' Contribution in Public Health

The Jewish people received much of their culture from contact with the Babylonians and Egyptians. Their contribution to biology was the recognition of infectious diseases. The laws of Moses include practical aspects of public health. Health of the group was preserved at the expense of the individual. The word "leprosy" as it is used in the Bible included skin eruptions and contagious diseases of various kinds. Lepers, considered unclean and to be avoided, were given little consideration or humane treatment. They were expelled from society and allowed to go their lonely way, without care or assistance; to protect the group from infection.

Evolution of Writing Media

While evaluating biological observations and concepts of primitive societies the means of communication among individuals has been referred to repeatedly. This factor had great influence on the cultural development of groups and has made possible the preservation of accomplishments for succeeding generations. Individuals and cultures living in the remote past with no means of communication, would be totally unknown to us if it were not for their preserved records. Man first learned to communicate his thoughts by signs and later by symbols. By making use of both signs and symbols together and the sound mechanism associated with the vocal cords he learned to speak. This was a great advantage, but man could communicate only as far as his voice would carry. He then devised sketches and symbols that could be set on stone or other physical material and thus he greatly increased his facility for exchanging and preserving observations and ideas.

When man began to make use of writing, his own skill and the material available for writing became limiting factors. Early Chinese wrote on strips of bamboo. This material was fragile and would not last for a long period of time unless special care was provided. It is likely that only a small proportion of the treatises written on such material were preserved long enough to be useful to later generations. Few, indeed, are available at the present time.

Babylonians and other Mesopotamians used blocks of clay and stones which were cumbersome and inflexible for their writing material. Usefulness of these materials was limited and only under special conditions were the records preserved for the enlightenment of succeeding generations.

Egyptians made a great step forward when they learned how to make papyrus. This is a crude paper-like material made from the pitch of a tall sedge, Cyperus papyrus, native to the Nile region. Many Egyptian manuscripts, written on papyrus have been discovered and translated. Those of Ebers and Edwin Smith provide virtually all that is known about early Egyptian biology and medicine. Papyrus was flexible and could be rolled up on a scroll for safekeeping. The Egyptians recorded their observations more extensively than the Mesopotamians partly because their writing medium was more usable.

The use of spoken and written language is one of the greatest accomplishments made by man which sets him apart from all other members of the animal kingdom. Facility in communication is perhaps the most important

8

single factor in the building up of a civilization. A limitation of the Babylonian civilization was the complex and cumbersome means of writing which required actual pictures to be drawn on clay blocks.

The Egyptians also used complex symbols in their hieroglyphics but they developed a much improved writing material, papyrus. Modern civilization is dependent on paper, printing, and the publication of facts and ideas.

REFERENCES

Breasted, J. H. *A History of Egypt.* New York: C. Scribner's Sons, 1909.

Breasted, J. H. *Translation of the Edwin Smith Surgical Papyrus.* Chicago: Univ. Chicago Press, 1930.

Breasted, J. H. *The Dawn of Conscience.* New York: C. Scribner's Sons, 1933.

Breasted, J. H. *Ancient Times.* 2nd Ed. Boston: Ginn and Co., 1944.

Brinton, C., J. B. Christopher and R. L. Wolff. *A History of Civilization.* Vol. 1, Englewood Cliffs, N. J.: Prentice-Hall, 1955.

Buck, A. H. *The Dawn of Modern Medicine.* New Haven: Yale Univ. Press, 1920.

Coonen, L. P. The Prehistoric Roots of Biology. *Sci. Monthly* 73: 154-165, 1951.

Coonen, L. P. Biology in Ancient Egypt. *The Biologist* 34:79-85, 1952.

Coonen, L. P. Herodotus on Biology. *Sci. Monthly* 76:63-70, 1953.

Coonen, L. P. Biology in Old China. *The Biologist* 36:3-12, 1954.

Coonen, L. P. Biology in Ancient Palestine. *The Biologist* 38:3-12, 1955.

Dawson, W. R. *The Beginnings, Egypt and Assyria.* New York: P. B. Hoeber, Inc., 1930.

Ebbels, B. *Translation of the Papyrus Ebers.* Copenhagen: Leven and Munksgaard, 1937.

Frankfort, H. *The Birth of Civilization in the Near East.* Bloomington: Indiana Univ. Press, 1951.

Frazer, J. G. *The Golden Bough* (12 vols.) Vol. 1, 2. London: Macmillan and Co., Ltd., 1926.

Glanville, S. R. K. ed., *The Legacy of Egypt.* Oxford: Clarendon Press, 1942.

Jastrow, M. *The Civilization of Babylonia and Assyria.* Philadelphia: J. B. Lippincott Co., 1915.

Meyer, A. W. *The Rise of Embryology.* Stanford: Stanford Univ. Press, 1939.

Morse, W. R. *Chinese Medicine.* New York: Paul B. Hoeber, 1934.

Needham, J. *Science and Civilization in China.* Vol. 1, Cambridge: The Univ. Press, 1954.

Rawlinson, G. trans. *The History of Herodotus.* New York: Tudor Publ. Co., 1956.

Reed, C. A. Animal Domestication in the Prehistoric Near East. *Science* 130:1629-1639, 1959.

Rostovtsev, M. *History of the Ancient World,* Vol. 1. Oxford: The Clarendon Press, 1926.

Sarton, G. *A History of Science: Ancient Through the Golden Age of Greece.* Cambridge: Harvard Univ. Press, 1952.

Singer, C. *From Magic to Science.* New York: Dover Publ., 1958.

Winter, H. J. J. *Eastern Science.* London: J. Murray, 1952.

Little is known of the specific ideas of the early Greek philosopher-scientists. Fragments of their writings that have survived indicate that their objective was to find one basic element that would explain the functioning of the physical world. Thales (639-544 B. C.) of Miletus, for example, considered water to be the basic material from which the world and living things were made. The earth was visualized as a disc on a sea of water. Life, he thought, originated from the water. Thales lived in the Ionian colonies on the coast of Asia Minor and traveled extensively. He coined the word "philosopher" and is credited with several specific observations in nature, including the prediction and observation of an eclipse of the sun that occurred on May 28, 585 B. C.

Chapter 2

BIOLOGY IN ANCIENT GREECE

Anaximander (611-547 B. C.), a pupil of Thales, wrote an extensive poem, On Nature. He considered not water alone to be involved in the formation of the earth and living things, but an ethereal substance called apeiron that was necessary to produce heat and cold. The earth was described as spherical. Spontaneous generation of plants and animals was presented as the source of origin and the descent of higher animals from lower forms was visualized as a sequence of evolution. Life, he thought, originated in the water but through adaptation over long periods of time, terrestrial forms were developed. It can thus be seen that the first ideas on evolution did not originate with Charles Darwin. The subject was given careful consideration 23 centuries before Darwin's time. Evolutionary theory became more tangible

when Xenophanes (576-490 B. C.), a pupil of the mathematician, Pythagoras, correctly interpreted fossils as the forms of organisms that had lived in earlier periods of the earth's history.

Anaximenes (570-500 B. C.), considered air to be the primary matter and this substance, he believed, had the capacity to condense into water and earth. Heraclitus (556-460 B. C.), the great teacher of Ephesus, chose fire as the fundamental element. He believed the world to be governed by law, but not static law. It was dynamic and constantly in a state of flux. Fire caused change and made worlds rise and perish but water was antagonistic to fire. With reference to man, fire was reconcilable with the soul, while water caused disease. These first suggestions of a balance among elements associated with good health were brought together by Empedocles (504-433 B. C.) of Agrigentum. Fire, air, water, and earth were thought to originate from combinations of four fundamental qualities; hot, wet, cold, and dry (Fig. 2-1). All changes in the world were due to different mixtures of the four elements. Plants and animals were included in the system and were believed to have originated from specific combinations of the basic elements. They were identified with four constituent humors of the body: blood, yellow bile, phlegm, and black bile, that were supposed to originate from the heart, liver, brain, and spleen, respectively. This gave rise to the humoral theory of disease, later incorporated into the writings of Hippocrates and perpetuated in part until the last century. Symptoms associated with imbalance of the humors were sanguine, choleric, phlegmatic and melancholy, respectively.

Alcmaeon of Croton who lived about 500 B. C., was one of the first of the Greek philosophers to write specifically on medicine. He was interested in anatomy and physiology. Among his contributions are the description of the optic nerves, the distinguishing of the different kinds of blood vessels, and the identifying of the trachea. He was far ahead of his time in designating the brain as the center of higher activities in man. The brain was considered by contemporary anatomists as merely a glandular organ for secreting phlegm but Alcmaeon found that the brain had no connection with the nasal passages. On the other hand the lungs were connected by the trachea to the nasal passages and these organs were

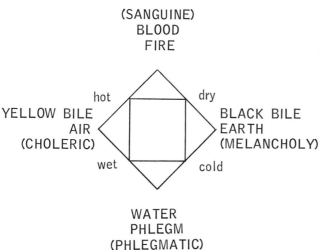

(SANGUINE)
BLOOD
FIRE

hot   dry

YELLOW BILE   BLACK BILE
AIR   EARTH
(CHOLERIC)   (MELANCHOLY)

wet   cold

WATER
PHLEGM
(PHLEGMATIC)

Fig. 2-1. Diagram illustrating the theory
of the four humors

considered by Alcmaeon to be the source
of phlegm.

Democritus (470-380 B. C.) of Ab-
dura in Thrace was deeply interested in
traveling and gaining knowledge. When
his father died and left him a large inheritance he traveled to Egypt and studied
mathematics and physical systems. He
returned to his home when the money was
spent and persuaded his brother to support him in further travel. Finally,
when he became established as a great
scholar, he was pensioned by the province
of Thrace to devote his full time and energy to travel and creative work. The
greatest contribution of Democritus was
his atomic theory. According to his theory, the universe is made of atoms which
move in space and all physical changes
are due to the union and separation of
atoms.

Aspects of his theory with biological implications were associated with
epidemics that were attributed to particles originating in celestial bodies.
Democritus studied and dissected many
animals including human beings and
found that lower animals as well as the
higher ones were complex. All organs
present in higher animals were thought
to be present in lower ones, but those
which could not be seen were considered
to be too small to be visible with the
naked eye. Democritus was one of the
first to attempt a classification of

animals. His first differentiation was
based on the color of the blood. Like
Alcmaeon, Democritus considered the
brain to be the organ of thought. Sensations, he believed, were due to the movements of atoms which eminate from the
objects with which people come in contact.
Sleep he declared to be a result of the loss
of atoms but the loss was on a smaller
scale than the loss that caused death.
Life itself was associated with the presence of atoms and death came when the
life-giving atoms had departed.

Medical Practice Among the Greeks

Modern medicine has taken much
from ancient Greek medicine. An examination of present day medical terminology
will show that numerous common words
and a great many more extractions are
from Greek roots. The close relation
between Greek and modern theory and
practice make the Greek period, actually
some 24 hundred years ago, seem much
closer to us than other, more recent,
historical periods. Greek medicine, at
its best, differed from those developments
of all earlier periods and most of those
that have occurred more recently, in
treating disease as a natural rather than a
supernatural phenomenon. The Greeks
assimilated the best thought and practice
from previous cultures, particularly the
Babylonian and Egyptian, and carried
medicine forward from its earlier beginnings.

Greek medicine had its origin in a
religious atmosphere. The Greeks had
many gods, several of which were active
participants in the cause or cure of disease. Early Greeks regarded Apollo as
the god of disease and healing. In the 5th
century B. C. he was largely replaced by
Asclepius who, according to Greek mythology, was the son of Apollo and Coronis
and the father of Hygeia. The staff and
holy snake of Asclepius are still the symbols of the medical profession. Greek
legend informs us that Asclepius became
so proficient in the healing art that he
was able to raise the dead. This brought
him into conflict with other gods whose
domain was being invaded. Greek mythology indicates further that Asclepius lost
his life when Pluto complained to Zeus
that the prolonged life on earth was cutting
down the population in Hades. Asclepius
was slain with a "thunderbolt." Although
he lost favor with the gods, the Greek
people appreciated his interest in health
improvement. They were pleased to

12

retain him as a god and temples were erected to his honor.

Asclepius may have been a real physician at an earlier time, who had much the same history among the early Greeks as Imhotep among the Egyptians. He was glorified, as time went on, and eventually deified. His name thus became woven into Greek mythology. Many practitioners, particularly those who worked with the poor and incurables, were priests of Asclepius. Healing was accomplished in the temples, located in the communities and along the countryside. Temples were not merely places of worship and religious ceremony but they were also sanatoria called Asclepicia. These were the first institutions provided for the care of ill people. Gradually they were replaced by hospitals and more modern sanatoria. In a temple, patients were reported to go to sleep and while they slept either a cure would be effected or information required for treatment would be given.

Among the Asclepians, secret knowledge was transmitted from father to son free of charge. Outsiders were required to pay large sums of money for the same training, if they were admitted to the guild at all. Each member took an oath in which he promised to share his knowledge freely with his colleagues but to withhold it from all others. There were, of course, wide variations in attitude and training among the Asclepians. Some were more superstitious and favored supernatural aspects of their practice whereas others belonged to the more rational school of thought.

Contemporary with Asclepian medicine, another kind of practitioner, the philosopher-scientist type developed and gave rise to the classical school of Greek medicine. These physicians were not necessarily irreligious, but they were naturalists who separated their practice from their personal religious beliefs. A group of physicians of this type became established on the island of Cos during the 6th century B. C. Tradition was built up among them for objectivity and critical evaluations of medical procedures. Other similar groups were located in the Greek colonies at Cnidus, Crotona, Rhodes, and Cyrene. The first medical communities or schools were thus established. They were schools of medical thought and tradition rather than teaching institutions in the modern sense. Teaching was done by individual masters and the students were

apprentices. Schools were thus composed of mature medical men who came together for mutual assistance and improvement in their practice.

The great physician, Hippocrates, (460-377 B. C.), who became the "father of medicine" was born and grew up on the Island of Cos (Fig. 2-2), a most favorable environment for a prospective physician at that time. Little is known about the early life of Hippocrates but his father belonged to the guild of physicians.

Fig. 2-2. Map of Athens and surrounding area

While a young man, Hippocrates traveled widely and became familiar with the cultural accomplishments of contemporary Greeks. He learned, practiced, and taught medicine on his home island and became the foremost member of the school that later became known as the "School of Hippocrates." The chief agents that were employed in medical practice were sunlight, fresh air, pure water, exercise, and a proper diet.

In practice, the Hippocratic physicians treated the individual patient and not the disease. Furthermore, the whole body was considered, and not merely a part that seemed to show symptoms. Methods, in general, were conservative and the healing powers of nature were taken into account. The physician took the attitude that he was merely helping nature to provide a cure by prescribing improved diet or other environmental modifications. Only when these methods were inadequate did he resort to more violent treatments such as blood letting to re-establish a favorable balance among the humors. The theory of the four humors, as presented in the Hippocratic writings, was basically similar to that developed by Empedocles but it had undergone some modifications. As pointed out earlier, Empedocles had considered the brain to be the source of phlegm, but later writers transferred this function to the lungs.

More than fifty books, attributed to Hippocrates, were collected at Alexandria in the 3rd century B. C. and became the Corpus Hippocraticum. It is not known which, if any, of these books were actually written by Hippocrates. They represent the thinking of the school at Cos, but were probably not written by the same author. Several of the books deal with diet, one describes epidemic diseases and another gives symptoms by which common diseases may be recognized. Several books deal with fractures, dislocations, ulcers, and wounds all of which include excellent descriptions and conservative treatments.

One of the best known of the Hippocratic books is entitled, On Air, Waters and Places. This treatise relates disease with environmental conditions in different parts of the known world and also gives consideration to the importance of hereditary stock and social institutions that may modify the effects of climatic conditions. Like all other Hippocratic books, this volume stresses the naturalistic approach to prevention and cure of disease. Great stress is placed on observation of the symptoms and disease process in individual people.

The famous book On the Sacred Disease, a discussion of epilepsy, makes a strong case for the natural in contrast to the supernatural explanation of disease. The author begins with the statement that this dreaded disease is no more sacred than other diseases. It must have a natural cause like other diseases but the cause is not understood, therefore, it has been considered supernatural or sacred. When ignorance is dispelled and the disease is eventually understood, there will be nothing sacred about it.

Three of the Hippocratic books, The Law, The Physician, and Oath deal with professional attributes and ethics of the physician. These writings reflect the unprotected social position of the medical man. He had to rely on himself for the establishment of a good reputation among his patients and he could not afford failure. Therefore, it was customary for physicians to reject cases that were considered incurable and thus to protect themselves in every way possible from failure or suspicion of malpractice. The following oath that was taken by Greek physicians and is now administered to graduating medical students suggests the care that was taken to keep the conduct of the doctor on a high ethical plane and above reproach.

"I swear by Apollo Physician, by Asclepius, by Health, by Panacea and by all the gods and goddesses, making them my witnesses, that I will carry out, according to my ability and judgment, this oath and this indenture. To hold my teacher in this art equal to my own parents; to make him partner in my livelihood; when he is in need of money to share mine with him; to consider his family as my own brothers, and to teach them this art, if they want to learn it, without fee or indenture; to impart precept, oral instruction, and all other instruction to my own sons, the sons of my teacher, and to indentured pupils who have taken the physician's oath, but to nobody else. I will use treatment to help the sick according to my ability and judgment, but never with a view to injury and wrongdoing. Neither will I administer a poison to anybody when asked to do so, nor will I suggest such a course. Similarly, I will not give a woman a pessary to cause abortion. But I will keep pure and holy both my life and my art. I will not use the knife, not even, verily, on sufferers from stone, but I will give place to such as are craftsmen therein. Into whatsoever houses I enter, I will enter to help the sick, and I will abstain from all intentional wrong-doing and harm, especially from abusing the bodies of man or woman, bond or free. And whatsoever I shall see or hear in the course of my profession, as well as outside my profession in the intercourse with men, if it be what should not be published abroad, I will never divulge, holding such things to be holy secrets. Now if I carry out

*this oath, and break it not, may I
gain forever reputation among all
men for my life and for my art; but
if I transgress it and forswear myself, may the opposite befall me."
Hippocrates 460-377 B. C.*

Aristotle, the Biologist

The Greek philosopher, Aristotle, was one of the greatest biologists who ever lived. He and his associates undertook the tremendous task of writing down in a series of books everything known at that time. Greek catalogues list 146 books that are attributed to Aristotle. Many manuscripts have been lost. Some were copied by copyists who were not accurate and thus the manuscripts were confounded. Four important works on biology have been preserved which contain Aristotle's methods, observations, deductions, and theories.

1. Natural History of Animals. Ten books (3 considered spurious) containing observations about animals.
2. On the Parts of Animals. Four books of anatomical works.
3. On the Generation of Animals. Five books on reproduction.
4. On the Psyche. Three books on the living principle.

Aristotle is known to have written on botany and other biological subjects but these books have been lost.

Perhaps Aristotle's greatest contribution to modern science was his demonstration of the scientific method. Much of his knowledge was based on his own observations and deductions. A vast amount of information was collected, classified, recorded, and evaluated. Conclusions and interpretations were drawn from the data.

Aristotle (384-322 B. C.) was born at Stagira, on the Strymonic Gulf. It was an agricultural area and slaves did the manual labor. An absolute monarchy had developed under the leadership of a series of strong rulers. Aristotle's father was physician to the ruling Macedonian king, Amyntas II, and Aristotle grew up in the court. He learned medicine from his father and had the best opportunities for education that were available at the time. Amyntas and, particularly, his son Philip who succeeded him on the throne, were cultured men who did much to attract scholars to their court. The cultured environment was favorable for the development of a young scholar.

At the age of 17, Aristotle went to Plato's school, the Academy at Athens. Instruction was given in a grove of trees where the teacher and his pupils met and discussed their problems. Aristotle was connected with Plato's school for some 20 years, but he did other things during part of this period. When Plato died, Aristotle, then 37 years of age, expected to become master of the Academy but he was disappointed and went to the Island of Lesbos (Fig. 2-2) where he studied marine biology. At age 42, he was recalled to the court by King Philip where he became tutor for the king's son and royal heir, Alexander.

Aristotle influenced Alexander greatly, but in the latter part of his tenure, Alexander assumed more responsibility in government and became more interested in military pursuits than in academic accomplishments. When Philip was assassinated, young Alexander took the throne and entered upon his career of military conquest. Aristotle returned to Athens and established his school called the "Lyceum" (Gr. luminous or light bearing) in a garden. Here he walked and talked with his students.

When Alexander died in 323 B. C., there was much unrest and civil strife in Greece. Aristotle had been closely associated with Alexander and the fallen government. He was under suspicion when the revolutionary forces came to power and he fled from Athens to save his life, spending his last year in exile. He died in 322 B. C. at the age of 62.

Aristotle was a keen observer and interpreted most of his observations accurately but he was not an experimenter. Chemistry and physics had not been developed and therefore, an accurate study of physiology was impossible. There was no substantial body of facts in any field and no consistent scientific nomenclature. Under such circumstances one would expect some inaccuracies of observation and reasoning. The centuries preceding Aristotle had yielded him little but vague speculation. In his own words translated and quoted by Romanes (1891), we get a picture of the problem he faced: "I found no basis prepared; no models to copy. Mine is the first step and therefore a small one, though worked out with much thought and hard labor. It must be looked at as a first step and judged with indulgence. You, my reader, or hearers of my lectures, if you think I have done as much as can fairly be required for an initiatory start, as compared with more advanced departments of theory, will acknowledge what I have achieved and pardon what I have left to others to accomplish.

It is the glory of Aristotle that both his observations and reasoning can stand present-day comparisons as well as they do. Considering the handicaps he had to face and the enormous range of his work in biology alone, it is surprising that he went as far as he did. His were original investigations. Aristotle was, indeed, a great pioneer of biology.

Aristotle's Knowledge of Marine Animals

Marine fauna seemed to interest Aristotle even more than land animals. His observations and interpretations of the structure and habits of sea animals were remarkably accurate. Aristotle's writings on marine biology refer frequently and with particular intimacy to places on or near the island of Lesbos. Here he spent at least two years and it is probable that most, if not all of his observations on marine life were made during this period. No doubt much of his philosophy was developed during his stay at the seashore at Lesbos. He noted the abundance and variety of marine life and became interested in the adaptations and apparent intelligence of animals. In speaking of the sea, Aristotle says, "Now the sea is not only water but much more material than fresh water, and hot in its nature, it has a share in all parts of the universe, water and air and earth, so that it also has a share in all living things which are produced in connection with each of these elements."

One might picture the great observer in a boat on a clear day, when the shallow water was calm, watching sea animals in their native haunts. Remembering that he had no instruments and was under the necessity of making all observations with his naked eyes, it is remarkable, indeed, that he was able to describe so accurately such small objects as eggs and developing embryos of molluscs and fish. Motivated by an intense curiosity, he watched these animals methodically day after day, recording what he discovered. No doubt

he talked frequently with the local fishermen and received enthusiastically any bits of information they were able to give.

An example, illustrating his method of study, can be taken from his description of a certain mollusc called the "cuttlefish" or sepia. The cuttlefish was a common article of food in the Mediterranean countries and many kinds were known to fishermen. Aristotle knew most of the common kinds and described them with far more accuracy than would be possible from a mass of fragmentary information gleaned from fishermen. Their morphology, habits, and development were recorded with such faithful accuracy that little can be added. He began with an outline of the general form, described the body and fins, the eight arms with their rows of suckers, and mentioned the abnormal position of the head. The eyes were observed and two great teeth forming a beak with which the animals could cling to rocks and sway back and forth like ships at anchor. Aristotle observed the two long arms in sepia and noted their absence in the octopus. After making careful dissections of several species and noting differences, he described the eggs and embryos and yolk sac attached to the head and noted that in certain males, observed in the breeding season, one of the arms was modified into a long coiled whip-lash, used in copulation.

At Lesbos Aristotle made many keen observations. Starfish were in such abundance as to be a pest to the fishermen. Scallops had been exterminated by a period of drought and the continual working of the fishermen's dredges. There were no spiny fishes, sea-crawfish, spotted or spiny dogfish. In this region all the fish, save only a little gudgeon, migrated seaward to breed. Big purple murex shells were observed at Cape Lectum and different kinds of sponges were found on the landward and seaward side of Cape Malia.

Reproduction and Embryology

Aristotle was interested in problems of reproduction and described with minute detail the breeding habits of certain marine organisms. He traced the development of at least two molluscs from the egg to the adult and noted that the egg is undifferentiated. In describing the development of the octopus he said that breeding occurs in the spring; the female lays numerous eggs and broods over them. After about fifty days the eggs burst and little creatures creep out like little spiders in great numbers. The characteristic form of their limbs is not yet visible in detail but their general outline is clear. They are small and helpless and many perish.

The eggs of the cuttlefish, he said, look like bunches of grapes stuck together by a moist, sticky substance extruded by the female and are not easily separated from one another. At first they are white but they become larger and black after the sticky material has been extruded. A young cuttlefish is first distinctly formed inside the egg and when the egg bursts, it comes out. The inner part is formed as soon as the egg is laid and is something like a hailstone. From the white substance the cuttlefish grows, being, however, attached to the head in the same way as the developing bird is attached to the belly.

Regarding the breeding habits of the crustacea, Aristotle said that crustacea copulate by fitting their tails to one another. Males have fine spermatic ducts and females a membraneous uterus alongside of the intestine. Aristotle compared minutely, different kinds of eggs. In birds' eggs white and yellow yolk was found to be separated, but fish eggs were of one color and the corresponding matter was completely mixed. Fish had one umbilicus like birds, connecting the embryo with the yolk. In cartilaginous fish the embryo was connected with the whole egg. The embryo, he said, gets nourishment from the yolk and as it is being consumed the flesh encroaches upon it and grows around it.

Most fish he found to be externally oviparous, laying perfect eggs. The "frogfish" was similar to cartilaginous fish, except that the outside of the egg was harder and growth was more rapid. Eggs grow, of necessity, because they have superfluous yeasty matter in them. It was impossible for them to attain their whole growth in the uterus, because these animals have so many eggs. They are small when set free and grow quickly so that the race will not perish, as it would if much time were spent in growth. As it is, most of the eggs laid are destroyed before hatching. Hence the class of fish is prolific, for nature makes up for destruction by large numbers. Some fish, Aristotle observed, actually burst as the eggs increase in size. An example was

the fish called "belone" (some kind of pipefish) probably Syngnathus acus that has a pouch to carry eggs which bursts when the eggs are mature.

Speaking of fertilization Aristotle says, "The eggs do not arrive at completion unless the male sprinkles his milt upon them." Further he says that the males have their milt and the females their eggs at about the same time of the year, and the nearer the female is to laying, the more abundant and the more liquid is the milt formed in the male. The union of the fishes is brief so that it has not been observed by many fishermen, nevertheless their copulation has been seen. Aristotle, erroneously, supposed copulation to take place in teleosts generally, before oviposition, even though he knew that the eggs must be influenced by the male element after they are deposited in the water.

A chapter in Aristotle's work that is attractive to embryologists deals with the mode of reproduction of cartilaginous fish. Aristotle knew that most fish are oviparous, that is, they deposit eggs that hatch outside the body of the mother. He observed, however, that a small group of fish bring forth actively living young. This group of cartilaginous fish he called "Selache" and described them as sharklike fish which produce a perfect egg within themselves but are externally viviparous, that is, they give birth to living young. One exception, the frogfish, was noted which he says, "lays a perfect egg externally." He observed that whereas eggs of the cartilaginous fish that are sheltered by the mother are soft-shelled and moist, the eggs of the frogfish are solid and firm for protection outside of the mother's body. Young of both oviparous and viviparous fish are produced from the egg in the same way but development differs in some respects from that of birds. The egg of the bird is separated from the uterus before it is perfected, but in most of the cartilaginous fish, the egg is still attached to the uterus when perfect. Since eggs of cartilaginous fish are protected by the mother, they do not have a surrounding shell, but only a thin membrane that breaks before birth.

Among the Selacheans, Aristotle knew of one form in which the resemblance to mammals goes even farther than the mere production of living young. One of the shark-like fish called "Galeos" lays eggs within itself. These eggs are deposited in the womb and acquire an attachment to it, much like the placenta of a mammal. They have a delicate membrane that connects the yolk sac of the embryo with the parental tissue providing a temporary union through which the blood of the mother nourishes the young. Physiologically, this arrangement for nourishment is like that of viviparous mammals that nourish their young through the placenta.

Aristotle said that the spiny dogfish has its eggs close to the midriff, above the breast-like formation. Eggs shift into each of the two horns of the womb and descend, and the young develop with the navel string attached to the womb so that, as the egg substance is used up, the embryo is sustained to all appearances, just as in the case of quadrupeds. The navel string is long and adheres to the under part of the womb and also to the center of the embryo in the place where the liver is situated. If the embryo is cut open, even though it no longer has the egg substance, the food inside is egg-like in appearance. Each embryo, as in the case of the quadruped, is provided with a chorion and separate membranes. At first the embryo has its head upward, but when it is completed and becomes strong the head is downward. When the egg descends, as soon as it is detached, the young is born. Even in the embryo, the internal organs, such as the liver are large and supplied with blood.

This description attracted little attention until the 17th century when it was discovered by the Danish anatomist, Nicolaus Steno (1638-1686). The observation was again forgotten, until the middle of the 19th century when the German physiologist, Johannes Müller (1801-58), found that Aristotle's description was correct. Müller showed that there are a few selachia which resemble mammals and that the so-called "placenta" in these fish is derived from the yolk sac itself and not from the allantois, as in mammals. Aristotle was apparently aware of the difference between the yolk sac and the placenta. His complete and accurate account shows how wide his survey of this class of fish must have been. The 16th century naturalist, G. Rondelet (1507-66), based his great work dealing with Mediterranean marine creatures, on the work of Aristotle.

Aristotle's Contribution to Ecology

Aristotle was a keen observer of the habits of fish and, no doubt, took accurate notes of his observations. He was interested in the relation between the animal and its environment, studied adaptations of sea animals and took particular interest in the migrations of fish. Following is a summary of his account of the habits of a certain catfish, Parasilurus Aristotelis. The eggs are deposited in shallow water, generally close to roots or close to reeds. They are sticky and adhere to the roots. The female, having laid her eggs, goes away but the male stays and watches over the eggs, keeping off all other fish that might steal the eggs or fry. He thus continues for forty or fifty days, till the young are sufficiently grown to escape from the other fishes. Fishermen can tell where he is on guard, for, in warding off the fishes, he sometimes makes a rush in the water and gives utterance to a kind of muttering noise. Knowing his earnestness in parental duty the fishermen catch him by the hook while he is on guard. Even if he perceives the hook, he will still keep by his charge, and will even bite the hook in pieces with his teeth.

For many centuries the only notice taken of this account was to laugh at it. Catfish in Europe do not care for their young in this fashion, though some can make a noise with their gill covers. About the middle of the 19th century Louis Agassiz studied the habits of the American catfish and observed that the male looks after its young, just as described by Aristotle. Agassiz had catfish sent to him from the Achelous River and found them to follow Aristotle's description exactly.

Aristotle also observed and described the torpedo and angler fish, both of which are aided in obtaining food by an electric discharge. Following is Aristotle's description of the habits of these two fish. In both of these fish the breadth of the anterior part of the body is much increased. In the torpedo, the two lower fins are placed in the tail. This fish uses the broad expanse of its body to serve as a fin. In the angler, the upper fins are placed behind the under fins which are close to the head. The torpedo stuns the creatures that it wants to catch, overpowering them by the force of shock in its body, and feeds upon them. It hides in the sand and mud and catches all creatures that swim within reach of its stunning power. The angler stirs himself up a place where there is plenty of mud and sand and hides himself there. He has a filament projecting in the front of his eyes that is long, hair-like, and rounded at the tip. It is used as a bait. Little fish on which the angler feeds swim up to the filament taking it for a bit of seaweed that they eat. Then the angler raises the filament and when the little fish strike against it, he sucks them down into his mouth. That these creatures get their living thus, is evident from the fact that even though sluggish themselves, they are often found with mullets in their stomachs and mullets are swift fish. Moreover, the angler is usually thin when taken after having lost the tips of its filaments.

Aristotle's Classification System

Aristotle had no formal classification system, but conceived the evolutionary concept and distinguished animals according to function. By examining his definitions, a classification scheme can be drawn up, based mainly on reproduction. The first great division separated the red-blooded (vertebrates) from those without red blood (invertebrates). Subdivisions were made according to breeding habits, type of eggs, and modes of reproduction.

Aristotle characterized animals according to their way of living, actions, habits, and bodily parts. He divided them into land and sea animals and noted that certain of the latter, such as fish, live entirely in the water, whereas others such as the otter, beaver, and crocodile spend most of their time in water but breathe air and reproduce on land. Some water animals swim, others creep, and some are adherent. Animals can easily be divided into large divisions such as birds, fish, and whales and Aristotle observed that some can readily be further divided into such groups as inkfish, shellfish, and crayfish. Aristotle's careful discrimination in placing animals is evidence of his keen observation of relations. He knew that mammals have lungs, breathe air, are warm-blooded, and viviparous. Therefore he placed dolphins, and whales with the mammals rather than the true fish.

Among the animals without red blood Aristotle recognized four classes. Three of these, Malakia, Malacostraca, and Ostracoderma, are made up largely of marine animals. Today his Malakia

would be placed in the class Cephalopoda, his Malacostraca with the Crustacea, and his Ostracoderma would be made up of certain miscellaneous molluscs and scattered representatives of lower phyla.

Theophrastus, the Botanist

Aristotle's work on botany was lost and it is fortunate that the work of Theophrastus (380-287 B. C.) on plants was preserved to represent plant science of the Greek period. Theophrastus was born on the Island of Lesbos, where he may have met Aristotle. He went to Athens, attended Plato's Academy and later transferred to Aristotle's Lyceum. Theophrastus was devoted to Aristotle and succeeded him in the Lyceum where he continued Aristotle's policies and remained for 30 years after Aristotle died. Theophrastus was a good observer and teacher but he lacked the great capacity and inspiration of Aristotle.

Writings of Theophrastus on the history of plants were prepared as scrap books with stories of plants and folk lore mixed in abundantly. Practical values of plants and methods of gathering those useful for drugs are the only significant botanical contributions. Theophrastus prepared descriptions of plants and plant parts that were quite accurate, but wordy and cumbersome. A number of his terms such as "carpos" for fruit, "pericarpion" or "pericarp" for seed vessel, "metra" for the core of the stem, have retained their usefulness for descriptive purposes in modern botanical literature.

Theophrastus was interested in plant reproduction including seed germination and embryology and he recognized several methods of reproduction. Lower plants, like lower animals, he considered to originate spontaneously whereas higher plants developed from seeds. His description of germination came from first-hand observations and represented the best account presented before the 17th century. Theophrastus distinguished the monocotyledons from the dicotyledons and gave good descriptions of the sequence of events in seed germination in each category. Vegetative propagation was also recognized. It could occur from the roots, pieces removed from a branch, or from the trunk. Cross fertilization was described in the date palm.

REFERENCES

Aristotle. *De Partibus Animalium*. trans. A. L. Peck. London: W. Heinemann, Ltd., 1937.

Aristotle. *De Generatione Animalium*. trans. A. L. Peck. London: W. Heinemann, Ltd., 1943.

Aristotle. *Historia Animalium*. trans. T. Taylor. London: Robert Wilks Co., 1809.

Aristotle. *Historia Animalium*. trans. D'Archy Thompson. Oxford: Clarendon Press, 1910.

(There are other translations of Aristotle's works and a number of books and articles about Aristotle not listed here which may be located through the card catalogue.)

Breasted, J. H. *Ancient Times*. 2nd Ed. Boston: Ginn and Co., 1944.

Brock, A. J. *Greek Medicine*. New York: E. P. Dutton and Co., 1929.

Cohen, M. R. and I. E. Drabkin. *Source Book of Greek Science*. New York: McGraw-Hill, 1948.

Coonen, L. P. Theophrastus Revisited. *The Centennial Review* 1:404-418, 1957.

Edelstein, E. J. *Asclepius*. Baltimore: The Johns Hopkins Press, 1945.

Heidel, W. *Hippocratic Medicine, Its Spirit and Method*. New York: Columbia Univ. Press, 1941.

Hertwig, R. *A Manual of Zoology*. trans. and ed. J. S. Kingsley. New York: Henry Holt and Co., 1902.

Jaeger, W. *Aristotle*. London: Oxford Univ. Press, 1948.

Lewes, G. H. *Aristotle*. London: Smith, Elder and Co., 1864.

Lones, T. E. *Aristotle's Researches in Natural Science*. London: West, Newman and Co., 1912.

McKeon, R. *The Basic Works of Aristotle*. 4th Ed. New York: Random House, Inc., 1941.

McRae, C. *Fathers of Biology*. London: Percival and Co., 1890.

Needham, J. *A History of Embryology*. Cambridge: The Univ. Press, 1934.

Osborn, H. F. *From Greeks to Darwin*. New York: The Macmillan Co., 1915.

Reymond, A. *History of Sciences in Greco-Roman Antiquity*. London: Methuen and Co., 1927.

Romanes, G. J. Aristotle as a Naturalist. *Contemporary Review,* Vol. 59, 1891.

Ross, W. B. ed. *Aristotle Selections.* 12 Vol. New York: C. Scribner's Sons Co., 1927.

Singer, C. *A Short History of Anatomy and Physiology From the Greeks to Harvey.* New York: Dover Pub., Inc., 1956.

Shippen, K. B. *Men, Microscopes and Living Things.* New York: The Viking Press, 1955.

Taylor, A. E. *Aristotle.* Rev. ed. New York: Dover Publ., 1955.

Thompson, J. A. *The Great Biologists.* London: Methuen and Co., 1932.

Thompson, D. W. *Aristotle as a Biologist.* Oxford: Clarendon Press, 1913.

Wilson, G. *Great Men of Science.* Garden City, N. Y.: Garden City Publ. Co., 1929.

Upon Alexander's death in 323 B. C., his empire fell apart. The Greek lands came under the rule of Macedonian successors, although the Greek people never easily submitted to foreign rule and frequently united in leagues to fight for and maintain at times a precarious independence. Constant warfare and civil strife characterized the period that followed. The Alexandrian conquests, however, had laid the foundation for a new culture called by historians, the Hellenistic culture. Combined were features of the classical Hellenic period and features of the oriental cultures taken over by the Greeks. In Greek history the period from 323 B. C. to 146 B. C. (when Rome conquered Greece) is known as the Hellenistic Age. Really, though, Hellenistic culture was the dominant culture of the Mediterranean World from about 323 B. C. to about 500 A. D. One of its most salient features was the continuation of scientific investigations.

Following the death of Alexander, many Greek scholars moved to other areas where conditions were more conducive to their scholarly work. These scholars carried with them manuscripts and other tangible products of the Greek culture as well as an attitude and aptitude favorable to learning. It must be remembered that in ancient times there was no public education. Information was communicated in the forum or in the street and relatively few people were literate. Several cities and provinces in the Mediterranean region benefited from the migration of Greek scholars. Two great centers of culture developed, one at Alexandria, Egypt, and one at Rome, Italy. Alexandria in the east reached a high level in general culture and in some limited areas of biology shortly after the fall of Alexander in the 3rd century B. C. In the 2nd century B. C. other Greek cities such as Pergamum, Rhodes, and Antioch shared with Alexandria the cultural leadership. Rome, to the west of Greece, developed slowly and reached its highest point in the period around the time of Christ.

Alexandria, at the mouth of the Nile River, was one of several cities of the same name to be named by Alexander, after himself. He had been an ambitious general with a strong desire for power and conquest. In his great military campaign he led armies into Asia Minor, down the coast through Syria and into Egypt. He then turned eastward and marched through Mesopotamia, into

Persia, and as far east as India. As new areas were conquered, mostly in the Persian Empire, Alexander made certain governmental changes to keep the conquered peoples under his control. In each new governmental unit, some Persians and some Greeks were appointed to serve together as administrators under Alexander's close supervision. He hoped that the Greek and Persian peoples would become united and form one great empire. The whole enterprise changed suddenly when Alexander died.

Alexanders generals took immediate control of his empire and divided the army and the conquered territory among themselves (Fig. 3-1). One of the generals,

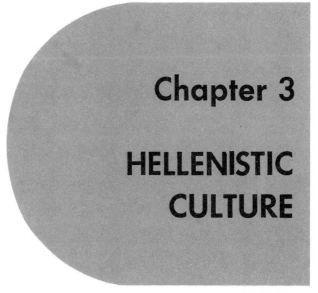

Chapter 3

HELLENISTIC CULTURE

Ptolemy I, took his part of the army to Egypt and established the Greek capitol of Egypt at Alexandria. The name "Ptolemy" was taken by all the rulers of Egypt from 323 to 30 B. C. Ptolemy I was a cultured man and an author. Ptolemy II (Philadelphus), son of Ptolemy I, was even more enthusiastic for science and culture than his father. He attracted Greek scholars to Alexandria with scholarships or grants for research and attractive working conditions. A great library was built by Ptolemy I and further developed by Ptolemy II, where manuscripts were gathered and copied and where scholars studied. It was called a "temple of Muses" and became the first "museum".

The Muses in Greek mythology were the nine daughters of Zeus and Mnemosyne who became patron goddesses of the humanities as follows: Cleio, muse of history; Euterpe, muse of lyric poetry;

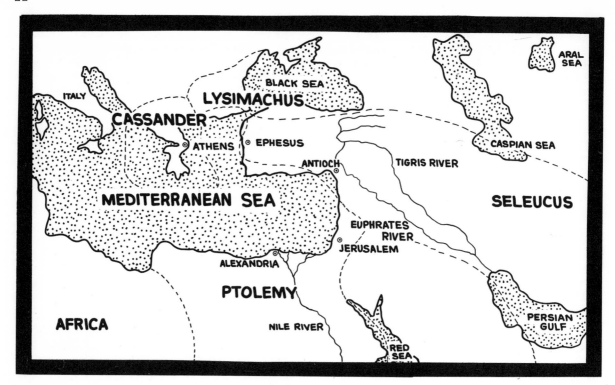

Fig. 3-1. Map showing the divisions of
Alexander's Empire among his generals

Thaleia, muse of comedy; Melpomene, muse of tragedy; Terpsichore, muse of dance and music; Erato, muse of erotic poetry; Polymnia, muse of hymns; Urania, muse of astronomy, Calliope, muse of epic poetry. Seven of the muses were thus patrons of literature, one of history, and one of science (astronomy). Temples to particular muses and to all of them combined had been erected in Greece, but the museum of Alexandria was the greatest.

The Alexandrian Museum was not merely a show place for specimens or a storage place for manuscripts. It was a great institution where literary and scientific studies were carried on. A public walk and an enclosed meeting place were important parts of the museum. There were living quarters for scholars and a common dining room where scholars were served their meals. A part of the royal palace was also included and supervision was provided by a priest who was appointed by the king. Both lodging and maintenance were furnished free of charge to the research workers who lived together and made use of the facilities for learning. The museum had great influence on the progress of science. Complete freedom was apparently enjoyed by the scholars in their search for truth.

Several hundred thousand papyrus rolls were housed in the great library at Alexandria. This alone, however, did not establish the wide reputation for the institution. It was the distinguished scholars who studied there and their contributions which gave it lasting significance. Most of these scholars were men of letters but some were scientists. Eratosthenes, the great mathematician and geographer of antiquity was one of the librarians.

Basic biology was not developed at Alexandria but some practical aspects of medicine rose to a high place. Two great anatomists were Herophilus and Erasistratus. The writings of both of these men were lost but references to their work by contemporaries give evidence of their great accomplishments.

Anatomists of Alexandria

One of the two great anatomists of the period, Herophilus, was reported to have worked with some 600 human bodies. He described the brain as the center of the nervous system and made critical studies of the membranes and sinuses of the brain identifying the fourth ventricle as the "organ of the soul." Herophilus also worked out the structure of the eye, studied the digestive tract, and named the duodenum. The shape of the liver was found to be different in different persons. (It is now known that the liver responds readily to body conditions and infections undergoing many modifications.) He studied the circulatory system and noted the strong walls of the arteries and weak walls of the veins. The pulse was compared in illness and in health but Herophilus did not relate the pulse to the beating of the heart. He distinguished tendons from nerves; Aristotle had confused these two structures. He also worked out the anatomy of the genital organs. Herophilus was a strict follower of Hippocrates and supported the doctrine of the four humors.

The other great anatomist of the Alexandrian period, Erasistratus, was a contemporary and rival of Herophilus. Because Herophilus was an anatomist, Erasistratus called himself a physiologist. He scorned Hippocrates and turned away from the bleeding methods that were associated with the doctrine of the four humors. Erasistratus was a follower of Aristotle and was said to be his nephew. He described and named the valves of the heart. Like Herophilus, he distinguished between arteries and veins and showed that both arteries and veins carry blood. Others had considered the arteries to carry only air. Erasistratus also studied wounds, found lymphatic glands in the digestive tract, and observed the lymph carrying digested fat (i. e. chyle). Sensory and motor nerves were also distinguished from each other in the anatomical studies of Erasistratus.

Following the reign of Ptolemy II, the atmosphere in Alexandria was not as favorable for scholarly accomplishment as in earlier periods. Later Ptolemys were not scholarly and enlightened. They withdrew support from research. In some cases learned men were persecuted by tyrants and politicians. The freedom and incentive necessary for science to thrive were lacking.

At this time medical men were the only people who took an interest in biology and they were only concerned with practical applications. Some anatomy was perpetuated and plants were studied for their medicinal values. After the death of Cleopatra, last of the Ptolemys, in 30 B. C., Alexandria became a Roman city. Later, Alexandria was made a center by the Christian church. The Alexandrian period represented an extension of Greek culture.

Biology in Rome

Rome reached a high point in biology in the period between the 1st century B. C. and the end of the 2nd century A. D. Most Roman biologists were medical men and many were Greeks. Political leaders in Rome were more interested in building an empire than in developing culture and science and soldiers rather than thinkers were rewarded. Significant contributions were made in law and government but there was no parallel advance in science. Practical applications were made of Greek ideas in agriculture and medicine but there was little creative science. Rome's greatest contribution in biology was the development of hygienic measures. Because much of Italy was swampy and malaria was prevalent, cities were built on hills where the disease was less serious.

Sewers were constructed to carry wastes into the Tiber River and people were warned against drinking the river water. Culinary water was brought in great aquaducts to Rome where settling tanks were constructed to purify and aerate the water. Great fountains supplied some 85 gallons per day for each person. Baths were built and operated on a high plane at first, but later they degenerated into loafing places where people were more interested in sensual pleasure than wholesome exercise and bodily cleanliness.

Lucretius (Titus Lucretius Carus 96-55 B. C.), a cultured man who had been educated in Athens, spent most of his productive life writing a single poem entitled The Nature of Things (De rerum natura) which was unfinished at the time of his death. It is a long poem, contained in six volumes, dealing with the author's thoughts concerning nature. The poem begins with an invocation to Venus, goddess of creation. Following is a statement of objectives in which the author outlines his interest in "the nature of things," beginning, evolution, and dissolution. He attempted to explain the universe in common terms.

Such topics as reproduction, mental defects, demon superstitions, and plagues were discussed. Lucretius was not superstitious; but a clear thinker who tried to analyze nature and discover underlying causes. Thinking men, he contended, should be able to think out nature; their mission should be to banish superstition. Lucretius developed the atomic theory of Democritus through which atoms were believed to form worlds, infinite in number and space. This theory formed an early beginning of the modern theory developed many centuries later by Dalton and Berzilius. Lucretius adapted the atomic theory to living as well as non-living things. The soul was described in terms of atoms and dreams were believed to depend on floating particles in the air. Lucretius also developed a theory of heredity which anticipated the work of Mendel. He suggested a hereditary mechanism for plants, animals, and finally, man.

Pliny (23-79 A. D.), a literary man in Rome who held important positions in governmental and military units, compiled an extensive encyclopedia of natural history that had great influence through the centuries that followed until the renaissance. Although Pliny's natural history was widely read, it had little scientific value. It was uncritical and represented a mixture of animal stories, folk lore, and summaries of earlier observations in nature. As its popularity increased and more copies were required, it was changed by copyists and became increasingly more inaccurate. It was the best work on biology available to large groups of people and it did much to stimulate man's interest in nature. The only book that was more widely used than Pliny during long periods of time hereafter was the Bible.

Contemporary with Pliny was a Greek scholar, Dioscorides, who had become a Roman military surgeon. He was interested in improving medical services in the complex Roman Empire. Drugs obtained from plants represented a critical item in medical practice and Dioscorides performed an invaluable service by identifying and describing many plants with medicinal value. Some names that he attached to plants have persisted and are now used in plant identification. The work of Dioscorides was compiled in a book about plants called an "herbal". Later Dioscorides' "herbal" was illustrated with pictures of the plants he had described. This increased its usefulness and the work had great influence for centuries after its original preparation. Dioscorides has been properly recognized as one of the founders of botany.

Galen (131-200 A. D. Fig. 3-2) was born of Greek parentage at Pergamum in Asia Minor. He had excellent opportunities for education and at the age of 18 was familiar with Platonic, Aristotelian, Stoic, and Epicurean philosophies and had already spent two years in the study of medicine. He then traveled and studied medicine and philosophy in the cultured centers of the time: Greece, Phoenicia, Palestine, Crete, Cypress, and finally in Alexandria. With his education completed in 158 A. D., he returned to his native city, Pergamum, where he practiced medicine and served as physician and surgeon to the gladiators. He supervised the diet of men who fought in the arena and treated their wounds. Here he wrote the first of his many medical treatises.

Fig. 3-2. Galen of Pergamum, great anatomist of the Roman period

Six years later he moved to Rome where he established a medical practice and lectured on medical subjects. He was successful in his profession and won recognition when he healed the great philosopher, Eudemus, and treated other distinguished persons. Because of his success he was called a "wonder worker". Galen was confident of his own skill and critical of contemporary medical sects and theories. Enmity between Galen and his fellow physicians forced him to leave Rome. He was later brought back to be the physician to the Emperor,

Marcus Aurelius. From then on, much of his time was devoted to writing and practicing medicine among the dignitaries in the court of the Emperor.

At the time Galen was establishing his philosophy, Christianity was making itself felt in the Roman Empire. It is likely that Galen remained a pagan and never joined the Christian church but he was sympathetic to Christianity and much of his philosophy was incorporated in the Christian theology. Galen accepted the principle of a divine intelligence as the originator and ruler of the world. He referred to the Mosaic story of creation but was critical of the implication that something was created from nothing.

Galen wrote some 256 treatises on subjects dealing with medicine, philosophy, mathematics, grammar, and law. Fifteen of these were on anatomy, based on the dissection of apes. The majority were medical in nature but Galen was interested in many fields. His great book, entitled On Anatomical Preparations, was the standard medical text for 1200 years. This is perhaps the longest "run" a textbook has ever enjoyed. Much of his medical knowledge was based on Hippocrates but Plato and Aristotle also took an important place in providing his background philosophy. Because of prejudice and superstition, prevalent at the time, Galen was not permitted to dissect human bodies. Most of his first-hand information was obtained from dissections of such animals as sheep, oxen, dogs, bears, and apes, which he presumed to be similar to human beings. He began his description of anatomy with a study of the hand and proceeded to describe the other extremities. From the extremities he went to the digestive tract, respiratory organs, brain, spine, blood vessels, and genital organs. The work was done with care and was carried out in great detail. Unfortunately for later generations of anatomists, it was based on apes instead of men. Galen's work remained the undisputed, authoritative "human" anatomy for some fourteen hundred years, until the time of Vesalius.

In describing the circulatory system (Fig. 3-3), Galen followed the blood from the liver to the heart, where it was supposed to pass through pores in the septum from the right to left heart. Here he imagined that the blood became mixed with air from the lungs to form "vital spirits" or pneuma, the life-giving property of the organisms. Pneuma were carried with the blood to the various parts of the body. He believed that a "boiling up" or "fermenting" process heated the body and provided the motion to carry the blood into the body. He supposed that waste from combustion or "soot" went from the right heart to the lungs and out of the body. For the blood it was a one-way passage through the body. New blood he supposed to be produced, presumably in the liver, to maintain the blood volume. The blood pumped out from the heart, he thought, was used in the body and never returned to the heart. The "vital spirits," however, he believed were circulated back and forth in the blood vessels, and carried the life-giving properties to the different parts of the body. This description of circulation was regarded as infallible during the long period from the 2nd century A. D. until Harvey demonstrated the continuous circulation of the blood in the 17th century.

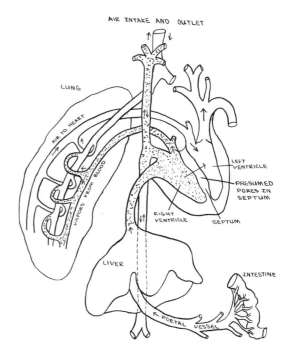

Fig. 3-3. Diagram illustrating Galen's description of the circulatory system

Reasons for the Decline of Greek Science

By the end of the 2nd century A. D. Greek science was virtually dead. The Alexandrian and Roman periods merely represented an extension, but the decline was in progress for centuries before the end came. It would be of great interest to know the reasons for the disintegration of the high intellectual pattern established by the Greeks. There is no simple explanation, but several factors were involved. Epidemic diseases, particularly malaria, were associated with war and conquest. The people were insecure and often demoralized. It is difficult to maintain an intellectual life when there is constant fear of illness and death. Moral and political decay contributed to the insecurity of the people in the Roman Empire. Dictators, unsympathetic to culture, had replaced the scholar-leaders of an earlier age, and war and strife had disrupted the pursuit of culture. It is difficult to say categorically whether war or peace best support the advance of science. A survey of history suggests that war and the requirements of warfare have generally stimulated science. Peace seems not to be the major prerequisite for the advance of science, but in the ancient world with poor communication when centers of learning were destroyed, groups of intellectually-superior people were disbanded and social disintegration was all too prevalent. Then too, Rome developed colonies and took pride in material gains, rather than in the encouragement of an intellectual life.

It must be remembered that there was no printing at this time; each new copy of a manuscript required tedious copying by hand. Copyists were not always accurate and sometimes took the liberty to "improve" the manuscripts by omitting parts with which they did not agree or inserting their own ideas when opportunities were presented. Information was not widely disseminated and could easily be lost. When a local unit was disrupted the accumulated knowledge could be lost forever. People in other locations, or at a later period of time, who were interested in the same area had to start from the beginning and accumulate the same information. This made it virtually impossible under unsettled political conditions to bring together a substantial body of facts in any one area of learning, and there was little chance for the survival of a culture.

Philosophies that were developed in the Roman world particularly by the Stoics and Epicureans were not conducive to the development of science. Stoics, who were governed by reason, subdued emotion, and were indifferent to pleasure or pain might have been scientists but their energies were devoted to subjective rather than to objective experiences. There was too much philosophy in early science. Philosophical ideas developed by "pure logic" took precedence over those obtained from observation and investigation. A philosopher schooled in logic could tear down another's work by arguments because there was no established base in classification, terminology, irrefutable experimentation, and perhaps even more important, there was no parallel development in mathematics that permitted measurements to be made and quantitative data to be used in elevation.

It has also been suggested by some historians that the institution of slavery tended to keep science in the theoretical and "toy" stage. Advances in mechanics, for example, never went beyond the toy stage and never were applied as labor-saving devices. Masters loved their slaves, wanted to keep them around, and were not interested in devising mechanical systems to replace them. Labor-saving devices are invented when labor is expensive, necessity is pressing, or survival is threatened.

REFERENCES

Allbutt, T. C. *Greek Medicine in Rome*. London: Macmillan and Co., 1921.

Ashley-Montagu, M. F. Vesalius and the Galenists. *Sci. Monthly* 80: 230-239, 1955.

Clagett, M. *Greek Science in Antiquity* Part II. New York: Abelard-Schuman, 1955.

Coonen, L. P. Biologists of Alexandria. *The Biologist* 39:13-18, 1957.

Farrington, B. *Science in Antiquity*. London: Oxford Univ. Press, 1947.

Green, R. M. trans. *Galen's Hygiene.* Springfield, Ill.: Charles C. Thomas, 1951.

Greene, W. C. *The Achievement of Rome.* Cambridge, Mass.: Harvard Univ. Press, 1934.

Hadzsits, G. D. *Lucretius and His Influence.* New York: Longmans, Green & Co., 1935.

Hamilton, E. *The Echo of Greece.* New York: W. W. Norton Co., 1957.

Kilgour, F. G. Galen. *Sci. Amer.* 196(3):105-108, 1957.

Latham, R. E. trans. *Lucretius, On the Nature of the Universe.* London: Penguin Books, 1951.

Lucretius, *On the Nature of Things.* trans. H. A. J. Munro. London: G. Bell and Sons, 1929.

Needham, J. *A History of Embryology.* Cambridge: The Univ. Press, 1934.

Plinius, S. C. *Natural History.* English trans. H. Rackham. Cambridge, Mass.: Harvard Univ. Press, 1938.

Sarton, G. *Galen of Pergamon.* Lawrence, Kansas: Univ. Kansas Press, 1954.

Sarton, G. Forgotten Men of Science. *Saturday Review* 41:50-55, 1959.

Singer, C. *A Short History of Anatomy and Physiology From the Greeks to Harvey.* New York: Dover Publ., Inc., 1956.

Singer, C. *From Magic to Science.* New York: Dover Publ., 1958.

Theophrastus, *De Causis Plantarum* (On Plants) trans. R. E. Dengler. Philadelphia: Univ. Penn., 1927.

Wethered, H. N. *The Mind of the Ancient World, A Consideration of Pliny's Natural History.* New York: Longmans, Green & Co., 1937.

Wilson, G. *Great Men of Science* (Galen pp. 53-58) Garden City, N. Y.: Garden City Publ.

Wright F. A. *A History of Later Greek Literature.* London: Routledge and Kegan Paul Ltd., 1951.

The period of some 1000 years from about 500 A.D. to about 1500 A.D. has been called the Middle Ages. Little was accomplished in biology; in fact, there was virtually no original observation in any area of science during this long period. Some of the Greek manuscripts were copied and used in monasteries, but many were lost or destroyed. Some were taken to Persia by scholars who studied in the Greek centers and carried copies home with them. Others were moved to Persia by Greek scholars who were exiled or who were voluntarily seeking a favorable place to live and study. Manuscripts that were preserved in Persia fell into the hands of the Arabs when Persia was conquered in the 7th century A.D.

Chapter 4

MIDDLE AGES

The Arabs made use of the Greek works and extended some to make them more useful for practical application, but the Arabs conducted few if any original investigations in biology.

Greek works were also preserved in the Roman Empire and, after the fall of the Empire, in the Christian monasteries; but they had little influence until Latin translations were made many centuries later. The attitude of the ruling class in the later stages of the Roman Empire was not favorable to the development of science. Romans were practical people. Because agriculture was needed to support armies, and physicians were needed to care for wounded soldiers, technicians were trained to fill immediate, practical assignments, but there was no incentive for them to gain a broad background in science. Centers of

learning were periodically invaded and destroyed by barbarians and since there was no printing to preserve and disseminate knowledge, destruction or loss of accumulated manuscripts in a local center could be a decisive loss to all science.

There has been much discussion concerning the influence of the early Christian church on science. Some writers have associated the rise of Christianity with the fall of ancient science. Actually, the decline of Greek science began before the time of Christ and the Christians were obscure and unimportant for several centuries after Christ. Later, when Christianity became widespread, it did little to promote science and in some instances discouraged its revival. Most leading Christians were indifferent to nature and considered free inquiry and research to be sinful. It should be remembered, however, that the church exerted great social force during the Middle Ages. It was the one institution that was devoted to maintaining order, preserving society and the heritage from the past. The church provided support and security for its people after the Roman Empire had fallen into decay, but it provided no incentive for inquiry in nature.

Medicine in the Middle Ages

Because of its practical applications, medicine fared better during the Middle Ages than other areas of biology. The tendency for men to want to live and avoid illness and death, kept alive their interest in medicine. Greek medicine was perpetuated but little progress was made after the time of Galen. It was customary among those who studied classical medicine to learn merely what was available from the Greek texts that were copied, compiled, and interpreted, but no original investigations or new observations were recorded. There was no attempt to replenish the store of facts and ideas lost or forgotten. Furthermore, the materials in existence were written in a language not understood by most people and not available to more than a few scholars connected with monasteries. The common practitioner had at his disposal only inferior but usually more practical Latin treatises on drugs and surgery.

Since most of the physicians and compilers of medical texts during the Middle Ages were monks, Christian monasteries became the centers of medical learning.   Medicine was again in the hands of religious organizations, as it had been in earlier periods when the priests of Imhotep and Asclepius controlled the theory and practice.   Monks were primarily concerned with their religious duties; and to them and their superiors, medical work was of secondary importance.   Many church people had little use for the medicine that was available.   They emphasized the importance of the soul while minimizing the body and bodily ills.   To many Christians, disease was a punishment for sin or a result of possession by devils or witches. Treatments required prayer, penitence, and supplication; every cure was a miracle.   Some of the less spiritually minded people argued that the body should be strengthened physically to enable it to withstand the attacks of the devil, but such arguments had little influence in church institutions.

At the Council of Clermont in 1130 A.D. the practice of medicine by the monks was forbidden because it interfered too much with religious activities. Medicine then fell largely into the hands of the secular clergy.

Biology Among the Persians and Arabs

The Arabs in Eastern Europe and Asia created little in science but they preserved the Greek contributions more successfully than the Christians in the Western World.   When the school at Athens finally closed in 529 A.D., most of the remaining Greek scholars were exiled to Persia.   With them went the remaining Greek manuscripts.   In the years that followed, Greek thought became fused with Persian thought.   When Mohammed conquered Persia in 631 A.D., the Arabs learned about Greek science from the captive Persians.   Greek works were translated into Arabic which became the universal language.

Mohammed placed conquest by the sword as the first means of expanding the faith.   Arabic forces swept into North Africa, Egypt, Syria, Mesopotamia, Armenia, Persia, Spain, Afghanistan, Baluchistan, a large portion of Turkestan, a smaller portion of India, and the islands of Crete and Cyprus. As the empire grew and gained strength, the incentive for education and culture rose.   Translation projects were undertaken through which Greek manuscripts were made available to Arabic scholars.

This enabled the Arabs to assimilate much of the Greek knowledge of medicine and philosophy.   A period that has been designated "the golden age of Arabic medicine" developed in the 9th and 10th centuries A.D.   The rise of a universal language had its influence on science and particularly medicine.   Arabic was concise and especially well adapted for scientific writing.   This characteristic of the language proved valuable in the translation and application of technical Greek works.

The Arabs were more active in the physical sciences, such as astronomy, mathematics, and chemistry, than in the biological sciences.   All acids and alkalis known before the last century were known in the laboratories of the Arabs. Many practical inventions such as the magnifying glass, windmill, and linen paper (necessary for printing) were made. Words used in modern physical science, such as alchemy, nadir, azimith, aldurism, cipher, alcohol, and algebra came from the Arabs.   Arabic numbers, much more useful than the Roman numerals for scientific usage, were introduced.   Any who doubt this should try multiplying with Roman numerals.

Avicenna

One of the most illustrious of the Arabic scholars was the physician-philosopher, Ibn Sina, known in the Western World by the Latin name, Avicenna.   He was born in the year 980 A.D. in the province of Balkh, now Afghanistan.   His first study consisted of a mastery of the Koran which he completed at the age of seven.   About that time his father moved the family to the city of Bokhara which was the capital of Turkestan.   Here the boy continued his education with the study of arithmetic and logic.   He became interested in medicine which he studied from the works of Aristotle and Galen.

At the age of seventeen, Avicenna was a practicing physician and was successful in curing the Samanid Sultan of Bokhara from an ailment.   With this recognition, Avicenna was appointed court physician and invited to study in the Sultan's library where translation of Greek manuscripts were kept.   At the age of 22, Avicenna left Bokhara and traveled from court to court healing rulers, practicing medicine among the common people, and philosophizing.

His great success and increasing popularity led to his imprisonment through the influence of jealous rivals. While in prison Avicenna began writing his famous book, Canon of Medicine which was later completed in the city of Ispahan (Isafahan) in the court of a friendly prince. Here Avicenna found the peace and security that he needed to continue his work of writing and practicing medicine.

The writings of Avicenna demonstrated his ability to observe, retain ideas, and make use of logic. His main contributions were in two general fields, medicine and philosophy. The philosophical treatise considered best by his followers was The Book of Theorems and Propositions. Some other treatises were: Guide to Wisdom, composed by Avicenna when in prison; The Fountains of Wisdom; several treatises on logic, one of which forms a part of the work entitled, On the Soul; an epistle on Human Faculties and Their Perceptions; and a series of mystical treatises. Avicenna's philosophical contributions have been classified in five basic areas: logic, physics, psychology, metaphysics, and ethics.

Over 100 medical works have been attributed to Avicenna. The major medical contribution was the Canon of Medicine, a storehouse of facts, in which the author attempted to codify the whole medical knowledge of the time and to correlate the facts with the systems of Aristotle and Galen. It was composed of five volumes: the first two were devoted to physiology, pathology, and hygiene; the third and fourth described methods of treating disease; and the fifth was a materia medica dealing with the nature and properties of substances used to treat disease. Although it was voluminous, it was clear and easy to read, exemplifying the simplicity possible in using the Arabic language.

It should be pointed out that, although most of Avicenna's written work was theoretical, he was a practical physician. His abilities in using the medical art in healing the sick were attested by the fact that he was a court physician for many rulers. Three of Avicenna's more practical medical writings were as follows: (1) On Vision, Haemolytic Jaundice, and Meningitis. Avicenna anticipated the modern explanation of vision. He understood the difference between obstructive and haemolytic jaundice and was the first to provide a good description of meningitis. (2) Malignant Cancer. Avicenna had experience with tumorous growths and cancer and described cases in considerable detail. His descriptions and methods of treatment are quite acceptable by modern standards. The only hope of cure of malignant disease, he said, is surgical treatment in the early stages. Excisions must be wide and bold; all veins running to the tumor must be included in the amputation. Even this is not sufficient; the affected area should be cauterized. Even then, Avicenna added, cure is not certain. (3) Use of Anesthetics. It is clear from the discussion that Avicenna effectively used for anesthetics in his operations drugs that had been initiated by the Chinese centuries before.

The Arabic literature as it moved west to Salerno, Bologna, Toledo, Montpellier, and Paris, carried many misconceptions. It was characterized by an over-adherence to the classical Greek authorities with a magnification of errors and imperfections introduced by copyists. The prevalence of astrology, aversion to anatomical studies, degradation of surgery, (Avicenna ranked this as an inferior branch of medicine), and the predilection toward cautery and laudable pus in surgery, all had an adverse influence on the development of medicine in the West. It is well to note, however, that the medical literature from the Arabs ran much higher in degree of perfection than that obtainable directly from the West. Two men were chiefly responsible for the early translations of the major medical works of the Arabic culture into Latin. They were Constantinus Africanus (1020-1087) of Salerno, and Gerard of Cremona (1140-1187), who worked in Toledo. These men lived near the Arab-Christian border where they were able to gain much from the Arab literature and introduce it into the western culture.

Following translation, Avicenna's work had great influence in the West. It became available at a time when the West was looking into the theoretical aspects as well as the practical side of medicine. For some five centuries the Canon of Medicine was accepted as a guide in European universities.

The western world finally obtained the works of the Greeks through a roundabout course. The writings of Aristotle, for example, came through several successive translations. From the Greek they were translated into Persian, next to Arabic, and in the 11th and 12th centuries into Latin. Early in the 13th century, Michael Scot translated more of Aristotle's work from Arabic to Latin. From Latin the Greek works were translated into German and other modern languages.

Medical School at Salerno

The first important medical school of the Middle Ages developed at Salerno in southern Italy and was officially founded in 1150 A. D. This location was close to Sicily, where the Greek-Arabic influence had become concentrated. The world-famous medical school at Salerno was not a church institution but a lay organization composed of a group of men interested in medicine. Medical papers were written by the members of the school; some contained clinical descriptions of such diseases as dysentery and urogenital irregularities. Therapeutic agents such as mercury ointments for skin diseases, and iodine for goiter, were described. Excellent work in surgery was done by members of the Salerno school.

Western Universities

Stimulus from the Greek works, again available in the West, resulted in co-operative group activities designed to accumulate and use the new knowledge. This movement, promoted by scholars who had already come together in a few centers, resulted in the founding of the western universities. (Fig. 4-1) The

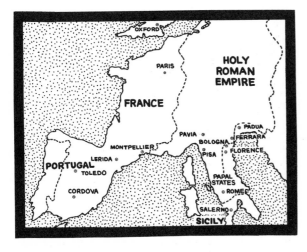

Fig. 4-1. Map showing locations of early western universities

universities reflected a rebellion against the narrow provisions for education offered by monasteries.

The University of Paris was said to have been founded in 1110 A. D. (chartered in 1200 A. D.) by a group of free lance teachers who came together in Paris and gathered around them groups of students who wanted to learn. Instruction at first was informal and personal but when the institution became popular and there were not enough teachers to work individually with the increased numbers of students, classes were organized and the lecture method was employed. Greek classics formed the basis of the curriculum. There was no appreciation for science nor the scientific method. By modern standards, the class work would be considered superficial indeed. It was "book learning" and became known as the scholastic method of teaching. The teacher's task was merely to pass on the information available to him. He took no interest in helping his students to think independently and he took no responsibility himself for adding to the store of knowledge. Anyone who could read the works of Aristotle and other classical authors could be a teacher. The tendency among students was to memorize facts and to recite back the information they were given by the teacher. They were inclined to sharpen their wits and their senses rather than to develop reasoning power.

Two great figures, who rose above the level of their colleagues, became established at the University of Paris during the 13th century. They were the German, Albertus Magnus (1206-80), and the Englishman, Roger Bacon (1214-94). Albertus, a member of the religious order of Dominicans, was a follower of Aristotle. He considered it his special mission to harmonize the teaching of Aristotle with church doctrines. When he found statements in Aristotle's writings that did not agree with his own observations, he was courageous enough to state his disagreement. For example, Aristotle had said that the heart was the seat of the soul but Albertus attributed this function to the brain. Unfortunately, however, he followed Aristotle in some mistakes that had been corrected by later Greeks.

Albertus was interested in physics and geology as well as biology. He described and classified mineral elements, without the aid of modern instruments, into a system that was good as far as it went. Free arsenic was discovered by Albertus and he made important chemical combinations with this element. In biology he made scholarly beginnings in describing and classifying plants. His descriptions of plants, like those of the elements, were good as far as they went, but he had no natural basis for classification and knew nothing about minute structures. In his later life, he went back to his native Germany and located in Cologne, where he became a bishop in the Church. He did some exploring in the great mineral deposits of Germany which have since become important politically as well as economically.

Roger Bacon, an Englishman who had studied at Oxford and later at Paris, was a Franciscan monk. His interests were in physical science rather than biology but he made indirect contributions to biology. He was against the scholastic method of education, prevalent at his time, and demonstrated the values of observation and experimentation. So many strange things happened through his experiments that he was accused of witchcraft and sent to prison. When Pope Clement III was suffering from a stone in his bladder, Bacon was summed as a consultant. The Pope was so impressed with Bacon's scientific attitude and wide knowledge, that he commissioned him to write two volumes, some 900 pages, on science. In the course of his work, Bacon studied and wrote on optics, lenses, and theories of light. He advocated the use of lenses for correction of eye irregularities and traced the function of sight to the brain. His greatest contribution was the introduction and demonstration of the experimental method.

Other leading universities established in the same period were Oxford University in England, founded in 1167, and Montpellier in southern France, founded in 1181. This latter university became famous in the 13th century for its medical program and with other early universities exerted a profound influence on social, political, and intellectual trends at that time. The early Italian universities at Bologna and Padua developed a wide reputation in the field of medicine. Early development of the University of Bologna will be described in more detail as an example of the university movement.

University of Bologna

Bologna became a center of learning during the period of the Roman Empire and the beginnings of a university were established at that time. But no real organization occurred until the 13th century when a law school was officially founded. It is difficult to establish an exact date when the institution might be considered to have university status. An early reliable reference is associated with the election of Pope Gelasius II, in 1118. At that time Bologna was described as a university. The word "university" connoted only the corporation, in which religious leaders and rulers aided the schools and granted important privileges. European universities developed as collections of colleges held together by the legal advantages afforded by the university. Schools licensed by the Vatican could offer course work in law, theology, philosophy, and later, medicine.

A spontaneous association developed at early Bologna between teachers and scholars because of the eagerness of young men to acquire knowledge. The students controlled the institutions and, at first, operated them quite independently without any connection with political or religious authorities. Interested students sought qualified teachers. Men with special "faculties" for particular subjects were chosen to teach and, eventually, groups of such men with appropriate qualifications became known as "faculties." The "Universitas" thus developed as a group of units (colleges) made up of teachers and scholars. When a teacher or master moved from place to place, his students went with him. Lectures at Bologna were at first held in the private apartments of teachers, and only at the beginning of the 15th century did the colleges meet in places especially designed for instruction. It was during the 15th century that the School of Medicine, or School of Artists (medicine belonging to the liberal arts) was provided a special building. To insure quietness for lectures and study, noisy shops and industries were not permitted in the vicinity of the university.

The student-university that originated in Bologna played a new role in the history of education. This institution was as different from anything that preceded it as it was unlike any modern institution. Students paid the teachers for instruction, for the use of the benches, and sometimes for the rent of the meeting place. Teachers were obliged, under penalty of fine, to have the rooms cleaned and renovated every year before the beginning of the lectures. In Paris and the English universities, colleges were established where teachers and students lived together, but in Bologna, students were lodged in the houses of their masters or in boarding houses controlled by municipal authorities. Houses occupied by students were protected, and the students' needs were given first consideration. In case of the sale of the house, students could not be evicted at least until the end of the academic year. Students were exempt from taxation on food and living expenses; a fact recorded on a marble tablet on the customs house in Bologna.

Scholars were encouraged by the townspeople to come to Bologna, where they were treated with great respect. A cherished law forbade the University to move elsewhere, for it was considered to be the "city's most precious treasure". The death penalty faced anyone who dared to attempt to move the University or induce students to leave Bologna. The same penalty applied to teachers who, without permission from their students and the University, left to teach elsewhere. Large numbers of students came from other countries, often from rich families, and some brought their tutors with them. In the 16th century, the records show that several thousand students from different countries were registered at Bologna. Among them were German nobility and intelligentsia, princes of sovereign houses, students who later became cardinals and bishops, and others who acquired fame as physicians and scientists.

Lectures were divided into two categories, ordinary and extraordinary, based mainly on the status of the lecturer. Ordinary lectures were given in the forenoon by qualified teachers whereas extraordinary lectures were less formal reviews or repetitions given often in the evenings by visitors or advanced students. Teachers were given the professional title "doctor" and later the academic title "professor". Graduation at Bologna was divided into two parts: the private examination and the public examination. The private examination was the real test of knowledge acquired, whereas the public examination was a mere ceremony, much like the commencement exercises of modern universities.

The Bologna School of Medicine was formally organized in the 13th century, although medicine was taught at Bologna for many years before. Teachers of

medicine did not have a fixed salary but, like other professors, were paid fees by their students. A popular teacher received large sums and could amass great wealth. Later, the municipality assumed the responsibility of paying a fixed salary to three teachers who occupied particular chairs in medicine; one was for teaching the practice of medicine, one, the philosophy of medicine, and the third, astrology.

At the beginning of the 13th century, Ugo of Lucco, a famous surgeon, who had developed simple methods for the treatment of fractures, was given a high salary to come to Bologna as a lecturer. Friar Theodoric of Lucco (1205-98) son of Ugo also became a famous physician; the first to advocate simple treatment of wounds. He maintained that the formation of pus was not necessary to healing, and that drugs applied to wounds sometimes actually hindered the healing process. In one of Theodoric's books, directions were given for the use of anesthesia during operations. Sponges were drenched in narcotics, such as opium or mandrake after which they were dried and stored. Before the operation they were soaked in hot water for an hour and then applied to the nose of the patient, who was instructed to breathe deeply. The operation was not begun until the patient was asleep. Practical, widespread use of anesthesia was not developed until some 6 centuries later.

Another great surgeon of the School of Bologna was William of Saliceto (1201-77). His book on surgery became popular and was used for several centuries. The name of Taddeo Alderotti is also associated with the School of Medicine at Bologna. This famous physician, who began teaching about 1260, was immortalized in the verses of Dante. Dante studied at Bologna and may have attended Alderotti's lectures. Medical students attended lectures on practical and theoretical medicine and on natural and moral philosophy. A standard requirement was attendance at lectures and discussions on the works of Hippocrates, Galen, and Avicenna. Two other required subjects were surgery and astrology. The most distinguished occupant of the chair of astrology at Bologna was the poet and philosopher, Cecco D'Ascoli, who, in 1327, was burned at the stake, a victim of the Inquisition.

In the Middle Ages, surgery was generally a subordinate subject considered to be manual craft. Nevertheless,

Bologna holds an important place in the history of this discipline. Licenses were granted to those who passed appropriate examinations but licensed surgeons were not classed as medical "doctors". For the degree in medicine, the candidate was required to be twenty-four years of age, to have five years standing in the study of medicine, and he must also have lectured on some medical book. The surgery license required considerably less training.

Teaching of anatomy during the early 13th century consisted mainly of the work of Galen with no actual dissection. Autopsies became established procedures connected with law enforcement before they were acceptable in medicine. The first male autopsy on record was performed in 1281 and the first female autopsy was made some thirty years later. Henrie de Mondeville (1260), a pupil of

Saliceto, became a famous teacher of anatomy. He prepared drawings at Bologna and later taught at Montpellier. Mondino (1270-1326), also a great anatomist at Bologna, wrote a textbook which was used in virtually all European universities for 3 centuries after its preparation. There was no attempt to make new discoveries, but Mondino set out to verify the work of the Greeks by actual observation. It is doubtful that he dissected human bodies, but he studied numerous domestic animals and advised his students to learn anatomy by actual dissection.

During the 15th century, the Bologna School of Medicine, which had been founded as an independent institution, came more and more under the influence of the Church, which exercised a decisive influence in the choice of professors.

REFERENCES

Brehaut, E. *An Encyclopedist of the Dark Ages: Isidore of Seville.* New York: Longmans, Green and Co., 1912.

Campbell, D. E. H. *Arabian Medicine and Its Influence on the Middle Ages.* London: K. Paul, Trench, Trubner and Co., 1926.

Clagett, M. *Greek Science in Antiquity.* Part II. New York: Abelard-Schuman, 1955.

Corner, G. W. *Anatomical Texts of the Earlier Middle Ages.* Washington, D. C.: Carnegie Inst. Wash., 1927.

Elgood, C. *A Medical History of Persia.* Cambridge: The Univ. Press, 1951.

Haskins, C. H. *The Renaissance of the Twelfth Century.* Cambridge, Mass.: Harvard Univ. Press, 1933.

Haskins, C. H. *The Rise of the Universities.* New York: P. Smith, 1940.

Holmyard, E. J. *The Ordinall Alchemy.* Baltimore: Williams and Wilkins, 1929.

Holmyard, E. J. *Alchemy.* New York: Penguin Books, 1957.

Hopkins, A. J. *Alchemy, Child of Greek Philosophy.* New York: Columbia Univ. Press, 1934.

Lassek, A. M. *Human Dissection, Its Drama and Struggle.* Springfield, Ill.: Charles C. Thomas, 1958.

Rashdall, H. *The Universities of Europe in the Middle Ages.* London: Oxford Univ. Press, 1936.

Sarton, G.   *The History of Science and the New Humanism*.   Cambridge, Mass.:
   Harvard Univ. Press, 1937.

Singer, C.   *Greek Science and Greek Medicine*.   Oxford: Clarendon Press, 1922.

Singer, C.   *From Magic to Science*.   London: Ernest Benn, Ltd., 1928.

Singer, C.   *A Short History of Anatomy and Physiology From the Greeks to Harvey*.
   New York: Dover Publ., Inc., 1958.

Taylor, F. S.   *The Alchemists*.   Henry Schuman, 1949.

Taylor, H. O.   *The Medieval Mind*.   Cambridge, Mass., Howard Univ. Press, 1949.

Thomas B.   *The Arabs*.   Garden City, N. Y.: Doubleday, Doran and Co., 1937.

Thorndike, L.   *A History of Magic and Experimental Science*.   8 Vol. New York:
   The Macmillan Co. 1923-58. (Vol. 1-4 cover period of Middle Ages).

The 14th to 16th century period was marked by a revival in Greek science and a rebirth of science in general. This was a transitional stage from the Middle Ages to the Modern Age called the Renaissance. It was a culmination or flowering of the Middle Ages characterized by physical and intellectual discovery and not a sudden break with the past. America was discovered and explored and sea travel became common. New coast lines, continental areas, and oceanic islands were discovered with strange plant, animal, and human inhabitants. Gunpowder, which had been discovered in the 12th century, came into practical use and markedly changed the mode of warfare and conquest. The religious

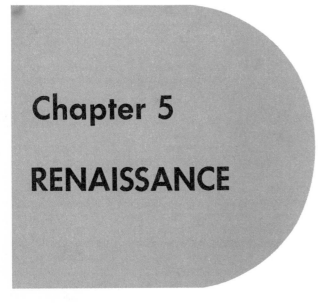

Chapter 5

RENAISSANCE

reformation that occurred in the latter part of the Renaissance brought with it a critical attitude toward general culture as well as religion. There was a wholesale development in the basic sciences, particularly mathematics and astronomy.

Perhaps the most important single development was the use of printing from movable type. In addition to making knowledge more accessible, printing brought a stimulus to new discovery. There was much more incentive to discover and present a new Greek or Latin manuscript if it could be printed and distributed. When only single copies of a manuscript could be made from an old text, it was futile to try to dispurse it widely, but when numerous replicas were possible it seemed worth the time and effort required to find and reproduce old texts. By the end of the 15th century

many of the works of Aristotle, Theophrastus, Dioscorides, and Pliny were available to the educated public. This does not mean that all these manuscripts were discovered for the first time since their original production. Some were not actually lost, but only neglected. Some had been discovered and translated when previous revivals occurred, particularly in the 9th and 12th centuries, but the first sustained interest on the part of large groups of people came in the Renaissance centuries. Not only did the Greek texts appear, but Latin translations were made which could be read by more people. The work of Pliny was written in Latin and therefore became much more readily available than the works of Aristotle, Theophrastus, and Dioscorides which required translation from the Greek. Some translations had already been made from Arabic to Latin by Africanus, Gerald of Cremona, and Michael Scot, but now the movement was in full swing.

When the Renaissance awakening was eventually extended to original observations and experiments, printing had great importance. For the first time it was possible for an investigator to record on permanent printed pages his results and interpretations. These pages could be widely distributed and other investigators, even at a distance, could have access to his work. It was no longer necessary to start from the beginning with each study. A new investigator could go on from the place where his predecessors left off. Printing also provided for critical review by contemporaries, and opportunities to compare experimental results and interpretations. Numerous copies could be prepared for wide distribution and it was no longer necessary to depend on a single manuscript that could be lost or distorted.

In the Renaissance and the periods following, many fields of biology were developed simultaneously. In this outline of the history of biology it will no longer be possible to follow a chronological sequence. The fields of botany, anatomy, and surgery will be used to illustrate the developments in biology during the Renaissance. These areas developed to a higher level at this time time than most other branches of biology.

Botany

Plants with medicinal value were known to the early Chinese and other groups who lived at earlier periods. Hippocrates and his fellow Greek physicians were interested in plants. Aristotle wrote about plants but unfortunately his botanical works were not preserved. The work of Theophrastus including observations on reproduction and seed germination and descriptions of some 500 plants was preserved. The Roman surgeon, Dioscorides, described many plants particularly those with medicinal value. Although foundations of botany were laid by the Greeks, little progress was made in the long period that elapsed before the Renaissance awakening. Throughout the ages, plant science has been closely associated with medicine. Botany was, therefore, an important part of the medical curriculum and many botanists were professors of medicine.

Foremost in the revival of botany were a group of herbalists called the "German fathers of botany." These men made use of the newly invented printing and also used wood carving for illustrating plants as they appeared in nature. Some herbalists did the technical work of illustrating plants themselves, but others engaged artists to do the illustrating. The first member of the German group was Otto Brunfels (1489-1534), a monk who fled from the church and became interested in medicine. He took the text of his herbal from Dioscorides but the drawings were made from actual plants in nature by an artist, Hans Weiditz. Serious discrepancies occurred when Weiditz drew plants from Germany which did not fit the original text based on the Mediterranean region. Plants which did not match the descriptions of Dioscorides had no names. Brunfels called them "nameless waifs."

The discrepancies that occurred in Brunfel's herbal were overcome by the next German father, Jerome Bock (1498-1554), in his Kreütter Buck (1539). He described plants in his own garden from his own observations. His artist, David Kandel, drew the same plants which Bock described. The location and surroundings of each plant were recorded along with the description. Bock's illustrations were not as good as those of Brunfel, but his descriptions were original and considerably better because he described what he saw.

The third "father" was Leonard Fuchs (1501-66), a well-educated physician and professor at the University of Tübingen. The text and illustrations of Fuch's herbal, published in 1542, were more elaborate, better documented, and more concise than either of those which appeared earlier. Fuchs described some 400 German plants and also about 100 foreign specimens. Three collaborators, two artists and one engraver, worked with Fuchs in preparing his illustrations. This herbal was the best one prepared during the period and it had great influence on the art of describing plants. Fuchs was sarcastic about the superficial work of others and he was particularly caustic in his statements about most physician's knowledge of plants.

Valerius Cordus (1515-44), the fourth member of the group, was a pharmacist as well as a botanist. He was a true scientist with broad interests. After observing and describing the plants in his own country, he went to Italy to see the plants that Dioscorides and others of the ancients had described. Unfortunately, this brilliant and versatile man died, in Rome, from a fever when he was only 29 years old. His botanical work was published in 1561, several years after his death, by Conrad Gesner. In addition to his work on plants, Cordus had other accomplishments in pharmacology; he was the first to describe the anesthetic properties of ether. This was done in 1540, but it was 3 centuries later when practical use was made of the discovery.

The illustrations from nature in the herbals did much to increase the popularity and practical usefulness of these books. People who could not read the Greek or even the Latin text could learn much from the pictures. Later herbals, written with a great many pictures and a small amount of written material, could be used by uneducated women to pick out certain plants of medicinal value (simples) which they collected and sold to druggists. Virtually all plants had some value and the industry of collecting simples became an important one.

Although the German fathers led the way in the development of botany, interest soon developed in other countries of Europe. Surveys made in distant lands such as Mexico and India added new and strange plants to the lists and collections. In an age of discovery and exploration it was quite natural to undertake surveys of the flora of distant lands. Explorers in America and Asia returned to Europe with news about strange plants as well as leaves, fruits, and seeds of actual specimens. A new kind of natural-ist thus developed, the scientific explorer, who was interested in new knowledge of natural history and was willing to undergo the hazards and hardships of an explorer for no other purpose than the accumula-tion of scientific facts. Established scientists such as physicians, professors, and curators of botanical gardens were usually required to remain at home and younger, more adventurous scientists made the trips. Those at home were stimulated to make their descriptions more detailed and more accurate to keep pace with new developments. The whole movement promoted a higher quality of botanical research.

William Turner (1510-68), the lead-ing English botanist of the period, was a critical writer who demonstrated the true scientific spirit. His herbal appeared in 1561. In Switzerland two brothers, Jean and Kaspar Bauhin (1560-1624) led the Swiss school of botany. Jean engaged in a project of mass production and prepared some 3500 rather sketchy descriptions of plants. Kaspar developed an index or concordance of species, collected dried specimens of plants, and built a herbarium for critical study and comparisons among species. More and more plants were be-coming known and some method of sys-tematic arrangement became necessary. To fill this need, Bauhin developed a sys-tematic arrangement of names and de-scriptions, that represented a beginning and eventually led to the binomial system of nomenclature.

In Italy, Pietro Andrea Mattioli (1500-77) published, in 1554, a commen-tary on Dioscorides, that was reprinted in many successive editions. This work became popular and many copies were sold. So great was the authority and in-fluence of Mattioli that discoverers of new plants in various parts of the world followed a practice of sending information they accumulated to him to be included in his next edition. Another Italian, who made contributions in plant studies was Andrea Cesalpino (1519-1603). He im-proved upon the system of nomenclature developed by his predecessors and de-veloped a binomial system anticipating that of Linnaeus.

Following the stimulus that came with the herbals, botanical gardens were developed for scientific as well as medici-nal and ornamental purposes. Such gar-dens were already associated with medical schools but as time went on, they attained broader significance for basic research. Among the earliest botanical gardens was the one established at Pisa about 1544 by Luca Ghini (1490-1556). A few years later a botanical garden was established at Padua. Florence also had such a gar-den in about 1550.

Even botanical gardens where living plants could be kept did not fill all the re-quirements for making material available to investigators. Plants grow only dur-ing certain seasons of the year, and they are usually not available in the winter. To make it possible to keep plants on hand at all times, a group of Italian bota-nists led the way to establishing herbaria for preserving dried specimens. The keeper of the botanical garden at Pisa, Luca Ghini, began drying and preserving plants between sheets of paper soon after his botanical garden was opened. In the 1550's he is known to have sent preserved specimens from his garden to Mattioli. Cesalpino gathered and preserved plants for the grand duke of Tuscany at about the same time. A few years later Ulisses Aldrovandus (1522-1602) prepared a her-barium of about 4000 plants which is still preserved at the University of Bologna.

Anatomy

Anatomy is tangible and observable and therefore was better developed in the ancient and medieval periods than other areas of biology such as physiology. The human mind resolves tangible problems more readily and effectively than intangi-ble relations which require experiments for analysis. Beginnings in animal an-atomy, like those in botany go far back in history. Extensive anatomical work, in-cluding numerous human dissections, was done at Alexandria before the time of Christ. Galen dissected many different animals, including apes, but no human bodies. His writings, considered for centuries to be infallible documents on human anatomy, were based on lower animals. A few human dissections were made during the Middle Ages, but they were infrequent and had no lasting influ-ence. Pigs were used mostly for anatom-ical studies at the Salerno school. Anatomists there were interested in the structure of the human body, as was Galen, but human dissections were not considered proper and were, therefore, so rare that most of the human anatomi-cal knowledge had to come from specula-tion based on other animals. As the history of anatomy is now considered in perspective, it is surprising that the studies based on pigs and apes were as useful as they were to anatomists who were primarily interested in human anatomy.

With the new medical schools in the Renaissance, public dissections called "anatomies" were organized to provide opportunity for more people to see the internal parts of the human body and to make the best possible use of the few human bodies available for dissection. Most professors of anatomy had been trained in the scholastic pattern of the day and had never actually made a dissection. Because they considered the task below their dignity and did not care to soil their hands, technicians or prosectors were employed to make the dissections. It was much more pleasant and less confusing for the professors to handle and observe the clean pages of Galen. The professor sat some distance above the operating table in a room built like an arena and read Galen aloud. If the reader and the dissector were well-synchronized, the students around the table were supposed to see the anatomical parts as they were being described by the reader. Actually, neither the professor who was some distance away, nor the students who were seated around the arena, could see clearly the parts being dissected. The only person who really saw what went on was the prosector and he was only supposed to work, not to talk. If a discrepancy occurred between the description and the dissection, the written word of Galen was invariably accepted rather than the observation of the body laid out for inspection. Curiously, in such circumstances, the body itself was considered wrong; and Galen, who had never seen a human body dissected, was considered right.

There were some real anatomists who lived during the Renaissance. The greatest were Leonardo da Vinci and Andreas Vesalius. They were not satisfied with the kind of dissection they observed in the anatomies and preferred to use the knife themselves.

Leonardo da Vinci

Leonardo da Vinci (1452-1519 Fig. 5-1) was one of the great anatomists of all time. He became famous not only in anatomy but in most every phase of Renaissance art and science. Leonardo was born in Vinci, near Florence, Italy, and spent his early years in Florence and the surrounding country where he observed the birds and the insects in the meadows. He studied trees and flowers on the hillsides and represented the things he saw with sketches on whatever material he had at hand. His father recognized his artistic potential and when Leonardo was fourteen years of age he was apprenticed to Verrochio, one of the leading artists of the Renaissance. Art in this period was characterized by reality. External structure of human beings, as well as that of other animals, was extensively studied, especially for the preparation of statues and other pieces of sculpture which were popular at that time. In order to make them life-like, the artists scrutinized living examples with the greatest of care. Curiously, artists became more proficient in anatomy than anatomists.

Fig. 5-1. Leonardo da Vinci, Renaissance artist and anatomist

Leonardo attended anatomies whenever they were held in this vicinity. He performed dissections on animals and probably on human bodies while he was still a young man. Later he was granted permission to carry out anatomical studies at the hospital of Santa Maria Nuova in Florence. Leonardo's approach to anatomical science was new and refreshing. All of his contemporaries and most of his predecessors followed precisely the work of Galen and that of earlier Greek and Alexandrian anatomists. Mondino of Bologna who had dissected numerous animal and human bodies preferred to dissect fresh bodies and stated frankly that he had no interest in the preserving method then prevalent that consisted of masserating or drying the bodies to make the inaccessable parts more readily observable. Leonardo followed Mondino and set out to dissect actual, fresh human bodies for the purpose of studying them in all of their beauty and to represent them properly in art. He showed scientific interest and curiosity in his early undertakings. He also showed originality and skill as a technician in working out devices for observation and experiment.

During the course of his anatomical studies, Leonardo was reported to have dissected some thirty human bodies. His findings were recorded in 129 notebooks well illustrated with detailed sketches. The successful results of his experiments showed that he anticipated some modern techniques in studying the soft parts of the body. The eye structure, for example, which was soft and difficult to dissect was placed in the white of an egg. The mass was heated until the albumen coagulated and the soft structures were held firmly enough to enable him to cut transversely without the loss or distortion of the finer structures. Leonardo also developed methods of injection for the hollow ventricles of the brain surrounded by thin membranes which were easily distorted and lost. By using a syringe, Leonardo filled the ventricles with melted wax. After the wax had solidified he was able to dissect with precision and follow three ventricles of the brain. Leonardo also made some vivisection experiments on animals. In one experiment he observed the heart beat of a pig. This was done by drilling through the chest and inserting pins to hold out the body wall.

The Renaissance period was an exciting time for its leaders. New information was being obtained in many areas of culture and it did not seem impossible for a person to be interested in, or even to master, all branches of knowledge known at that time. Leonardo was interested in many artistic and scientific developments. He was attracted to anatomy from the standpoint of art but soon he became so absorbed in it that he carried on anatomical studies for their own sake. In 1510 he wrote that he hoped to master the whole field of anatomy during that year. Furthermore, it was his intention to write an encyclopedia on man, but he never accomplished

this goal. This was the fate of many others of Leonardo's objectives. He was a perfectionist, who was never satisfied, nothing was ever considered finished, but he was always experimenting to make his accomplishments better. Some 16 years were devoted to a bronze statue of a horse that was never really completed. He worked 12 years on the famous painting of the last supper on a monastery wall in Milan, Italy. Three years were spent in getting the twist of the lip of Peter exactly right. He never did feel satisfied with his accomplishment.

Leonardo had scientific curiosity but he did not stick to his objective as a scientist must. He did not make any lasting contribution at the time but demonstrated the scientific spirit. A scientist must have curiosity strong enough to make him resort to observations and experiments but he must also have persistence to carry his experiments to completion. Leonardo had the curiosity but not the persistence. His treatises on anatomy, however, and his illustrations show that he had great skill as an artist and great ability as an anatomist. By using illustrations to show structural characteristics, he was able to present a large volume of information with only a few words.

Some 20 notebooks and bound volumes of Leonardo's work including some 4000 pages are now available. Many have only sketches and drawings; others are covered with minute writings running from right to left on the page rather than from left to right. Had the notebooks been known in the 16th and 17th centuries Leonardo probably would have been recognized as the father of anatomy. Unfortunately, the notebooks were lost until the 18th century.

Vesalius

Andreas Vesalius (1514-1564 Fig. 5-2) the leading anatomist of the Renaissance, followed in the tradition of Leonardo da Vinci and made dissections with his own hands. Vesalius was born in Brussels, Belgium, the son of an apothecary-physician who had descended from a long line of physicians. While a young boy Vesalius dissected mice, moles, cats, dogs, and weasels on his mother's kitchen table. Equipped with a keen intellect and a strong motivation, he began his training for medicine at the University of Louvain. He did not receive sufficient challenge at Louvain so he transferred to the University of Paris when he was 18 years old (1532). Here he was engaged for 3 years in the study of medicine and as a part-time assistant in anatomy.

Fig. 5-2. Andreas Vesalius, Renaissance anatomist

At Paris he came under the influence of Sylvius (1478-1555), a sophisticated anatomist of the Renaissance who had studied and taught classical languages, Greek, Roman, and Hebrew, until he was 50 years old. Sylvius had become so interested in treatises on anatomy by Greek and Roman authors that he developed a series of classical lectures on the subject. In 1536, Sylvius published a text on anatomy based on the works of Galen. He did no original research but merely organized and repeated Galen's work. Vesalius served as an assistant to Sylvius and soon surpassed his master. As they worked together, Vesalius expressed doubts concerning some of Galen's work and insisted on describing structures as he saw them. He quarreled with Sylvius on many points and when he learned that Galen had never actually dissected a human body, he lost all confidence in Galen's work. He called the anatomies "detestable ceremonies" in which barbers

do the cutting and instructors who direct from a distance "sing like magpies of things whereof they have no experience."

Vesalius soon became dissatisfied with the University of Paris and left without graduating. He began his own independent study of anatomy, obtaining specimens from graveyards and execution chambers. In his own room he assembled the bones of the human skeleton. Each bone was handled so much that he could recognize it by touch with his eyes closed. Because of his medical background he was assigned to caring for the wounded in the Belgian army and his knowledge of human anatomy was greatly increased. Now he realized more than ever that Galen's account of human anatomy was full of errors.

He went to Venice for a time and engaged in study and anatomical practice. When he made public dissections he surprised his observers by dissecting and lecturing at the same time. At Padua he completed the work for the doctor's degree and accepted a professorship in 1537, when he was 23 years of age. Here he became a popular professor, giving demonstration-lectures that were attended by hundreds of students. He lectured in Latin rather than Greek so the practitioners as well as the scholars could understand him. In 1540 Vesalius assembled the bones of an ape and those of a man and demonstrated before a large audience, some 200 differences in which Galen was in error.

The great book of Vesalius, The Fabric (Structure) of the Human Body, was first published in 1543. Vesalius was assisted in this book by a student of Titian who prepared the illustrations. It is a rare combination of Renaissance art and modern anatomy with the bones, muscles, blood vessels, nerves, internal organs, and the brain shown in proper perspective. The illustrations are not mere diagrams but accurate representations of the structures in the living body. Vesalius followed Galen in his description of the heart. When he came to the septum between the two sides, he was puzzled but postulated invisible pores through which the blood passed. The book represented Vesalius' concept of the human body, a most beautiful object, a piece of the handiwork of the Almighty.

It was not easy for Vesalius to break with the Galen tradition. His former professors, Sylvius and Günther, called him an "unprincipled upstart." Even his assistant at Padua tried to discredit him. Unfortunately, Vesalius did not have the drive to overcome opposition. He became discouraged at the age of 31 and burned most of his scientific writings. In the latter part of his life Vesalius was physician to the King of Spain.

Vesalius has been called the "father of modern anatomy." This title is well deserved because he presented the first accurate description of the structure of the human body to be recorded and passed on to future generations. It is quite possible that Leonardo da Vinci might have been given this title if his notebooks had been known at the time of Vesalius. Vesalius left a consistent, printed, well-illustrated record to document his anatomical studies.

Surgery

The history of surgery is interwoven with that of anatomy and that of medicine, but it has a distinguishable pattern of its own. At certain periods of history it has been set apart arbitrarily as an application of lesser importance or a trade, and not a respectable one at that. Through long periods of history medicine was interwoven with superstition, but surgery was a more realistic area in which the operator could see what he was doing. Because of the lack of communication, each civilization had to do its own pioneering in surgery. After the time of Galen, surgery underwent a long period of starvation that lasted until the time of Leonardo da Vinci and Vesalius. A few surgeons developed, such as Guy de Chauliac (1300-1370), but through many centuries there were no effective surgeons.

Surgery in ancient times and in the Renaissance was handicapped by two main factors. The first was the pain that was caused by the incision into the body and the manipulation of the internal organs. Few persons had the stamina to undergo surgery without anesthesia; and when they did, the shock was often fatal. The second handicap to the progress of surgery was the lack of knowledge about infection. Practically all surgical procedures resulted in infection, and most infections were fatal. The most noted surgeon of the Renaissance was Ambroise Paré.

Paré

Ambroise Paré (1517-90) was a Frenchman, trained as a barber-surgeon, who attained a high position as a military surgeon. He became acquainted with the ancient and medieval as well as the current knowledge of surgery and became great in spite of his humble scholastic background. Not trained in Greek, he spoke and wrote in his native vernacular. His formally-trained contemporaries snubbed him, but he rose above their criticism and had remarkable success. Humble in his practice, he was often quoted as saying "I dressed the wound and God healed the patient."

The accepted treatment for gunshot wounds at the time was boiling oil poured over the wound causing great suffering and many complications. One day on the battlefield the supply of oil ran out. The patients not treated, to the surprise of Paré, got well more quickly than usual when treatment was administered. This led Paré to experiment by using less oil and finally he gave it up all together. A clean wound would heal satisfactorily with no treatment. Paré revived the ancient dictum of Hippocrates, "first do no harm", and capitalized upon it. He discovered that pain and infection were not necessary for good surgery. The notion prevalent among physicians that copious pus formation on a wound was a good sign indicating that the healing processes were operating was not true. Pus formation was supposed to represent a discharge of unhealthy humors from the body. Other physicians and surgeons before Paré had opposed the idea of laudable pus, but Paré was first to bring substantial evidence into the argument.

Paré's next contribution was a method of stopping bleeding following amputations that were common in the Middle Ages and Renaissance because of the lack of aseptic surgery. Infection, particularly gangrene, was usually associated with surgery, and limbs frequently had to be removed to save the life of the patient. The common method for stopping bleeding was by cautery. Paré found that better results could be accomplished by ligaturing the blood vessels. This was less painful and more effective. Artificial limbs were also introduced by Paré to replace losses through amputation. Another accomplishment was to induce labor in a woman suffering from uterine hemorrhage. Paré performed autopsies and wrote a treatise on the legal aspects of surgery. He published 8 major works that had great influence on surgery and medicine.

REFERENCES

Ashley-Montagu, M. F. Vesalius and the Galenists. *Sci. Monthly*. 80: 230-239, 1955.

Atkinson, D. T. *Magic, Myth and Medicine*. Cleveland: The World Publ. Co., 1956.

Belt, E. *Leonardo the Anatomist*. Lawrence, Kansas: Univ. Kansas Press, 1956.

Chauvois, L. *William Harvey*. New York: Philosophical Library, 1957.

Cole, F. J. *A History of Comparative Anatomy*. London: Macmillan and Co., Ltd., 1944.

Crombie, A. C. *Augustine to Galileo, the History of Science*. London: Falcon Press, 1952.

Cushing, H. W. *A Bio-Bibliography of Andreas Vesalius*. New York: Schuman, 1943.

Galilei Galileo. *The Dialogues Concerning Two New Sciences*. trans. H. Crew and A. de Salvio. New York: The Macmillan Co., 1933.

Graham, H. *The Story of Surgery*. Garden City, N. Y.: Doubleday, Doran and Co., 1939.

Gumpert, M. Vesalius. *Sci. Amer.* 178:24, 1948.

Guthrie, D. *From Witchcraft to Antisepsis*. Lawrence, Kansas: Univ. Kansas Press, 1955.

Hall, A. R., *The Scientific Revolution 1500-1800*. Boston: Beacon Press, 1956.

Hillier, L. A. *Surgery Through the Ages*. New York: Hastings House, 1944.

Kester, H. *Copernicus and His World*. New York: Ray Publ., 1945.

Keynes, G. ed. *The Apologie and Treatise of Ambroise Pare'*. Chicago: Univ. Chicago Press, 1952.

Lassek, A. M. *Human Dissection, Its Drama and Struggle*. Springfield, Ill.: Charles C. Thomas Co., 1958.

Lind, L. and C. Asling. *The Epitome of Andreas Vesalius*. New York: The Macmillan Co., 1949.

MacCurdy, E. trans. *The Notebook of Leonardo da Vinci*. New York: Empire State Book Co., 1957.

McMurrich, J. P. *Leonardo da Vinci, the Anatomist*. Baltimore: The Williams and Wilkins Co., 1930.

Mizwa, S. P. *Nicholas Copernicus*. New York: The Kosciuszko Foundation, 1943.

Packard, F. R.   *Life and Times of Ambroise Paré*.   2nd ed.   New York:
    Paul B. Hoeber, Inc., 1925.

Santillana, G. de   *The Crime of Galileo*.   Chicago: Univ. Chicago Press, 1955.

Sarton, G.   *Six Wings, Men of Science in the Renaissance*.   Bloomington: Indiana
    Univ. Press, 1957.

Saunders, J. B. de C. M. and C. D. O'Malley.   *The Illustrations from the Works of
    Andreas Vesalius*.   Cleveland: The World Publ. Co., 1950.

Saunders, J. B. de C. M.   *Andreas Vesalius, the Bloodletting Letter of 1539*.
    New York: Henry Schuman, 1947.

Shippen, K. B.   *Men, Microscopes, and Living Things*.   New York: The Viking Press,
    1955.

Singer, C.   *A Short History of Anatomy and Physiology From the Greeks to Harvey*.
    New York: Dover Publ. , Inc., 1957.

Vallentin, A.,   *Leonardo da Vinci, The Tragic Pursuit of Perfection*.   trans.
    E. W. Dickes. New York: Halcyon House, 1941.

Although the early universities were important in the awakening of intellectual activity and the general recovery from the low cultural level of the Middle Ages, they did little for the development of science. A few university men such as Albertus Magnus and Roger Bacon promoted scientific accomplishment but the general effect was often a hindrance rather than an advantage to science. The University of Paris, one of the most influential of the early universities, provided courses in such subjects as music, art, theology, law, and medicine but none in science. Latin was the language used at the university and therefore, the first tool subject required. The vicinity of Paris around the University is still called the Latin Quarter. Elementary and secondary schools were poorly developed and the curriculum was not standardized. Some students were better prepared by previous training than others to profit by university courses. Furthermore, many students were very young, i.e., 12 to 15 years of age, when they attended a university. In terms of the age at which students were allowed to enter, the institutions would be comparable with present-day secondary schools rather than universities. Francis Bacon, philosopher and statesman who became Lord Chancellor of England, completed his university training at the age of 15. Sir Humphrey Gilbert, English navigator and explorer, was at the university from age 12 to 16.

The main objective was to preserve the knowledge of the past and little or no concern was given to creative activity. As long as the universities were small, the students could be given individual attention according to their needs and interests, but when they became larger and pressure was exerted by the church and state, more formality was required and rigid government policies had to be established. Functions of universities have been re-evaluated many times in the centuries that followed. Today a primary function of such institutions is to add to the fund of knowledge through research, as well as to preserve and teach things already known.

Freedom of thought and real incentives for the development of new ideas are necessary for wholesome growth in science. It is not surprising, then, that the real advance in science followed the work of independent but curious men who did original work themselves for the love of learning and who met together of their own free will to discuss learned subjects.

This spontaneous movement resulted in the development of the so-called "academies." The word academy had been used some 2000 years before to identify Plato's school where discussions were held in a grove of trees. It was revived to describe a gathering of people for the purpose of learning. Individuals engaged in original investigation met primarily to discuss the subjects in which they were interested.

The curiosity and enthusiasm that stimulated the academy movement was exemplified by the versatile experimenter Leonardo da Vinci. He entered into discussions with many different groups that were devoted extensively to science,

Chapter 6

ACADEMIES, JOURNALS, AND MUSEUMS

but the discussions usually involved other interests such as painting and sculpture as well as science. Two free thinkers of the next century, Francis Bacon (1561-1639) and René Descartes (1596-1650, Fig. 6-1) had much to do with establishing the atmosphere in which the academy movement flourished

Bacon was an effective writer and popular lecturer, but he lacked the objectivity necessary for a modern scientist. He gathered many facts but did not sift and coordinate them in a scientific manner. In order to pursue the scientific method, the investigator must have the judgment necessary for sorting and applying facts as well as the ability to discover them. The true scientist must formulate hypotheses and design and conduct experiments to test these hypotheses. Bacon discovered facts but lacked the

46

Fig. 6-1. René Descartes, French
philosopher and physiologist

ability to put them together and make the
applications that might have justified his
inclusion among scientists in the modern
sense. Several indirect contributions to
science came from his work. He fought
against the scholastic methods of teaching
and advocated criticism but he did not
realize the first premise of science today;
that the fact finder must provide the first
criticism, that is, the investigator
should be his own critic and should present
only facts and conclusions that he himself
can verify.

Bacon became the father of the English school of philosophical thought and
originated much of the philosophy perpetuated by John Locke and others. He considered the earth to be the center of the
solar system. In this respect he did not
follow Nicholas Copernicus (1473-1543)
who a hundred years before had identified
the sun rather than the earth as the center
of the universe. Bacon had a philosophy
somewhat like that of Aristotle in which a
great plan was visualized for the origin
and governing of the earth and its inhabitants. Science was considered important
only as a tool to fill in the details of the
plan already established and functioning.
In spite of his inadequacies by modern
standards, Francis Bacon started a movement for free discussion that can be traced

to one of the most important events in the
history of science, the organization of
academies, one in particular, which became the Royal Society of London.

Descartes was a French thinker who
followed the mechanistic viewpoint in
developing a theory of the universe. Like
Francis Bacon, he was a founder of modern philosophy and a progenitor of the
scientific society movement. His best
known and most significant work, Discourse on Method, developed an objective
system for discovering and verifying
truth. He believed that truth can be obtained only through objective methods.
Religious truth, in spite of its claim for
supernatural origin, he insisted, should
be subjected to the same criteria and criticism as scientific truth. His forthright
proposals for criticism of truth regardless of its source became a point of bitter discussion in religious circles. The
earth was considered by Descartes to be
infinite. Man could not and was not expected to understand all of the activities
of the earth or its inhabitants, but little
by little the whole picture could be pieced
together. Therefore, intensive rather
than encyclopedic work was considered
necessary to understand the details of
natural phenomena. Descartes himself
made a beginning when he employed algebra and geometry and constructed physical models to explain natural phenomena.

In the latter part of the 16th century,
small academies developed and flourished
in several parts of Europe. Some were
promoted by princes and other prominent
people who became patrons or honorary
members, thus lending their support to
the movement and often acquiring some
interest in the study of nature. Laboratories were established for experimental
work, and collections of plant and animal
specimens promoted scientific activities.
These developments were sporadic and
depended largely on the interest of the
members. They were supported for the
most part by wealthy and influential
people, but interest in science rather
than material support was responsible
for their origin. When interest lagged,
the activities were postponed or abandoned. One of the first men to be definitely identified with scientific academies
was Nicholas de Peiresc (1580-1637), a
wealthy and influential Frenchman who
served for many years as a voluntary
agent for the exchange of knowledge
among individuals and organizations in
different countries. He was acquainted
with prominent investigators in all the

countries of Europe and knew of virtually everything being done in science in Western Europe at the time. He followd the work of Galileo carefully and repeated some of Galileo's observations with the telescope.

Early Academies

The academy movement developed earlier and more effectively in Italy than elsewhere in Europe. One of the first academies met at Naples in the home of Giambattista della Porta (1543-1617) in the latter part of the 16th century. To gain membership in this group which became known as Academia Secretorum Natural, a person was required to discover a new fact in natural science. Experiments were performed at the meetings and some 20 books of results and discussions were compiled.

A better known early academy was the Accademia dei Lincei (Academy of the Lynx) founded in Rome in 1603 or before. The word "lynx" was selected to suggest the motto, sharp eyesight and keen observation. A symbolical picture of a lynx with upturned eyes holding in its paws the powers of darkness became the standard to symbolize the struggle between scientific truth and ignorance. The society was founded by Duke Federigo Cesi (1585-1630), a rich young Italian and skillful experimenter. At first only three men met with Cesi at his home to discuss studies in which they were interested. In 1609 the membership had increased to 32. Among the new members were Della Porta, Peiresc, and Galileo.

Galileo made a microscope for the society and another member, J. Faber (1574-1629), an entomologist gave the instrument the name, "microscope." A charter member, Francesco Stelluti (1577-1653), used the microscope in preparation of a zoological study on bees which became the first scientific report to be published (1625). Other important publications from the society were botanical and astronomical observations and descriptions of plants and animals of Mexico. Following the death of Cesi in 1630 the society became inactive and was revived many years later (1870) in a more modern setting.

The Accademia del Cimento (Academy of Experiment), was established at Florence, Italy, under the patronage of the Grand Duke Ferdinand II (Medici) in 1657. It was the first academy to be formally organized. Although it had an active life of only ten years (1657-1667), it exerted a great influence in the development of science. There were nine members, including Castellio and Torricelli, disciples of Galileo; Giovanni Borelli (1608-1679), a mathematician with interests in biological mechanism; and Francesco Redi (1621-1697), who disproved the spontaneous generation of flies. It was the first institution whose members devoted themselves extensively to publication of science. The members all wrote together without signing their individual names; the actual writing was done by the secretary. The Report of Experiments, printed in 1666, was devoted mostly to physics. It contained original descriptions of the first barometer, which had been invented by Torricelli in 1643; the first true thermometer, and the hydrometer. Reports of the first experiments demonstrating the expansion of water on freezing, universal gravity of bodies, and the property of electrical matter were also included in this volume.

The French Academy of Science originated from a small group of curious men who at first held secret meetings similar to those held by groups in Italy and other European countries in the latter part of the 16th and early 17th centuries. Marin Mersenne (1588-1648), a skillful writer, who popularized the work of Descartes and Galileo in France, was the leader. The first meetings were spontaneous gatherings in the homes of the members but more formal meetings were held in public places as early as 1630. At that time, Cardinal Richelieu agreed to accept the organization and not prosecute the members. The French Academy of Science was formally organized in Paris in 1666 by Louis XIV. Regular sessions were then held in the Royal Library which was used both as a meeting place and as a laboratory for demonsrrations. Descartes and Peiresc did much to lay the foundation for the French academy. M. Thevenot (1620-1692), who became the patron of the microscopist, Swammerdam, was one of the most influential members.

A similar movement was promoted in Germany; a group of scientists was meeting at Leipzig as early as 1651 but formal academies were not organized until a later date. The Berlin Academy of Science was founded in 1700. Similar developments occurred in Denmark, Hol-

48

land, Switzerland, Belgium, Portugal, and other European countries.

The first real contributors to science after the Middle Ages were, thus, curious amateurs who came together spontaneously to discuss problems in which they were interested. Historians have called these organizations "curiosity cabinets". They were only loose organizations whose members came together for interest and amusement but they made significant and lasting contributions in science.

Royal Society of London

"Curiosity cabinets" developed in England during the latter part of the 16th and early part of the 17th centuries, but no formal organization was affected at that time. An attempt at such an organization was begun in 1616 by Edmund Bolton, an eminent scholar, who obtained hearings among government leaders during the reign of James I (1603-1625). The King and his advisers were favorably impressed, and it was discussed in parliament where the plan was favorably received. Plans were drawn in considerable detail and members were tentatively chosen, but the king died before the organization became a reality. In 1645, during the reign of Charles I, a group of scholars including John Wilkins, Jonathan Goddard, and George Ent began holding meetings in London, sometimes at the homes of the members and sometimes at Gresham College.

In about 1648, some members moved to Oxford where they formed a similar scientific group. John Willis, the anatomist, whose name is attached to the circle of Willis in the brain, along with other residents of Oxford, joined and broadened the organization to discuss anatomy and physiology, as well as physical science. The group at London continued to meet at Gresham College or elsewhere in London and called their society the "Invisible College." When members from Oxford happened to be in London they attended the meetings, and a connecting link was maintained between the two scientific groups.

Civil War and political strife in London in the 1650's made the meetings of the society more difficult. Gresham College was used for a time as a military garrison and was not available for scientific meetings. During this period, the Oxford group carried on the tradition of

the society. When conditions were more favorable in 1660 the London meetings were revived and the society grew rapidly in strength and prestige. In 1662, it was incorporated as the Royal Society of London under a charter signed by Charles II. The establishment of the Royal Society was one of the most significant events for scientific development in England; meetings have been held continuously since the official founding and numerous journals and books have been published. It should be pointed out that most of the early officers and members of the Royal Society were not connected with universities but were independent experimenters and free thinkers.

The first secretary of the Society was Henry Oldenburg (1615-77), a native of Bremen who had come to England as a diplomatic agent. At Oxford he became acquainted with the physicist Robert Boyle and other men interested in science. He was not an experimenter but a versatile writer with great enthusiasm for scientific subjects who carried on a massive correspondence with scientists and societies all over Europe and spared no time or energy in promoting the Royal Society.

Robert Hooke

Another early leader in the Royal Society was Robert Hooke (1635-1703). Throughout his life he was closely identified with the Society, and he did much to shape its destiny. His particular background and interests prepared him for his responsibilities. At the age of 18 he entered Christ's Church College at Oxford University where he attracted the attention of Robert Boyle and was soon engaged as his assistant. Hooke developed a profound respect for Boyle, who was only 8 years his senior. This respect developed into admiration, and a warm friendship developed that continued throughout their lives. As an assistant to Boyle, Hooke worked on the construction of an air pump, a mechanical device of inestimable usefulness. Hooke was interested in air and air pressure and undoubtedly contributed much to the development of "Boyle's Law," that is, the volume of a gas is inversely proportional to the pressure, presented by Boyle while Hooke was his assistant. Hooke was primarily a mechanic and physical experimenter, but many of his contributions had biological implications. His interest in the microscope, that led not only to its development but also to its usefulness, is his main connection with biology. The contributions of Hooke in the physical sciences are many and varied.

Hooke's first scientific publication was a small tract that appeared in 1661, dealing with the surface tension phenomenon. This paper won attention at the Invisible College, which at that time consisted of about 20 distinguished experimental scientists. When the loose, spontaneous organization received royal patronage and a charter in 1662 it became a fashionable society greatly enlarged by an influx of gentlemen not trained in science. The real scientists were soon greatly outnumbered and outvoted by the non-scientists. This new trend in membership made necessary some revision in organization and direction to maintain the original objectives and keep the organization functioning on a high plane. Some enlightenment in science had to be provided for the new members. To fill this need the position of Curator of Experiments was created and Hooke, then 26 years of age, became the first curator and the only professional scientist employed by the Society. His duties were to furnish experiments as demonstrations for the weekly meetings and to carry out other research officially recommended to him. In the next year (1663), after the founding of the society, he was elected a fellow. For many years, Hooke furnished three or four experiments for each weekly meeting.

Since England was a sea power, much of the experimental work was related to navigation. Hooke invented a wheel barometer and designed a method for keeping weather records. It was the need for a portable timepiece in navigation that inspired him to improve the watch by inventing a better spring. From navigation he became interested in astronomical observations that, in turn, led him to make improvements on the telescope. This involved lenses and led quite naturally into the broader field of optics including other applications of lenses, particularly in the microscope (see next chapter).

Following the death of Henry Oldenburg in 1677, Hooke and Nehemiah Grew became joint secretaries of the Royal Society. Hooke held his position for 5 years and edited 7 numbers of Philosophical Transactions. He was offered the position as permanent librarian in 1679 but declined and the post was given to William Perry. When Hooke died in

1703 the Fellows of the Royal Society attended his funeral in a group, paying tribute to his part in founding and maintaining the Society.

The Royal Society of London has taken an important place in the promotion of biology in the years since its founding. Illustrious men such as Sir Joseph Banks have accepted positions of leadership and have been successful in maintaining the high scientific level envisioned by its founders. Accomplishments of later leaders will be cited in succeeding chapters.

Scientific Societies in the United States

During the 17th century the American colonists were busy settling a new land and had little time for scientific and cultural activities. The Boston Philosophical Society, patterned after the academies of Europe, was founded in the latter part of the 17th century and functioned for a few years. Newtonian philosophy, based on rigid natural laws that could be expressed mathematically, found its way into America and influenced the trend of thought during the establishment of the United States as a free nation.

In the 18th century, stimulus and encouragement for scientific work came from Europe, particularly from French scholars through Benjamin Franklin (1706-1790), Thomas Jefferson (1743-1826) and others who established a close cultural alliance between France and America. In 1727 Franklin gathered a small group of curious men around him in Philadelphia. Meetings were held on Friday evenings and natural history and philosophical subjects were discussed. This mutual improvement society, called the Junto, developed into the American Philosophical Society many years later after long periods of inactivity. Similar societies were established in other principal cities in the United States as security and stability developed among the people and time became available for cultural pursuits. The first state academy was the Connecticut Academy of Arts and Science founded in 1799.

A later trend was in the direction of specialization according to content or practical applications of areas of science. Medical societies were first to develop independent status. In 1781 the Massachusetts Medical Society was incorporated. During this same period other specialists formed agricultural societies, chemical societies, geological societies, and others. Similar to the early European societies most of these were loosely organized, meeting enthusiastically when interest was high and disbanding when interest lagged. Out of these early beginnings have come substantial and influential societies of entomologists, botanists, and other biological specialists now organized on a national and international level. Another trend has been in the direction of broad associations or unions of organizations with common interests to tie them together. The American Association for the Advancement of Science (A. A. A. S.), for example, has a membership approaching 100, 000. The weekly periodical Science reaches the entire membership and annual meetings are attended by thousands of scientists. A recent addition to the major organizations in America is the American Institute of Biological Sciences (A. I. B. S.) which is a union including most of the biological societies in America. The first large meeting of this society was held at the University of Minnesota in 1951.

Effect of Societies

The general effect of early scientific societies was to stimulate observation and experiment and to develop a new spirit of curiosity. These developments were effective in bringing scientists together and in providing an opportunity for them to discuss their interests with each other. A medium was also provided for preservation and publication of scientific works, thus making them more readily available to wider circles of people. New tools such as the microscope, telescope, thermometer, hydrometer, and barometer were developed. All of these had an important influence on the development of more precise experimental procedures. Laboratory facilities and laboratory methods came as a result of the activities of these groups. Public lectures were also provided, enabling more people to become informed about science.

Awards for Scientific Achievement

One of the noteworthy activities of the Royal Society was the establishment of awards or prizes for meritorious work in science. This did much to stimulate activity among people who otherwise might not have directed their talents in scientific pursuits. The oldest and most prized of the medals awarded for outstanding achievement by the Royal Society is the Copley medal, established from a legacy of Sir Godfrey Copley, F. R. S. (i. e., Fellow of the Royal Society). In Copley's will, dated 1704, the sum of 100 pounds was left in trust to the Royal Society to stimulate scientific research. The interest from the fund was used, in the immediate years that followed, by the curator of the society to provide demonstration experiments at the meetings. Beginning in 1736, however, the use of the interest was changed in order to exert greater influence on the development of science. A prize was established to be given each year to the author of a valuable scientific discovery or experiment. In recognition, a gold medal valued at 5 pounds was prepared with a portrait of Copley on one side and the coat of arms of the Royal Society on the other. This has become an annual award to the author of an especially worthy contribution. In 1881, the Copley family increased the fund sufficiently to provide a gift of 35 to 50 pounds, depending on the interest rate of the endowment funds, along with the medal. More than 200 scientists have received the honor at the present time. Among the American biologists to receive the Copley medal were Theobald Smith (1859-1934), bacteriologist; and Thomas Hunt Morgan (1866-1945), geneticist.

An award of particular interest to biologists is the Darwin medal, established for the promotion of biological study and research. This medal was made possible by the Darwin Memorial Fund, established to commemorate the work of Charles Darwin, F. R. S. (1809-1882). A silver medal and a grant of 100 pounds is awarded biennially by the Council of the Royal Society. Among the American biologists to receive this honor were Henry Fairfield Osborn (1857-1935) and Thomas Hunt Morgan.

Scientific Journals and Leaders in Publication

Perhaps the most important factor for perpetuating and developing science is the medium for disseminating scientific accomplishments. Greek science, and that of other ages before the advent of printing, suffered for want of an adequate means of transmitting and preserving ideas and observations. At present, this important function is accomplished by scientific periodicals, many of which are available in all fields of science and in many languages, to record and transmit scientific findings.

Beginnings in publication were made by the early academies but the first scientific periodical was published in France by Denys de Sallo (1626-69), beginning in 1665. Sallo was a patron of science, and took it upon himself, with the help of assistants, to review scientific work and prepare abstracts or summaries of accomplishments to be circulated among scientists. Through the influence of his friend Jean Baptiste Colbert, who was Minister of State under Louis XIV, a provision was made whereby it became possible to continue to circulate such material at regular intervals. The project was acceptable to the government and the publications were well received among scientists. The title Journal des Savants (Journal for those learned in the literature of science) was chosen for the periodical. It began as a review journal, but later original accounts of observations and experiments were included. As time went on, it became devoted more to original than to review articles. Similar publications were soon established in England, France, Italy, and Germany.

One of the most important publications of all time was the Philosophical Transactions of the Royal Society of London which had its origin 3 months after the Journal des Savants. It began as a personal project of the first secretary, Henry Oldenburg who maintained a correspondence with other societies and with corresponding members of the Royal Society, and published reviews of work completed and in progress. Like the French periodical, the emphasis in Philosophical Transactions gradually changed from reviews to accounts of original investigation. Monographs by the microscopists Malpighi, Hooke, and Grew, and the letters of Leeuwenhoek were published in this medium. Through the great influence and tireless effort of secretary Oldenburg, a precedent for high quality in scientific publication was established.

In the foreword of each volume of Philosophical Transactions a statement is made in which the Society as such disclaims responsibility for the material in the articles included. No conclusions are considered final and absolutely authoritative. The responsibility for accuracy rests with the authors, who are specialists in their fields. When consulted by the government or another agency, the Society never gives an opinion as a Society; but qualified fellows are asked to reply and give their opinions. No scientific body has better claim to authoritativeness, but this society denies the legitimacy of such a claim. Science can grow to maturity only when there is a general understanding that the last word has not been said on any subject. There must be no dogma to hinder inquiring minds in their continuing search for truth.

The next major development in the publication of scientific periodicals, that occurred in the next century, was in the direction of more specialization in particular fields of science. The Englishman, W. J. Hooker (1785-1865), began publication of The Botanical Magazine. His son, Sir J. D. Hooker (1817-1911), continued the publication for many years. Another important leader in botanical publications was the Swiss botanist, Augustin de Candolle (1778-1841). His studies included extensive morphological and physiological investigations in which he became a world authority. He contributed to the French journal Annales du Museum d' Histoire Naturalle and edited the book entitled French Flora.

Another contributor to the Annals of the Museum of Natural History was the French comparative anatomist Georges Cuvier (1769-1832). The German physiologist, Johannes Müller (1801-1858) studied medicine at the University of Bonn and became professor of physiology. He edited the German periodical Archiv für die Physiologic and wrote the book entitled Handbook of Physiology, which was responsible for introducing experimental physiology in Germany.

Parallel with the movement toward specialized journals was the development in Europe as well as in America of specialized societies. Principal among these was the Linnean Society, which took the name of the great Swedish taxonomist and was devoted largely to classification of plants and animals. The Linnean Society Transactions were published first in 1791 and have been continued until the present time.

Museums

The word "museum" originated from the Greek Temple of Muses at Alexandria and came to be applied to places of culture and contemplation. The great museum at Alexandria in the 3rd century B. C. was mainly a library or a research institute where written manuscripts were collected, preserved, and used by scholars. Some 400,000 volumes were col-

52

lected in the four principal departments: literature, mathematics, astronomy, and medicine. It is interesting to speculate on the differences that might have come in the history of science if this great library had been preserved. One section was destroyed by the Christian Bishop Theophilus about 90 A. D., and the remaining part was destroyed by the Mohammedans in 640 A. D. It was a most serious loss to intellectual achievement in the world. The word museum was lost entirely during the Middle Ages and was revived in the 17th century with a slightly different connotation. It was then applied to collections of rocks, animal and plant specimens, and other natural curiosities of various kinds. Human beings seem to have an inherent tendency to collect and to hoard objects of value and interest. Coins and curios have been collected by individuals throughout the ages. In the 16th century systematic collections of natural objects were brought together and museums with scientific value were established. They represented a natural development along with the academies and were used for displaying and preserving specimens, that were collected or prepared by investigators. The first museum on record to have a serious and scientific purpose was that of the geologist Georg Agricola (1490-

1555) who collected a useful series of rocks and minerals.

Museum collections of dried and preserved specimens served a valuable purpose for comparing and classifying individuals and groups of plants and animals. Many early naturalists maintained home museums; among the biologists, Vesalius made use of an anatomical museum, and Cesalpino prepared dried specimens of plants in a herbarium. These men and many others began to collect and preserve specimens for reasons other than sheer curiosity. A scientific purpose was the motivating factor and the first natural step was to work out means of systematizing their specimens. Practical demonstrations of actual specimens and dissections soon became a recognized function of the museum. Foundations were thus laid for the development of the modern museum as a research and teaching institution. John Hunter's Museum in London (Chapter 9) and the British Museum in the same city were two of the earliest and best Museums of this kind. In the United States the American Museum of Natural History in New York, the Smithsonian Institution in Washington and the Chicago Natural History Museum have followed in the same tradition.

REFERENCES

Abbot, E. A. *The Life and Works of Francis Bacon.* London: Macmillan and Co., 1885.

Bacon, J. *Advancement of Learning.* ed. J. Devey. New York: Collier, 1901.

Bates, R. S. *Scientific Societies in the United States.* 2nd Ed. New York: Technology Press, Mass. Inst. Tech., (1957) Columbia Univ. Press, (1958).

Brasch, F. E. The Royal Society of London and Its Influence upon Scientific Thought in the American Colonies. *Sci. Monthly.* 33:337-355, 448-449, 1931.

Brown, H. *Scientific Organization in Seventeenth Century France (1620-1680).* Baltimore: The Williams and Wilkins Co., 1934.

Cameron, H. C. *Sir Joseph Banks.* London: The Batchworth Press, 1952.

'Espinasse, M. *Robert Hooke.* Berkeley: Univ. Calif. Press, 1956.

Fäy, B. Learned Societies in Europe and America in the Eighteenth Century. *Amer. Historical Rev.* 37:255-266, 1932.

Kraus, M.   Scientific Relations Between Europe and America in the Eighteenth
    Century. *Sci. Monthly.* 55:259-272, 1942.

Montague, B.   *The Works of Francis Bacon.*   Philadelphia: Carey and Hart, 1844.

More, L. J.   *The Life and Works of the Honorable Robert Boyle.*   London: Oxford
    Univ. Press, 1944.

Ornstein, M.   *The Role of Scientific Societies in the Seventeenth Century.*
    Chicago: Univ. Chicago Press, 1938.

Porta, G. B. della   *Natural Magick.*   New York: Basic Books, 1957.

Roth, L.   *Descartes' Discourse on Method.*   Oxford: The Clarendon Press, 1937.

Shippen, K. B.   *Men, Microscopes and Living Things.*   New York: The Viking Press,
    1955.

Stimson, D.   *Scientists and Amateurs, a History of the Royal Society.*
    New York: Henry Schuman, 1948.

Weld, C. R.   *History of the Royal Society.*   2 vol. London: J. W. Parker, 1848.

Wolf, A.   *A History of Science Technology and Philosophy in the 16th, 17th and 18th
    Century.*   New York: The Macmillan Co., 1935-1939.

The 17th century brought profound changes in thought and great impetus in science. Such movements as the protestant reformation and the exploration of America broke the barriers that had in the past restricted new thought. Through the influence of the academies and independent activities of scientists and patrons, science had found its place and made a wholesome development. Publications now provided a medium for transmitting and preserving scientific accomplishments.

Galileo, the leading spirit of the period in physical science, wrote his observations and deductions and thus set them forth for anyone to criticize and

Chapter 7

THE MICROSCOPE, ITS MAKERS AND USERS

evaluate. Facts were the important elements of truth whether they fit the accepted dogmas of the time or not. Modern objective methods in science were thus established and made available for all to follow. Galileo's example of objectivity and his moral victory in the conflict with authoritarianism marked the change from the old order of authority to the new order of freedom of thought. As the main themes of modern biology began to emerge, new instruments such as the telescope, pendulum, thermometer, barometer, hydrometer, air pump, and watch spring were adopted for use in science. The most important of all instruments to biology, the microscope, was developed to practical usefulness during this period. This tool has opened new worlds in cytology, histology, and microbiology. Its history is of great significance to biologists.

Beginnings in the use of lenses can be traced to the Assyrians before the time of Christ. Ptolemy II in Alexandria wrote a treatise on optics dealing with indicies of refraction. Seneca, a Roman author and philosopher in the 1st century A. D., discovered that a globe of water in proper position would make handwriting appear larger and clearer. Lenses that show evidence of having been ground and polished were found in the ruins of Ninevah, Pompeii, and Herculaneum. The Arabs are known to have used lenses during the Middle Ages. Meissner, writing in the 13th century, spoke of spectacles recommended for the aged. In the same period Roger Bacon wrote in his Opus Majus of the remarkable optical accomplishments made possible by refracted vision. He mentioned not only the magnifying properties of lenses but also their properties in refraction and reflection.

An early use of magnification in scientific investigation and writing was that of Conrad Gesner, a Swiss naturalist, in about 1558. He wrote, among other things of biological interest, a book on shells in which he illustrated snails and other organisms with hard shells. Objects as small as the protozoan, Foraminifera, were sketched. These were barely visible to the unaided eye and could not be described in any detail without the use of magnifying lenses. The Dutch microscope makers Johann and Zacharias Janssens in about 1590 combined lenses in an effort to improve magnifying efficiency and resolving power. This resulted in the first compound microscopes. These instruments were built on the order of a telescope and were about six feet long. They had a barrel an inch in diameter with a lens on each end. Galileo heard of the accomplishment of the Janssens and modified the system of lenses to make telescopes. He went on to make many telescopes which he used to view the heavenly bodies, but he did not continue with the development of the microscope.

The publications from the Academy of the Lynx included illustrations which had been prepared from observations made with magnifying lenses. Figures of a honey bee were first presented in 1625 by Francesco Stelluti who improved these drawings and included them with a poetical treatise in 1630. A dorsal and lateral view of the bee were illustrated with remarkable detail. The magnification was given as five diameters. Between the two drawings of the whole bee, the mouth parts were sketched separately with a magnification of ten diameters. Stelluti is the man credited with the first scientific publication (1625) from the Academy of the Lynx.

Giovanni Borelli, a mathematician who had been a student of Galileo, also made use of lenses in biological investigations. In 1655 he described "whales" in the blood of a nematode worm. He also described fibers of textiles, spider eggs, and other natural objects requiring magnification for critical observation. The Jesuit father, Athanasius Kircher (1602-1680), described structures in the blood which some people have considered to be bacteria, but he did not provide illustrations to show what he had observed. It is probable that his magnifying equipment was capable of only about 20 diameters. Therefore, it is doubtful that he actually saw bacteria. From these beginnings the five classical microscopists, Malpighi, Leeuwenhoek, Hooke, Swammerdam, and Grew laid the foundation for the development and use of the microscope. It is interesting to note that these five men were born within a period of 14 years (1628-41). The momentum developed from their combined contributions did much to promote the mechanical improvements as well as the greater application of the microscope.

The oldest of the five classical microscopists was the Italian, Marcello Malpighi (1628-94), the son of an independent land owner with modest resources. His university training was obtained at Bologna where he became interested in lenses. The professor of anatomy, Massari, recognized him as a man of great ability and invited him to his home where Malpighi made use of the private library. This was before the time of public libraries when, even on a university campus, the only libraries were built up privately by professors. Along with other students, Malpighi made dissections at the professor's home. This experience along with the advice of a former teacher led him to the study of medicine. For his thesis subject he chose Hippocrates and found great interest and pleasure in studying the Greek physician and in tracing the early history of medicine. Following graduation he became Professor of Medicine at the University of Pisa where he

also carried on a private practice. Here he became acquainted with Professor Borelli who was primarily a mathematician but was interested in biology. Borelli had already made significant observations with the microscope. The two men worked together on anatomical and physiological studies including an investigation of the heart muscle.

After 3 years at Pisa, Malpighi returned to the University of Bologna to a career of teaching and critical microscopic investigations. He wrote letters to his friend Borelli and other investigators describing his observations. One letter to Borelli described the minute structure of the lung and gave the first complete description of the capillaries. In a later letter on fat tissues he described the flattened red corpuscles in the veins of a hedge hog. This was the first recorded observation of red blood corpuscles. He later wrote more formal monographs on the subjects of his investigation some of which were published in Philosophical Transactions of the Royal Society of London.

Malpighi described the minute structure of the liver and showed that bile released from the gall bladder was actually secreted by the cells of the liver. In the kidney he described the Malpighian corpuscles which bear his name. Through careful dissection he showed that the spleen was not connected with the stomach. It had previously been thought to be the source of "black bile" that was believed to go directly into the stomach. He described the Malpighian layer of the skin, the papillae of the tongue, and the structure of the cerebral cortex. When he looked through the eye of a screech owl he observed that the image was inverted.

Malpighi wrote an elaborate, detailed anatomical description of a silkworm, published as a monograph by the Royal Society in 1669. It included a description of the respiratory system made up of a system of air tubes, the central nervous system including the nerves to the eye and other sense organs of the head, and the digestive tract. The Malpighian tubules, connected with the intestine, were named after him. The silk forming apparatus was also described and illustrated by Malpighi.

In addition to the extensive studies in animal histology and anatomy, Malpighi made valuable studies in plant anatomy. One of his largest and best monographs,

entitled <u>Plant</u> <u>Anatomy</u> (<u>Anatome</u> <u>Plan-</u>
<u>tarum</u>), fills about 150 pages and is il-
lustrated with 93 plates and figures.
Various parts of the plant; the bark, stem,
roots, and seeds were described systematically and processes such as germination and gall formation were also included.
In his study on the structures of plants
Malpighi anticipated the cell theory.
Plants were described as composed of
separate structural units that he called
"utricles."

Malpighi was also interested in the
developmental anatomy of plants and animals. To follow the steps in development he used the chick which was the
most readily available material. Harvey
had initiated the study of embryology and
Malpighi supplied the next important step
with a series of illustrations showing
actual developmental stages. He did not
find the earliest stages but began with the
24-hour stage. In two memoirs, both
sent to the Royal Society in 1672, he presented 12 plates containing 86 figures with
some 24 pages of description. Considering the time when this study was made and
the instruments available to Malpighi,
this series on chick embryology was remarkable. The original drawings for one
of the two memoirs on the chick, made
with pencil and red chalk are still in the
possession of the Royal Society. Since
Malpighi was not able to see the developmental stages earlier than the end of the
first day (at that time the rudiments of
the embryo were established) he believed
that some structures at least were preformed in the egg.

The type of microscopes used by
Malpighi is not known precisely. Much
of his work was done with simple lenses
in sun light. He is also known to have
used an instrument with two lenses. His
contribution to microscopy was an example in critical use of the instrument for
probing into a new level of structures in
the internal anatomy of plants and animals.
The accurate observations and excellent
descriptions and diagrams anticipated the
work of the 19th century. He did not
originate new theories but took advantage
of the instruments available and made
keen observations. He demonstrated
what could be done with a microscope by
a person with some skill and an educated
mind. As a writer he was not prolific;
most of his observations were contained
in letters and short reports to the Royal
Society. Some of his major works
reached monograph size. He was an
original observer and a profound analyzer
of minute structures and relations.

Leeuwenhoek

Antony van Leeuwenhoek (1632-
1723 Fig. 7-1) was born in Delft, Holland,
the son of a basket maker. At 16 years
of age he went to Amsterdam where he
became an apprentice to a linen draper
under whose supervision he learned to
make and sell cloth. When this apprenticeship was completed he had qualified
as a draper and had been promoted to the
position of bookeeper and cashier of the
establishment. After 6 years in Amsterdam he returned to his home town, Delft,
married, and remained there the rest of
his life. He bought a house and shop and
set up a business as a draper but also
became qualified as a surveyor. In 1660
at the age of 28 he was made chamberlain
to the Sheriff of Delft, charged with the
care and cleaning of the Delft City Hall.
He was also the wine gauger and the town
revenuer.

Fig. 7-1. Anton van Leeuwenhoek,
Dutch microscope maker

Although he had several responsibilities, he devoted much time to a hobby
of grinding lenses. In this he was a perfectionist, always trying to make better
lenses with which to see more minute
objects. The lenses were mounted in
copper, silver, or gold plates which
Leeuwenhoek extracted and prepared
himself (Fig. 7-2). He was independent
and secretive, resenting any interference

even by people of high position, and was particularly distrustful of people who offered him advice. As time passed he became so intent upon his lens grinding that he neglected his family and was ridiculed by his neighbors who called him insane.

One man who appreciated Leeuwenhoek's discoveries with his lenses was the Dutch biologist, Regnier de Graaf, who wrote a letter to the Royal Society of London telling the Society of the remarkable things Leeuwenhoek was doing. The secretary of the Society, Henry Oldenburg, then wrote to Leeuwenhoek requesting an account of the discoveries. In response, Leeuwenhoek sent a letter entitled "A specimen of some observations made by a microscope contrived by Mr. Leeuwenhoek concerning mould upon the skin, flesh, etc., the sting of a bee, etc."

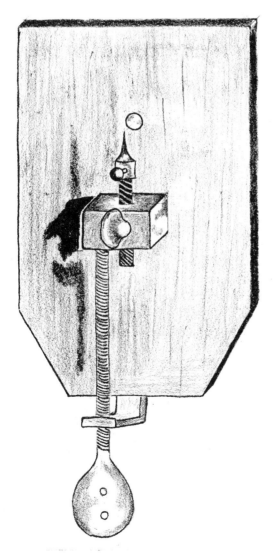

Fig. 7-2. One of Leeuwenhoek's microscopes

The letter was long, unorganized, and difficult to interpret. Leeuwenhoek was thanked by the Society and invited to send more letters concerning his achievements.

In 1673 Leeuwenhoek's letter was published in the Philosophical Transactions of the Royal Society of London. It contained rather crude and scattered observations of mold, mouth parts and stinging parts of a bee and a louse. Copies were sent to members of the Society with the suggestion that those who so desired might send encouragement, suggestions, and problems to Leeuwenhoek. The communication from the Society to its members included praise for Leeuwenhoek with the comment that he had observed the structures he described more accurately than any previous author. From the day of his first letter until the time of his death 50 years later, some 372 communications went from Delft to London, representing such widely separated fields as zoology, botany, chemistry, physics, physiology, medicine, and other unclassified subjects.

All of Leeuwenhoek's observations were described in letters written in his own Dutch language. The writings were more like conversations than formal letters. Many of his observations were left unpublished and were lost. In 1680, during his 48th year, he was elected a Fellow in the Royal Society. He also became a corresponding member of the French Academy of Science but he never attended a meeting of either Society nor signed the register. He seldom left Delft except for seaside excursions or holidays. As Leeuwenhoek's work became known he was visited by many curious people including royalty and celebrities but he was not flattered by their interest. He indicated in letters that these intruders only annoyed him and interfered with his work. Peter the Great was impressed with the microscope and the small objects made visible and requested a demonstration. As a special concession he was allowed the privilege of looking through Leeuwenhoek's microscopes. The Queen of England also paid him a visit. Leeuwenhoek refused to give or sell his microscopes and jealously guarded even the more inferior instruments in his laboratory, especially when visitors were there. He was quoted by one interviewer as saying that he didn't trust people, especially Germans.

Exact descriptions of Leeuwenhoek and his work are difficult to find, but his biographer, Clifford Dobell, has listed two books carrying first hand information: one was written by Thomas Molyneaux, a young Irish doctor, and the other was written when Leeuwenhoek was an old man by Vaughn Uffenbach, a German biographer. Molyneaux described a lens as being definitely ground (there was some suggestion that the lenses were blown by a glass blower), and placed between two thin, flat plates of glass about an inch broad and an inch and a half long. Leeuwenhoek told Molyneaux that he had other microscopes no one else had looked through that he saved for his own use. Molyneaux was impressed with the clearness of the image viewed through the instruments although he said the magnification was no greater than that of microscopes he had seen in London. Molyneaux found Leeuwenhoek to be complacent and confident but unschooled in languages. He felt that Leeuwenhoek was thus limited to his own reasoning, not being able to consult the writings of others. Von Uffenbach wrote of Leeuwenhoek in satirical terms. He scoffed at Antony's ideas of blood circulation and his statement that flies have eyes made up of a thousand or more independent units.

In the course of his work Leeuwenhoek observed muscle fibers of a whale and dried scales from his own skin, an ox eye with uniform crystaline structure, and hair of sheep, beaver, and elk. A fly was dissected and he marveled at the large size of the brain. The first major achievement that brought recognition was the discovery of microscopic organisms in water. Water from the tube in the earth that he used to measure rainfall was first observed. He found to his surprise that this water was teaming with what he called "wretched beasties." When water from other sources including the canals and swamps of Delft was observed more organisms of different shapes and sizes were seen. Leeuwenhoek never found out where they came from, but he knew they didn't come from the clouds in rain droplets and he was against the idea of their spontaneous generation.

The sharp taste of pepper fascinated Leeuwenhoek. He thought pepper must have little points which jabbed his tongue. Dry pepper could not be observed with the type of microscope he used, so he soaked the pepper for several weeks. When he finally looked at it he was so amazed with the organisms that he forgot to look for the barbs on the pepper. This was a new way to culture microorganisms.

Pepper infusions were employed by many other students of microbiology in the years that followed.

When Leeuwenhoek was in his fifties his teeth were well preserved, because, as he says, he rubbed them night and morning with salt, and cleaned the spaces between with a quill, and wiped them with a cloth. Even after his teeth were cleaned in this manner he observed that there was still a little white material between the teeth. An examination of this material revealed more "beasties." Some leaped around like pikes, he said, and others would move in one direction, then roll over and go the other way. Still others resembled cork screws. Following the observation of materials from his mouth he obtained samples from other people and made similar observations.

One morning after drinking hot coffee he observed some tartar from his teeth and to his surprise the "beasties" were dead. When he took a sample from the molars not touched by the hot drink the organisms were still alive. This led him to conduct an experiment which showed that the organisms could be killed in hot water. He drank hot coffee for another experiment in which he measured the quantity of perspiration. Leeuwenhoek's curiosity led him to set up another experiment in which he watched gun powder explode under the microscope. The experiment left him blind for several days.

He made so many scattered observations that it would be difficult to tabulate all of them. Magnifications of the objects he observed ranged from 40 to 270 diameters. The higher magnifications were considerably greater than those obtained by the low power of the present compound microscope. The more conspicuous discoveries are classified under major headings as follows:

1. Observation of the human sperm in 1677. A medical student named Hamm, was reported to have observed and sketched human sperm two years before (1675). Though Leeuwenhoek may not have been the first observer he was probably the first to recognize the significance of the sperm. His imagination, however, led him astray on one point. In one of his letters to the Royal Society he reported that he was able to identify the male and female producing sperm by inspection. In addition to human sperm Leeuwen-

hoek observed the sperm of dogs, rabbits, birds, frogs, fish, and insects.

2. Observations and sketches of bacteria from the substance around his teeth and also from pepper and hay infusions. Among Leeuwenhoek's sketches the three major groups, bacilli, cocci, and spirilla may be recognized.

3. Capillary circulation was observed in the tail of an eel, web of a frog's foot, and ear of a rabbit. The actual circulation of blood corpuscles was thus demonstrated. Corpuscles were described in fish, amphibia, birds, and mammals. In the course of his studies on blood he proved that it did not ferment.

4. Muscle fibers were observed in the iris of the eye, but their cellular nature was not recognized. Nerves in the brain were described as tubes.

5. Many independent organisms were observed, including ciliated protozoa, and rotifers from stagnant water and prepared infusions; intestinal protozoa including Giardia in human feces, marine protozoa including Foraminifera in the stomachs of shrimps.

6. Plant tissues and plant structures such as seeds were described.

7. The anatomy of insects including the mouth parts of the flea, the compound eye and stinger of a bee. The general structure of the cochineal insect was also observed.

8. Hairs were observed and found to be cylindrical. Descriptions of dried epithelial cells were also included in the Leeuwenhoek communications.

9. In the controversy over spontaneous generation he was on the side against the spontaneous origin of living things.

In his letters to the Royal Society he would frequently insert "I have observed" or "I imagine" or "I figure to myself" showing that he was accurate and scientific in his approach. He also gave in his letters insight to his plain, almost childlike character by inserting things about himself, his pets, and his habits. From these it may be concluded that he had a little, white, long-haired pet dog, and a horse that was a mare. He usually drank coffee for breakfast and tea in the afternoon, shaved himself twice a week, and got a rash on his hands when he sat in the sun. His choice recipe for a "hangover" was a great many cups of extremely hot tea on rising. Although he was sincere in his beliefs and jealously guarded what he believed to be true, he did on occasion change his opinions upon being presented more reasonable explanations.

In 1716 when Leeuwenhoek was 84 years old the University of Louvain in Belgium presented him with a medal in recognition for his work. The ceremony for awarding the medal was similar to that of the present-day universities in presenting distinguished service awards. As Leeuwenhoek grew older, his letters to the Royal Society were more concerned with his health and his diagnosis of the causes of his ill health. During the last 6 hours before he died on August 26, 1723, he left instructions for two letters to be translated into Latin and sent with some microscopes to the Royal Society. Maria, his maiden daughter, sent a box of microscopes as he had requested.

Dobell, the biographer of Leeuwenhoek, calls him the father of protozoology and bacteriology because he was the first man to see and correctly describe protozoa and bacteria. Some others have called him the father of microbiology. Robert Hooke and Marcello Malpighi also have a claim to this title. While actually not the original inventor of the microscope, Leeuwenhoek developed his simple lenses independently without the benefit of other discoveries and treatises on the subject. He was the first describer of many tiny animals that he called "beasties" or "animalcules." Leeuwenhoek's contributions may now be classified as false, silly, fantastic or true, fully or in part. If all observations were false, the fact would still remain that this man possessed a remarkable curiosity and thirst for knowledge. He was comparatively uneducated, yet he appreciated the scientific approach and advanced his theories without help from others. Compared with his critical and well-trained contemporaries such as Malpighi and Hooke, Leeuwenhoek was an amateur and perhaps a "putterer." His observations were scattered and incoherent, but he had a gift for hard work and saw many things with his microscopes.

Hooke

Robert Hooke (1635-1703), who was described in the last chapter in connection with the early history of the Royal Society of London, contributed to the development of the microscope and also to its usefulness. His numerous demonstrations of new developments and new uses for the microscope before the Royal Society did much to popularize the instrument as a tool for biological research. Also in his writings Hooke constantly urged more widespread and more critical use of the microscope.

Hooke's major written work, Micrographia, was published in 1665 when the author was 29 years old. This was primarily a series of microscopical observations in which Hooke described and discussed many demonstrations and inventions mostly associated with the development of the microscope. A contribution to the mechanics of the instrument was a scheme for using artificial lighting. Many of the demonstrations which he provided for the meetings of the Royal Society represented new developments on the microscope or new techniques for its use. Micrographia consists of 60 observations, 57 of which were viewed microscopically, and three were telescopic observations. The compound microscope was described in great detail and special attention was given to the matter of illumination. A method of focusing in sunlight by using a globe of water or a burning glass with oiled paper was suggested as a means of making the microscope more efficient.

In Micrographia, 4 important, fundamental concepts were presented. (1) a series of observations on the color of thin plates and a description of the phenomenon of diffraction; (2) a description of combustion as depending on something in the air and an association between combustion and respiration in the animal body including a physical explanation for energy release; (3) a correct explanation of the origin of fossils; and (4) the important biological observation of pores or boxes observed in sections of cork with the first use of the word "cell" to describe these open spaces.

In addition to the four fundamental contributions cited above, that were contained in Micrographia, there were many more observations of great significance. Examples of observations with biological significance are as follows: a description of bird feathers illustrated with detailed drawings, a description and functional interpretation of insect wings, descriptions of sponges that Hooke observed to be attached like plants but to have animal substance, a description of silk fibers, and a speculation that artificial silk may eventually be made from some glutinous substance drawn out mechanically in fine fibers. The book contains many illustrations of microscopic objects drawn by Hooke himself. These include the compound eye of a fly, a louse, a silverfish, a flea, and a stinger from a bee.

Later writings of Hooke presented originally as Cutlerian lectures included a series of papers devoted mostly to mechanical and physical subjects such as helioscopes, springs, pendulums, universal joints, gravitation, the earth's motion, and comets. The fifth one of these treatises, published in 1678, dealt in part with a biological subject and was called Microscopium. In this paper Hooke returned to microscopy which he had laid aside for many years because of the weakness of his eyes. The stimulus that brought him back to this subject was the 1677-78 correspondence addressed to the Royal Society by Leeuwenhoek. "Little Animals" were described in pepper water. Great excitement was aroused in the Society, and Hooke was asked to try to repeat the observations. He prepared cultures of organisms not only in pepper infusions but also in wheat, barley, and oats preparations and observed several sorts of tiny creatures. He also confirmed Leeuwenhoek's observations on blood, milk, and phlegm. Along with these observations, Hooke gave descriptions of the improvements made on the microscope.

Swammerdam

Jan Swammerdam (1637-80 Fig. 7-3) was born in Amsterdam the son of an apothecary who had a home museum with zoological specimens. The home atmosphere helped to stimulate young Swammerdam to an early interest in nature. From an early age Jan was characterized as nervous, intense, and stubborn. When he was in his middle twenties he entered the University of Leyden and began the study of medicine. He continued his studies in Paris and in about 1667 he was awarded the medical degree. His interest in basic biology increased and he did not immediately enter the medical practice but devoted himself to research. He had remarkable skill in making dissections of minute animals and parts of animals. At Paris he became acquainted with Thevenot, one of the founders of the French Academy of Science, who was impressed with his skill and promise as an investigator. Thevenot agreed to support him financially in his research.

In 1669 Swammerdam published a classical study of the metamorphosis of insects. Three main types of insects were recognized on the basis of their

Fig. 7-3. Jan Swammerdam, Dutch microscopist

metamorphosis: (1) no metamorphosis, insects that are complete when hatched from the egg and only need to grow larger (e.g., silverfish), (2) incomplete, those hatched without wings on which wings develop later (e.g., grasshoppers, mayflies), and (3) complete, those with larvae, pupae and adult stages (e.g., flies, bees, butterflies). Metamorphosis was used as a basis for classification. Studies on insects led Swammerdam to visualize a preformation from instar to instar in the development of insects (Chapter 16). He observed larval features later in the adult stage. This view was applied too generally by other investigators to other organisms. The theory was perpetuated for many years by less skillful microscopists who saw things that were not there. Swammerdam made excellent descriptions of the development of gnats and dragonflies. He also traced the development of the frog.

The remarkable observations were made possible by Swammerdam's skill in making dissections and interpretations. New techniques were developed to resolve specific problems. When studying the circulatory system he injected the blood vessels with wax to hold them firm for dissection. It was thus possible to observe the delicate valves in the lymphatic system. He dissected minute fragile structures under water to gain added support and to prevent tearing or destroying the frail tissues. When the structures for which he was searching were obscured by fat he dissolved the fat with turpentine. The modern technique of microdissection was developed to a high degree. Micropipettes were used for inflation and injection under the microscope. Some of his work contributed to the field of physiology. He studied respiration and muscular contraction in living specimens.

Swammerdam not only had poor general health in his youth, but he contracted malaria at an early age. Before he had really started his life's work he began to show early symptoms of mental instability, which became more serious as time went on. He did not work consistently for money and quarreled with his father who was financially able to assist him but who refused to support a mature son who was prepared but unwilling to practice his profession. In sheer desperation Swammerdam decided he must attempt to practice medicine as his only source of income. With limited financial help from his father, he went to the country presumably to regain his health and develop a medical practice in a leisurely way, but he spent long days and nights at his investigations. Accounts written at the time said he "worked like a madman", and his health became worse. He completed his classical study on the mayfly in 1675. This was a remarkable investigation in which the minute internal anatomy of the mayfly was described with great accuracy and detail. It showed what could be done with the microscope in in the hands of a skillful investigator and illustrator.

The father, not impressed with the scientific accomplishment and promise of Jan, withdrew all support. Swammerdam then tried to sell his books, specimens, and even his microscopes and dissecting tools to live. At this critical period the father died and left Jan a comfortable living, but another calamity interfered with his scientific career. He read the works of a religious fanatic, Antoinette Bouregnon, and became more interested in contemplation and religious devotion than in scientific accomplishment. He came to regard research in natural subjects as worldly and gave himself to adoration and worship. The last 6 years of his life were thus lost to science. He died in 1680 at the age of 43.

His scientific work lasted only about 6 years and conditions under which he worked were unfavorable during much of this time. Most of his work was not published until after his death. Hermann Boerhaave collected and published the material in 1737 under the title Biblia Naturae (Bible of Nature). It was only when the scattered work was brought together 57 years after his death that the great value of Swammerdam's work became appreciated. He was probably the first to describe blood corpuscles which he did in 1658 in connection with his study of the frog. Swammerdam worked with more minute structures than Malpighi and his drawings were superior to those of Malpighi. The Bible of Nature has been described as the finest collection of microscopical observations ever produced by a single worker. This volume includes a remarkably fine section on the internal anatomy of the bee.

Grew

Nehemiah Grew (1641-1712) was the son of an English clergyman. He was an undergraduate at Cambridge when his father found himself on the losing side of the Civil War. When Charles II returned to the throne and the Grews were under the necessity of leaving England, Nehemiah transferred to the University of Leyden in Holland where he studied medicine and graduated in 1671. He set out to practice in a small town but retained his interest in plant anatomy and soon moved to London where he could continue his research. In 1672 the first of his two great books was published under the title, Philosophical History of Plants. Ten years later (1682) he published Anatomy of Plants. His main contribution was a critical anatomical description of the parts of the flower. In some plants he observed that the pistil (female part) and stamens (pollen producing parts) were in the same flower. This suggested that some plants might be hermaphroditic like snails which had already been studied. The critical anatomical work of Grew was not fully appreciated until many years after his death.

The combined contribution of the 5 classical microscopists and other lesser microscope makers and users gathered a momentum that brought the microscope into practical usefulness. They did all that could be done with the instruments available to them. There was no further major improvement in the next 100 years. In the early 19th century further developments became possible and progress was again resumed.

More Recent Improvements

The most serious difficulty with early microscopes was chromatic aberration of the lenses. When lenses were made more convex, prisms were created which separated the different wave lengths in ordinary light and produced all the colors of the spectrum. A colorless object would be confused with all the colors of the rainbow which frequently resulted in misinterpretations. Newton who formulated a theory of light and color from studies on prisms, worked on the problem of chromatic aberration and concluded that it was insoluble. It is still insoluble as far as single lenses are concerned, but as early as 1752 it was found that chromatic effects could be avoided by cementing lenses together in such a way that one complemented the other in the prismatic effects. In 1766 the Swiss mathematician, Leonhard Euler, described two methods of avoiding chromatic aberrations: (1) use monochromatic light or (2) construct doublet or triplet lenses with different indicies of refraction. Achromatic lenses with corrections for color aberrations were not used in microscopes, however, until the 19th century. In 1827 G. B. Amici demonstrated corrected lenses and in 1830 microscopes with achromatic lenses appeared. The modern compound microscope with ocular and objective spaced properly by a body tube was then developed. Apachromatic objectives with better correction for color aberration removed the color fringes around the outside of the optical field and thus represented another improvement.

The next improvement made the microscope suitable for use of transmitted light. An optical axis and a moveable mirror were built into the instrument. When higher magnifications were made possible by more convex lenses it was found that a medium other than air between the lens and glass slide would improve the efficiency of the microscope. The immersion lens was first devised by John Dolland in 1844 with water the medium to fill the spaces between the lens and glass slide. This fluid improved the efficiency of the instrument considerably but cedar oil was found to have an index of refraction similar to glass and thus it provided a better medium. The oil immersion lens was developed for high power magnification and good resolving power. With this medium between the lens and slide the light rays follow from glass to oil and back to glass in the same plane. When the rays go from glass to air they diverge in other directions and are not concentrated on the object.

The next development in the microscope that made it suitable for studies of small organisms was the substage condenser. This is a glass lens placed under the stage that is designed to bring together the light rays and direct them more precisely through the prepared object. Ernest Abbe (1840-1908) developed this addition to the structural parts of the microscope in 1870. It has added greatly to the efficiency and usefulness of the instrument for studying small microorganisms.

Further improvements have centered around the manufacture of better lenses making it possible to resolve objects at 2000 to 3000 diameters. This line of improvement has apparently reached a maximum of efficiency at the present time, that is, the light microscope seems to have approached its greatest possible resolving power. The ultimate physical limits of refinement are associated with the light rays themselves. It is impossible to make an instrument with which to observe an object smaller than the wave length of light. Ordinary light waves are therefore too coarse to study extremely small objects. The present magnification and resolving power of the microscope are near the limit that can be obtained as long as ordinary light is used. In order to get higher magnification, instruments have been designed to make use of materials other than ordinary light.

The ultramicroscope operates with ultraviolet light which has a shorter wave length than ordinary light thus increasing the upper range from about 3000 to about 6000 diameters. Ultraviolet, however, cannot be seen with the eyes of man. Therefore, photographs are made on plates sensitive to ultraviolet light. The ultramicroscope has had some usefulness but has not been especially practical and has now been largely replaced by the electron microscope that has most of the qualities of the ultramicroscope and is capable of much higher magnification. The electron microscope makes use of waves of electricity that are much shorter than those of ultraviolet. It is therefore possible to resolve objects with this instrument that are in a smaller order of magnitude than those observable with either ordinary light or ultraviolet. Electric rays, like ultraviolet, are not visible to the eye. It is therefore necessary to expose a photographic plate and observe the object through the medium of a photograph rather than directly on the stage of the microscope. A fluorescent screen has been developed, however, that provides an image on the microscope and makes direct observation of the gross characteristics of the image possible. This is useful for focusing the microscope and making preliminary studies.

The electron microscope has proved especially valuable for the study of dead fixed objects. Its potential usefulness for analyses of living material is still in question. After being penetrated by the tremendous voltage required to operate the electron microscope, living materials are killed and the objects studied may not be representative of the living protoplasm. Furthermore, the techniques required for preparation of materials suitable for use on the electron microscope are exacting. Only small and discrete objects can be examined precisely. Electric rays do not penetrate structures with any appreciable thickness. Therefore, if the objects to be studied are as large as protozoa and many bacteria they must be carefully preserved and cut into extremely thin sections. Because ordinary microtomes are not capable of cutting sections sufficiently thin, further technical limitations restrict the usefulness of the electron microscope for living materials. As new tools are devised and techniques are improved, however, the electron microscope will undoubtedly have greater usefulness. Already viruses are being studied with remarkable precision.

REFERENCES

Allen, R. M. *The Microscope.* New York: D. Van Nostrand Co., 1940.

Beck, C. *The Microscope; Theory and Practices.* London: Raval T. Beck, Ltd., 1938.

64

Belling, J. *The Use of the Microscope*. New York: McGraw-Hill Book Co., 1943.

Cohen, B. A. *The Leeuwenhoek Letter*. Baltimore: Soc. Amer. Bact., 1937.

Corrington, J. *Working with the Microscope*. New York: McGraw-Hill Book Co., 1941.

De Kruif, P. H. *Microbe Hunters*. New York: Harcourt, Brace and Co., 1950.

Dobel, C. *Antony Van Leeuwenhoek and his Little Animals*. New York: Harcourt, Brace and Co., 1932.

'Espinasse, M. *Robert Hooke*. Berkeley: Univ. Calif. Press, 1956.

Gage, S. H. *The Microscope*. 17th ed. Ithaca, N. Y.: Comstock Publ. Co., 1941.

Hooke, R. *Micrographia*. 1665. Reprinted as Vol. 13 of R. T. Gunther, *Early Science in Oxford*. Oxford: Clarendon Press, 1923.

Munoz, F. F. *The Microscope and its Use*. Brooklyn, N. Y.: Chem. Publ. Co., Inc., 1943.

Sjöstrand, F. S. and J. Rhodin. *Electron Microscopy*. New York: Academic Press, Inc., 1957.

Shippen, K. B. *Men, Microscopes, and Living Things*. New York: The Viking Press, 1955.

Biology in the 17th and 18th centuries was dominated by systematists. New knowledge had been accumulated during the Renaissance and the next logical step was to classify it into useful systems. The movement to systematize and classify was promoted in the cultural areas such as literature, theology, and art as well as in science. Newton's book Principia, published in 1687, was the key to the period. Newton viewed the world as fixed and static with the earth and heavenly bodies precisely arranged in mathematical harmony. The same fixed and rigid system carried over to biology. Attempts were made to classify animals and plants according to a prearranged, fixed system. This pattern of biological classification continued until the publication of Darwin's Origin of Species in 1859.

For beginnings in classification of living things it is appropriate to go back to Aristotle who provided descriptions of many animals and made keen distinctions among them. His groupings were based mostly on such characteristics as mode of reproduction and habitat that are not valid for distinguishing natural groups. Aristotle did provide the concept of species as a fundamental unit of living things. The useful terms, genus and species, are simple translations of the Greek words genos and eidos, used by Aristotle.

There were some attempts after the time of Aristotle to classify animals and plants but most of the systems proposed were confused and unnatural. Among the "German fathers of botany" of the 16th century, Fuchs (Chapter 5) made the best contribution to classification. His descriptions were good and he differentiated genus and species groupings to some extent. The Italian, Andrea Cesalpino, anticipated the modern method by classifying plants according to flower and fruit characteristics. Kaspar Bauhin, Swiss botanist, began describing plants while he was studying at Padua and continued the project when he returned to Basel. During his productive career he described some 6,000 plants and systematized them to some extent.

A major contribution came from the work of the German Joachim Jung (1587-1657) who studied medicine at Padua and returned to his native Germany where he taught botany and carried on botanical research. None of his work was published during his lifetime but his manuscripts were preserved by his students and published in two small volumes in 1662 and

1679. Jung's material was written in a concise form and demonstrated his remarkable facility for classification. Buds and flowers were used as characteristics for distinguishing plants, but Jung like his contemporaries, did not understand the functional significance of these parts in sexual reproduction. Major biological problems have provided themes in different areas of biology. In the 17th century, reproduction in plants was a problem which stimulated much interest. It was resolved by Camerarius in 1694.

Jung coined many terms and phrases such as: simple in contrast to compound leaves, alternate and opposite leaves,

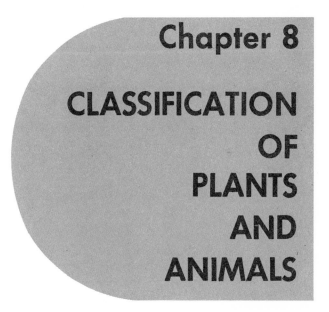

Chapter 8

CLASSIFICATION OF PLANTS AND ANIMALS

petiole, stamen, style, node and internode, that have persisted in plant taxonomy. In composite flowers, disc florets were distinguished from ray florets. A binomial system of nomenclature was used for identifying many of the plants described by Jung. In this system, a noun was used for the major group, that is the genus, and an adjective for the smaller subdivision of the genus, that is the species. Jung had come under the influence of the Cesalpino tradition while he attended the University of Padua in Italy. His use of the binomial system represented a development from earlier beginnings and approached the modern system that was developed by Ray and Linnaeus.

Ray

John Ray (1627-1705) ranks with Linnaeus as one of the founders of the biological science of systematics. As a biologist Ray was more profound than Linnaeus. He prepared the biological framework for a natural system of classification whereas Linnaeus, with his rare gift of discrimination, developed a more artificial system and promoted it to practical usefulness. Ray developed the idea of species as the smallest inseparable biological unit. He arranged species and larger groups on what he declared was the Creator's plan of numerical series for grouping like with like. Some of his groups were artificial, for example, he separated herbs and trees into two primary divisions of the plant kingdom. Although he was following the "Creator's plan" he visualized species as dynamic units subject to change in nature whereas Linnaeus considered them to be fixed and rigid. Ray thought plants must have a sexual method of reproduction but Linnaeus took little interest in the mechanics of reproduction.

Ray was the son of a blacksmith who lived at Black Notley near Braintree in Essex, England. He received his early training at the Braintree School and entered Catherine Hall, Cambridge, at the age of 16. After three quarters he transferred to Trinity College where he was tutored by James Duport, Professor of Greek. Much of the academic work done by a student at that time, and since in European universities, was done individually with the help and direction of a tutor. Ray was chosen a minor fellow at Trinity College in the year 1649 and a major fellow in 1651 when he obtained a university position as a cleric. In addition to his religious responsibilities, he tutored students in science and won a reputation as an excellent tutor. As he grew older he developed a passion for natural history and spent more and more time and energy in biological projects. Several students were attracted to him including Francis Willughby (1635-72), a wealthy young man with great ability and interest in natural history. During these years Ray and his students took excursions in England, Wales, and particularly around Cambridge, observing plants and animals. In 1660 Ray wrote a flora of the Cambridge vicinity, the first work of its kind.

In 1661 Ray was obliged to give up his fellowship and college life because of conscientious scruples that made him unable to subscribe to the Act of Uniformity. From this time on he pursued his scientific interests and depended chiefly, for support, on his former student and close friend, Willughby, who became his constant companion. The two men traveled together and observed and collected plants and animals. They formed a partnership and agreed that Ray would specialize on plants and Willughby on animals as they worked together. Ray set the pattern for taxonomy and based his classification of plants on the fruit, leaves, and the flower parts. In 1663 Ray and Willughby began a tour of Europe for the purpose of observing and classifying all the plants and animals they could find. They returned with a large collection of both plants and animals on which they meant to base complete systematic descriptions of the plant and animal kingdoms. In 1667 Ray published a Catalogus of British plants, a complete flora of the British Isles. Following his election as a fellow in the Royal Society in 1669, Ray with Willughby as co-author, published a paper entitled "Experiments Concerning the Motion of Sap in Trees" in Philosophical Transactions.

Willughby had done much work on animals but had completed only the sections on ornithology and ichthyology when he died in 1672 at the age of 38. His vast collection of notes was left to Ray to edit and publish. Willughby also left Ray a substantial annuity with a charge to educate his two sons and continue the biological projects the two men had planned together. Ray carried out the charges faithfully.

Ray used the Britannical collections for the ground work of his publication entitled Methods Plantarum Nova published in 1682, and his greatest work General History of Plants (Historia Generalis Plantarum), printed in three volumes, one in each year, 1686, 1688, and 1704. In the book on methods, Ray described the true nature of buds and used as major divisions of flowering plants the dicotyledons and monocotyledons. This difference was not a fundamental distinguishing characteristic and represented a poor choice. In General History of Plants, information concerning structure, physiology, distribution, and habits of plants was recorded. It contained some 18,600 plants, virtually all that were known at that time.

In 1684, Ray took up the work on mammals and reptiles that had been started by Willughby; the manuscript on fish was edited by Ray and published in 1686, and the work on mammals and reptiles in 1693. The Survey of the Quadrupeds and Reptiles is Ray's most important contribution to zoology. Although Ray was primarily a botanist, he was interested in animals and had made many observations that enabled him to continue Willughby's investigations and use a natural system of classification effectively. When he came to the mammals, Ray rejected Aristotle's classification based on three classes: animals with solid hoofs, those with cleft hoofs, and those with many toes, and devised his own system with only two classes: those having toes covered with horny hoofs and those in which the toes have only nails. After finishing the mammals and reptiles, Ray began working on the natural history and classification of insects. His best entomological work was on the order Lepidoptera.

The studies of insects were made under difficult circumstances after Ray's health had partially failed. With his family he moved back to his birthplace, Black Notley, where he planned to live leisurely but he had too much ambition and interest in his work to retire. Because he was unable to move about as he desired, his children and friends did much of his insect collecting. (He was married at the age of 46 and had teenage children when this work was in progress.) In spite of the difficulties, Ray managed to keep up his wide correspondence and to write his paper on the classification of insects, prepared for publication in 1704.

He also made significant observations on fossils and aspects of geology on his numerous field trips. His theories and comments on these subjects were expressed in his paper Physical, Theological Discourses, published after his death in 1713. In spite of prolonged ill health, Ray lived to the age of 78. The Ray Society for the publication of Ray's works on natural history was founded in his honor in 1844.

Ray's work as a botanist and zoologist was mainly concerned with descriptions and classification. He was content to devote himself to the business of observing, discriminating, defining, and arranging flora and fauna with which he had come in contact on his excursions. Ray insisted that the distinction should be based on the structure of the animal or plant, and not the color, size, or habit, a most important change from the approach of his predecessors.

Tournefort

The French biologist, Joseph de Tournefort (1656-1708), another contributor to the binomial system of nomenclature, traveled extensively describing and collecting plants. He used effectively the binomial system but his classification was artificial and inferior to that of Ray. He placed great emphasis on the names of the genera and described them in detail but species and varieties were given less attention. Tournefort was inferior to Ray in his philosophical viewpoint and his understanding of basic biology. He denied sexuality of plants and made little progress in discovering natural relations. His contribution however was an important link in the chain leading to the work of Linnaeus.

Linnaeus

Carl V. Linnaeus (Linné Latinized, 1707-1778, Fig. 8-1), was born in a rural district in Sweden and spent his early life in the modest home of a pastor who was a nature lover. Linnaeus gained an early appreciation of nature as he walked frequently in the woods with his father, observing plants and animals and discussing

Fig. 8-1. Carl V. Linnaeus, Swedish taxonomist

subjects in natural history. Most important for his later work, he learned to observe and to go to nature herself rather than to books for facts on natural subjects.

When Linnaeus was 20 years old he entered the University of Lund in southern Sweden. A year later he transferred to the University of Uppsala near his home. Professor Olaf Celsius, Professor of Theology, but also a botanist, was impressed by Linnaeus' understanding and appreciation of nature and invited him to live at his home and use his library. During this period, Linnaeus worked out a paper on the reproductive structures of plants and considered the possibility of distinguishing different plant groups on the basis of reproductive parts. This was published in 1730 under the title "Introduction to Floral Nuptials". Flowers were discussed as organs of reproduction. The work was not original but represented a careful review of the anatomical researches of others. He became acquainted with the structures, stamen and pistil, which later became the basis for his classification of plants.

Professor Celsius introduced Linnaeus to Professor Rudbeck, botanist and chief scientist at Uppsala. In 1732, on the recommendation of Rudbeck, the Uppsala Academy of Science provided an opportunity for Linnaeus to make a field trip into Lapland, a broad, unexplored territory which then included northern Sweden, Finland, and the Russian peninsula. This became the first extensive field trip in the history of science. Linnaeus traveled some 4,600 miles, partly alone and partly in the company of two Laps. His equipment consisted of a measuring stick, telescope, magnifying glass, knife, paper, facilities for drying plants and the Swedish equivalent of about $100 to pay his expenses.

After 6 months, he returned to Uppsala with specimens of plants and minerals and vivid impressions of the vast area of Lapland that was little known at the time. In the course of his travels he had observed many wild animals and discovered a hundred new species of plants. Three years later, Linnaeus was invited to make a botanical survey of the province of Delecarlia (a region of Sweden); this time with assistance, better equipment, and more adequate expense money. He later visited Germany, England, and France where he classified and described more plants.

In 1735, when Linnaeus was 28 years old, he became interested in Sara Lisa Moraeus whom he had met at Falun while on a lecture tour. He asked her father, Doctor Johan Moraeus, for her hand in marriage. The condition set by the father, who was town physician of Falun, was that Linnaeus should go to Holland, an important medical center at the time, study medicine and become a physician before the marriage. He offered to provide part of the money for the trip. Linnaeus who had already completed most of his medical training, accepted the challenge and went to Harderwijk, Holland, where he received his medical degree in a short time. He remained in Holland and spent much time observing plants and clarifying taxonomic problems which he had undertaken in Sweden and on previous collecting trips.

Linnaeus became physician extraordinary for a wealthy banker, Mr. Clifford, who had an extensive estate, museums, greenhouses, and botanical gardens with imported plants from all over the world. This was an ideal place for Linnaeus to try out his classification system and is now maintained as a park called Linnaeushof. One of Linnaeus' books was dedicated to Mr. Clifford. Hermann Boerhaave (1668-1738), the most famous physician in Europe, became interested in Linnaeus and helped to promote his career.

It was at Leyden in the Netherlands where Linnaeus published in 1735 the first edition of his famous Systema Naturae. The original edition contained only about a dozen pages but the great work was improved and enlarged through 16 editions during the lifetime of Linnaeus. In the 10th edition, published in 1758, binary nomenclature was used throughout. Zoologists use this edition as the basis for nomenclature. (Species Plantarum (1753) includes descriptions of all species of plants then known with binomial nomenclature used throughout. This book is the basis for plant taxonomy.) While in Holland Linnaeus worked in the botanical garden at Leyden and described it as a paradise.

Linnaeus was now famous and received offers for positions in various parts of the world. When he visited Oxford, Professor Dellenius became so interested in the Linnean system of classification that he offered half of his own salary to Linnaeus if he would remain and introduce his system at Oxford. Linnaeus was also offered a position with a collecting party to the Cape of Good Hope.

According to agreement, Linnaeus returned in 1738 to his native Sweden, attempted medical practice at Stockholm, and in 1739 married Sara Lisa. He did not care for the professional aspects of medicine and was not successful in his practice. When he had time and no patients he went to the slum districts and worked without pay among poverty-stricken people suffering from tuberculosis and venereal disease. Although he worked hard and long and made a sincere attempt to practice medicine he was not happy. An opportunity came to join the Swedish navy and eventually he was appointed head physician to the Swedish Admiralty and later physician to the queen. He was still not happy with his work and when he was offered the position of Professor of Physics and Medicine at Uppsala in 1741, he gave up everything else and went back to the University.

Later the chair of botany, formerly occupied by Professor Rudbeck, was open to Linnaeus and he again had the opportunities of working in the libraries and gardens that he loved at Uppsala. His fame spread and many students from foreign lands came to Uppsala purposely to work with the great systematist. He sent his students out on expeditions patterned after his own Lapland trip for the purpose of finding new plants and animals and observing living things in their native habitats. When Linnaeus had become established as Professor of Botany, he began to completely rearrange the botanical garden to fit his system of classification. The genus and species categories had been used by the predecessors of Linnaeus but they were vague. Linnaeus clarified them and introduced for the first time the class and order categories.

Linnaeus died in his home located in the corner of the botanical garden in 1778. Nine years later a large garden was given to the University by King Gustav III, and the home and garden of Linnaeus fell into decay. In 1917, the Swedish Linnean Society undertook the task of restoring the gardens used by Linnaeus. Plots were laid out according to Linnaeus' plan that had been carefully developed on paper but had not been completed in the garden itself while Linnaeus was alive. Today the gardens are arranged as Linnaeus planned them. Plants are placed according to taxonomic position based mostly on reproductive parts. To the right of the center aisle as one walks from the front to the rear of the garden, are the annual plants and to the left are the perennial plants. It is impressive to observe all of the plants in order, each identified by its latin name on a white marker with the name of Linnaeus listed after each species name. In the background the hothouses and head house are located as Linnaeus designed them. The home in the corner of the garden where Linnaeus lived for 35 years was restored by the Swedish government in 1937 and is now arranged as a museum.

Linnaeus Classification System

The system used by Linnaeus was fixed and rigid, characteristic of the times in the 17th and 18th centuries. Although natural relations were followed inadvertently, Linnaeus himself was not impressed, at least in his early life, by the pattern of evolution that was obvious in his garden. He was a special creationist and his objective was to classify plants and animals into a workable and useful system without reference to any evolutionary sequence suggested by these groupings. He was impressed by the diversity that he saw first in plants and later in animals. Plants and animals arranged according to the Linnean system now represent a demonstration of evolution.

Linnaeus had a rare genius for classification but he was not an original investigator. He was skillful in appropriating the best ideas of his predecessors and forming a useful system of classification. Cesalpino had arranged plants according to the flower and fruit but had placed too much stress on single characteristics. Linnaeus added the reproductive parts, mainly the pistil and stamens. Bauhin had used a form of binomial nomenclature in which he distinguished between genus and species. He had listed and described virtually all plants that were known at the time. Jung and his students had developed terminology useful in describing plant parts and distinguishing between types. Ray had worked out a natural system of classification and had applied it widely to plants and animals.

Although all parts of the Linnean system were used earlier, no one had promoted the binomial method and developed it to practical large-scale usefulness. This was the major contribution of Linnaeus. The value of the binomial system of classification might be appreciated by comparison with the system in use before it was developed. Although some attempts had been made in systematics, the descriptive system of Aristotle was still in use. Twelve words were the minimum used as an identifying description of a plant. This was quite satisfactory when only a few species were known but it became cumbersome and impossible as more were identified. Obviously, it was not suited for use in keys. The Linnean system as presented in the 10th edition of Systema Naturae consisted of the following taxonomic groups: class, order, genus, and species. Three of these groups: class, genus, and species were used in the earlier editions. The order grouping was used first in the 10th edition to separate categories of insects above the genus level. Wing characteristics were used as the basis for this distinction. The phylum, family, and the super and subgroups were added by other systematists.

Twenty-four main classes of plants were recognized by Linnaeus. This is not sufficient for the present day but was useful at that time. The lowest class, the Cryptogamia, was Linnaeus' waste basket in which he placed all of the lower plants that did not have recognizable reproductive structures. The life history had to be worked out before these could be properly identified.

Linnaeus made extensive descriptions of plants growing in his native Sweden, in the Netherlands, and also in various other parts of the world including America. He never visited America but observed American species in Clifford's garden and received specimens from many American biologists to be named and described. The plants studied were summarized in the publications Genera Plantarum and Species Plantarum.

In his later life he attempted to classify the fauna as well as the flora of the entire world. Linnaeus was a better botanist than zoologist but his binomial system was as well adapted to animals as to plants. In 1748, when he was 41 years old, he published a catalog of the fauna of Sweden in which he described some 300 species of beetles and a large representation of other animals. In the course of his work Linnaeus described about 4,000 species of animals compared with some 800,000 which have been described at the present time. Something over a million are now believed, by enthusiastic systematists, to be present on the earth.

When Linnaeus was an old man and had been unusually successful in classifying plants and animals, he decided to classify mankind. All human beings were placed in the same genus, Homo sapiens. No other members of the genus Homo were found living upon the earth although some fossil forms such as H. neanderthalensis have since been recognized. When Linnaeus classified the subgroups of man he did not employ the morphological type of characters that he had used so successfully on other animals but based his distinctions on attributes of mind and emotional status. He recognized four subgroups or varieties: Homo sapiens americanus, the American Indians, whom he characterized as contented; H. sapiens europaeus, the Europeans who, according to his observations, were lively; H. sapiens asiaticus, the orientals, who were haughty; and H. sapiens afers, the African negroes who were slow. Obviously these criteria are not objective and quite useless for classification. Shortly after this attempt by Linnaeus, Johann Friedrich Blumenback (1752-1840), German naturalist and father of physical anthropology, established the more persistent and familiar classification in which five races were recognized. As distinguishing features Blumenbach used skulls and other parts of the skeleton. The more obvious characteristic, skin color, was soon recognized by others and the five races became known as the white, red, yellow, brown, and black races. More recent attempts have been based on gene frequencies, particularly those associated with blood antigens.

Influence of Linnaeus

At the time Linnaeus made his major contribution in taxonomy, he had no better philosophical viewpoint than Cesalpino, Ray, and others of his predecessors. He was considerably less profound than Ray. Camerarius had shown in 1694 that plants have sexual reproduction, but Linnaeus was not aware of all of the fine points of Camerarius' contribution. Linnaeus did not conduct experiments and he made few observations except those necessary to identify organisms. In his early life he followed and strengthened the dogma of constancy of species. His idea of classification then was much like that of many laymen today, that the worthiest task of the biologist is to attach a tag or scientific name to every plant and animal. Classification is necessary to enable biologist to become acquainted with the fauna and flora but alone it is a superficial approach to biology. The true biologist is interested in the natural relations among living things and not merely in "pigeonholing" each organism with its group. Classification thus represents a tool rather than an end. The object of the modern taxonomist is to determine natural relations and then to place plants and animals properly in an appropriate system.

There is evidence that Linnaeus developed a concept of evolution in his later life when he tried to hybridize different distinct species of plants. The results of the experiment and comments on a natural origin of species were published in his Systema Vegetabilum in 1774. Students who followed Linnaeus were too busy naming and classifying plants to appreciate or remember his later interests in evolution.

At the time Linnaeus died (1778) Joseph Banks, President of the Royal Society of London, offered to purchase Linnaeus' herbarium for 1200 pounds. Linnaeus' son, who succeeded his father in the chair of botany at Uppsala and had control of the estate, refused the offer and retained the collection. The son of Linnaeus died 5 years later, in 1783, and Linnaeus' wife became heir of the collection. The new executor offered the herbarium, library, and manuscripts for sale to Banks at a price below Bank's original offer for the herbarium alone.

At the time Banks received the letter from Uppsala, he was entertaining at his home a young medical student, James Edward Smith (1759-1828), son of a wealthy silk merchant. Banks showed the student the letter and suggested that he ask his father to buy the collection. The young man accepted the suggestion, and soon he was the owner of a vast collection associated with the famous name of Linnaeus. This purchase elevated him socially, and he responded by touring Europe and talking about Linnaeus and the prized collection. Smith won recognition and in 1785 was elected a Fellow in the Royal Society. He disappointed some colleagues in the Royal Society when he promoted the organization of a new society honoring Linnaeus that was formally founded in 1788 and named the Linnean Society.

Officers in the Royal Society feared that the new society would become specialized in the narrow field of taxonomy. Eventually the house of Joseph Banks in Soho Square, London, became the home of the Linnean Society. This society has become a broad and important scientific body devoted mainly to the development of taxonomy but promoting natural history and evolution. The joint paper by Charles Darwin and Alfred Russel Wallace, July 1, 1858, announcing the theory of evolution by natural selection was presented at a meeting of the Linnean Society and was published in the Journal of the Proceedings of the Linnean Society for August 20, 1858.

The influence of Linnaeus on classification was reflected in botanical gardens that were developed later in Europe. Some of the most important were established by members of two families, de Jessieu and de Candolle, that have become prominent family names in the history of botany. The original botanists in the de Jessieu family were three sons of an apothecary who lived at Lyons, France. Several other distinguished botanists in later generations carried the same name. Bernard de Jessieu (1699-1777) established the Royal Botanical Gardens, that became the Jardin des Plantes in Paris, and a similar garden at Versailles. The arrangement of plants in these gardens was patterned after the Linnean system. De Jessieu tried to work out a more natural system and in some ways he improved on Linnaeus. His nephew, Antoine Laurent de Jessieu (1748-1836), continued the work on plant systematics and published his work that was based on a modified Linnean system. He followed Ray's distinction between the monocotyledons and dicotyledons for the main subdivisions in the plant kingdom. As pointed out earlier, this is an artificial and superficial distinction for separating major divisions, but it did provide a single characteristic for distinguishing plant groups. For further break down, de Jessieu used the Linnean categories: class, order, genus, and species.

The de Candolle family of botanists originated in Geneva, Switzerland, but most of the botanical work attributed to them was done in France. The most distinguished member of the family was Pyramus de Candolle (1778-1841). He was a profound botanist who made careful investigations and wrote significant books and papers, some of which are still in use. Best known are French Flora, and Elementary Theory of Botany. His classification was more natural than the classifications of Linnaeus and de Jessieu because he placed more emphasis on the morphological characteristics of fundamental nature than did his predecessors.

Later Developments in Classification

The influence of Linnaeus was also perpetuated in classification systems devised for animals. Three French biologists, Buffon, Lamarck, and Cuvier may be cited here for their contributions in natural history and particularly in the classification of animals. They will be discussed in later chapters in connection with comparative studies and evolution. Comte de Buffon (1707-1788) was a prolific writer who attempted to classify all animals in the world. He did much to stimulate other people who made significant contributions, but his own works in this area were not especially valuable. His Natural History which extended through many volumes contained a theory for the formation of the earth, a history of the plant and animal inhabitants and a description of many animals and plants. He was director of the largest zoological garden in Europe and had more biological material than any previous collector.

Jean Baptiste Lamarck (1744-1829) was more intimately connected with other developments in biology such as evolution, but he made significant contributions in classification of both plants and animals. He was a student of Buffon and followed Buffon in the Jardin des Plantes in Paris. Lamarck's method of classification and concept of evolution were more modern than those of any of his predecessors. He visualized a progressive series in the animal kingdom similar to that described by Aristotle. Unlike Linnaeus, he based his distinctions on function rather than structure. In his ladder-like classification, he placed organisms that responded only by reflex at the bottom. Those with a sensory system were in the middle and those with intelligence were on the top of the ladder. This classification was associated with his view on the inheritance of acquired characteristics to be considered later in connection with evolution.

George Cuvier (1769-1832) was primarily a comparative anatomist but he also contributed to the classification of animals. He lived at a time when worldwide explorations and collections were going on and became the leading scientist of the Napoleonic era in France. Much attention was being given to orderly arrangement following the tradition of Linnaeus, and Cuvier found a place for which he was well prepared. Educated in a military academy, he was precise and discriminating and thrived on discipline. Following graduation at the age of 18 he studied marine biology and became skillful with the pen. His writings and drawings of marine organisms came to the attention of scientists at the Jardin des Plantes who invited Cuvier to Paris to take a position in the Natural History Museum. A contribution to classification was the establishment of higher categories comparable with present phyla in the taxonomic system. His animal kingdom was divided into 4 major groups which he called Embranchements: I Vertebrata, II Mollusca, III Articulata, and IV Radiata.

Embranchement I, the Vertebrata, included the classes: Mammalia, Aves, Reptilia, and Pisces. Mammalia and Aves were identical with the classes of mammals and birds presently in use. Reptilia included the group we now identify as amphibia along with the animals now called reptiles. Pisces included the fish and some primitive chordates, such as the lamprey, that were known at that time. Embranchement II included the Cephalopoda, Gastropoda, Pteropoda (free-swimming marine animals) and Acephala (bivalve marine forms), now grouped with the Mollusca. Also included were the Cirripedia (barnacles) and Brachiopoda, a primitive group resembling superficially the mollusca but now placed in a separate phylum. Embranchement III included the Crustacea, Arachnida, and insects now in the phylum Arthropoda and the Annelida now placed in a separate phylum. Embranchement IV, the Radiata, included the Echinoderms and Polyps with radial symmetry and a miscellaneous collection of aquatic forms called Infusoria. Internal parasites known at the time and other forms that did not fit anywhere else, were placed in this group.

Significance of the Period

The period was marked by a culmination of interest in systematics. It resulted in a useful system of classification and stimulated further work in natural history. Little was contributed toward the solution of basic biological problems of natural relations, physiology, and reproduction but the theory of constancy of species was strengthened. Linnaeus had said repeatedly that no new species was ever created and this attitude remained the dominant one even though some individuals anticipated the theory of evolution. The artificiality of the system hindered progress in biology. Little attention was given to the life history of organisms.

A contrast between the aims of biologists then and now might be appropriate to conclude this discussion. At that time contributors were more interested in words and style than in the solution of basic biological problems. A search was made for types to fit a ground plan and the objective was to classify the entire animal and plant kingdoms according to the predetermined plan. There was an attempt to relate structure and function because structures were believed to be specially created for a purpose. The dominant view was against evolution. In contrast, the objective of the taxonomist today is to discover natural relations and to classify plants and animals accordingly. There is less interest in systems and names. The plan is visualized as determined only by actual relations among the organisms concerned. Individuals closely related are placed together whereas those more distantly related are farther apart. Correlations between structure and function are expected and the objective is to discover how structure and function are related. Evolution is the basic theme and the core of biology.

REFERENCES

Benson, L. *Plant Classification.* Boston: D. C. Heath and Co., 1957.

Clausen, J. *Stages in the Evolution of Plant Species.* Ithaca, N. Y.: Cornell Univ. Press, 1951.

Core, E. L. *Plant Taxonomy.* Englewood Cliffs, N. J.: Prentice-Hall, Inc., 1955.

Drachman, J. M. *Studies in the Literature of Natural Science.* New York: The Macmillan Co., 1930.

Jackson, B. D. *Linnaeus, The Story of his Life.* Adapted from Swedish by T. M. Fries. London, 1923.

James, W. O. Linnaeus 1707-1778. *Endeavour* 16:107-112, 1958.

Hagberg, K. *Carl Linnaeus.* trans. from Swedish A. Blair. New York: E. P. Dutton and Co., 1953.

Lawrence, G. *Taxonomy of Vascular Plants.* New York: The Macmillan Co., 1951.

Linnaeus, C. *Species Plantarum.* Stockholm, Sweden, 1753. (Facsimile ed. W. Junk, 1908.)

Linnaeus, C. *Genera Plantarum.* 5th ed. Lugd. Bot., Sweden, 1754.

Peattie, D. C. *Green Laurels, the Lives and Achievements of the Great Naturalists.* New York: Simon and Schuster, 1936.

Peattie, D. C. *The Road of a Naturalist.* Boston: Houghton Mifflin Co., 1941.

Raven, C. E. *John Ray Naturalist.* Cambridge: The Univ. Press, 1950.

Schifferes, J. Sciences Through the Ages. *The Book of Popular Science.* New York: Grolier Society, Inc., 1958.

Svenson, H. K. On the Descriptive Method of Linnaeus. *Rhodora* 47: 273-302, 363-388, 1945.

Tanner, V. M. Carl Linnaeus' Contributions and Collections. *Great Basin Naturalist.* 19:27-35, 1959.

Extensive comparative studies were made by Aristotle and other Greek, Alexandrian, and Roman scholars. Pliny the Elder (23-79 A. D.) wrote The History of the World, commonly called the "Natural History of C. Plinius Secundus" which included many comparisons in the world of living things. Galen made dissections of different animals and advised his students who were unable to dissect human bodies to work with animals as a substitute. He assured them that there was little difference in structure among all higher animals. Galen carried the presumed similarities too far when he dissected apes and described them as if they were human beings. Numerous descrepancies were later pointed out by Vesalius who carefully compared the bodies of men and apes.

Chapter 9
COMPARATIVE STUDIES

Gross anatomy, the most obvious and tangible field available for exploration by biologists, became the main area for comparative studies during the Renaissance. Leonardo made many anatomical studies which led to comparisons of different animals. In one study he compared the muscles and bones of man with the corresponding bones of the horse. Pierre Belon (1517-1564) published figures in 1555 comparing the skeleton of man with that of the bird. Although errors were made in homology, the basic similarity was observed.

Conrad Gesner (1516-1565), known as the "German Pliny," prepared descriptions and woodcut figures of all classes of animals including some mythi-

cal forms. Ulysses Aldrovandus followed Gesner's example and prepared a natural history (13 volumes), published posthumously. It included descriptions and woodcuts representing an interesting mixture of scientific accuracy and naive credulousness.

Bartholomaeus Eustachius (1524-1574) observed that, to understand the workmanship of nature, it is necessary to examine the anatomy of brutes as well as man. Another Italian anatomist, Carlo Ruini (1530-1598) at Bologna made a careful study of the horse and wrote two books, one on diseases of horses and one on the anatomy of the horse (1598). The latter, which was published after his death, was a classic. With these beginnings other animals were dissected and their anatomical features were compared with those of man. Hieronymus Fabricius (1537-1619), the great anatomist and teacher at Padua, and his students, William Harvey (1578-1657) Guilio Casserius (1561-1616), and Adrian Spigelius (1578-1635), all compared the structures of different animal species.

Harvey drew freely on different animals in his experiments on the circulation of the blood. He mentioned in his writings some 50 species that he had examined. Casserius succeeded Fabricius in the chair of anatomy at Padua and became the most skillful of the early comparative anatomists. In a monograph on the larynx Casserius compared the structures of about 20 different animals. Spigelius made a distinction between human and animal anatomy which resulted in the separation of the two areas. Through his influence human anatomy became a specialized discipline for medical men quite distinct from the broad field of comparative anatomy.

Botanists of the Renaissance made extensive comparisons among plants, particularly those with medicinal value, and prepared a foundation for Ray, Linnaeus, and other taxonomists who based their distinctions on observable similarities and differences. Further contributions in comparative anatomy of plants were made later by de Candolle and Lamarck in France.

With the development of the microscope the minute anatomy of both plants and animals could be investigated and compared. The classical microscopists, Malpighi, Leeuwenhoek, Hooke, Swammerdam, and Grew all made remarkable observations and laid the foundation for minute comparative anatomy in both plants and animals. Swammerdam's anatomical study of the mayfly was especially noteworthy.

The last quarter of the 17th century was especially important for comparative studies. The most prominant leader in comparative anatomy in England was Edward Tyson (1650-1708). In his early professional life he was a practicing physician and lecturer in London. He later abandoned human anatomy in favor of comparative studies. His early comparative work included critical studies of the female porpoise, male rattlesnake, tapeworm, roundworm (Ascaris), peccary (Dicotyles tajacu), and the male and female opossum (Didelphis marsupialis). All through this work Tyson took every opportunity to draw parallels and make comparisons.

Tyson's most significant contribution was the anatomical study (in 1699) of an immature chimpanzee that he called a pygmy. This animal was not only dissected and described in great detail but its anatomical parts were critically compared with those of man. The physical relation between man and anthropoid apes was thus indicated nearly two centuries before Darwin's Descent of Man (1871). Tyson made further comparisons with other primates and showed gradations among them. Similarities and differences among structural features of monkeys, apes, and men were pointed out and relations were suggested.

Tyson, the first Englishman to make extensive anatomical studies, was closely associated with the London and Oxford scientists such as Robert Boyle, Robert Hooke, and Christopher Wren, who were responsible for the founding of the Royal Society. John Ray acknowledged the value and assistance he had derived from the work of Tyson who contributed notes on Willughby's study on fishes. Much of Tyson's work was published in Philosophical Transactions of the Royal Society, some major contributions were printed as separate monographs but some remained in manuscript form at the time of his death. Several unpublished manuscripts are now in the libraries of the British Museum and the Royal College of Physicians. Recognizing the value of Swammerdam's work, Tyson sponsored a partial English translation of the monograph on the mayfly.

By the 18th century, comparative anatomy had become refined and highly developed. Comparative embryology followed in the 19th century along with comparative physiology. These more recent developments in biology required special tools and techniques and grew more slowly than the morphological sciences which depended for the most part on simple straight forward observations. Comparative studies on fossil plants and animals increased as more specimens were found and methods of dating fossils were improved. Interest increased in comparing fossils with present day forms to determine what changes have occurred in the evolution of certain lines. Two leaders of the 18th and early 19th centuries who made use of comparative methods were the English physician, John Hunter (1728-1793) and the French comparative anatomist and paleontologist, Georges Cuvier.

Hunter

John Hunter (Fig. 9-1) and his older brother, William (1718-1783) were sons of a Scotch farmer. In personal traits they were quite different. When John was a young man, William was already a successful physician who was well educated, well dressed, and a gentleman in every sense of the word. He

Fig. 9-1. John Hunter, English comparative anatomist

had been trained in medicine at the University of Glasgow and was a brilliant anatomist, obstetrician, and teacher in London. His specialty was the anatomy of the human genital tract and the course of pregnancy. It was largely through his influence that scientific methods were introduced in obstetrics.

At the time of William Hunter and dating back to early periods of civilization, midwives provided the services at childbirth. At first, they were women who had borne children and were thus qualified by experience to assist their neighbors in childbirth just as warriers or hunters who had been exposed to injury were qualified to render aid to their injured associates. As the organization of the community developed, some women took over the practice and performed the services regularly for gain. Thus the art of midwifery arose. At first it was a blessing and a comfort to the expecting mother, but later it became an impediment to the advance of scientific obstetrics. Midwives were often women of low caste who held their position jealously and effectively held out all intruders from their monopoly. Only in extreme cases when the efforts of the midwife were ineffective was a male physician invited to assist. Obstetrics was a courageous occupation for a man at this time when tradition decreed that men were not to take part in childbirth. In spite of this handicap William moved in the best social circles and developed a lucrative practice in obstetrics that he carried along with his research and private teaching. Through his influence, infant mortality was reduced considerably, and the prejudice against scientific methods in childbirth was broken.

John, the "kid brother", was quite the opposite. He was the youngest of the ten children of John and Agnes Hunter. Not successful in school nor willing to conform to social patterns in his home community, he was considered a worthless rough-neck. In his youth he discarded his wig. He couldn't write; he couldn't spell; he couldn't talk well; and his polished brother and other educated relatives were ashamed of him. Worse still, he became a drunkard when he was a young man and seemingly lost all pride in himself. At the age of 17, he went to stay with his sister at Glasgow and worked with his brother-in-law who was a cabinet maker. He showed great skill in the use of tools and soon was recognized as an excellent artisan.

Three years later William invited John to London to be an assistant in the private anatomical laboratory. John was interested in the new opportunity and rode on horseback to London to begin the new assignment. After a brief apprenticeship, his special task was to perform dissections that would be used by William for demonstrations in his classes. He also performed routine duties, including the cleaning up of the laboratory, and menial tasks that someone had to do in the anatomical laboratory. John showed remarkable skill at dissection and soon was doing many of the things that William otherwise would have done himself. By the second winter in London he had acquired sufficient anatomical knowledge to be entrusted with all demonstrations in William's practical class. John soon won a reputation as an excellent technician and became supervisor of the laboratory. He was widely recognized by students and physicians who had opportunity to observe his work.

In the summer of 1749 William obtained permission for John to study at Chelsea Military Hospital under William Cheselden and John succeeded with distinction. When Cheselden retired in 1751, John became a pupil of Percivall Pott at St. Bartholomew's Hospital. In 1754 he entered as a surgeon's pupil at St. George's Hospital where he was resident surgeon for one year. He then entered a partnership with William in William's private anatomical school. Now, recognized as an excellent surgeon, he showed more interest in basic biology than in the narrow practice of surgery.

William decided that perhaps he might salvage John and make him a cultured gentleman, so he provided an opportunity for John to go to Oxford. On June 5, 1755, John entered St. Mary's Hall at Oxford University. His stay at Oxford was less than one week. He did not appreciate the type of classical training which was provided at that institution. Later he said to Sir Anthony Carlisle, "They wanted to make an old woman of me, trying to stuff me with Latin and Greek." In London again, he enjoyed lively company, went often to the theater, and moved in elite social circles. He was well known among physicians and was recognized for his skill in dissecting. At the anatomical school he now gave lectures and carried on original investigations with his brother, William. Several significant contributions to comparative anatomy were made during this period. He traced the descent of the testes in the foetus, followed the nasal and olfactory cranial nerves, studied the formation of pus, and observed the nature of the placental circulation.

In October 1760, he became the staff surgeon in the Hodgson and Kappel expedition to Belleisle, and in 1762 he served with the British army in Portugal. It was here that he carried out his important studies on gunshot wounds that were finally published in 1794, a year after his death, under the title A Treatise on Blood Inflammation and Gunshot Wounds. When the Seven Years War was over in 1763, John returned to London and was soon recognized as a leading surgeon. He established an office at Golden Square and, in addition to his practice, he taught anatomy and surgery to private students. When the army awarded him half pay as a retirement benefit, he had time for his private interests in collecting and comparing specimens. Much of his time was now devoted to studies of comparative anatomy and physiology.

In 1764 he purchased ten acres of land and built a home at Earl's court, Kensington. Here he provided cages for live animals and laboratory space in his own home. Bees had become especially interesting to him and he kept several hives. His house was soon too small and he moved to a larger one where he kept more specimens and pets. Now there was more room in his home and his best students were invited to come and live with him; Edward Jenner was one student to whom Hunter became attached. The home museum grew and Hunter recognizing its value as a teaching medium preserved and displayed many dissected forms from which comparisons could be made.

The museum was designed to illustrate the entire phenomena of life in all organisms in health and disease. Hunter had intended to provide a catalogue of his observations in each department but this was never completed. He did prepare notes on matters pertaining to dissection, preservation, and embalming, that were of great value to other anatomists. At the time of Hunter's death more than 10,000 preparations illustrating the departments of science in which he was interested were in the museum. The museum was especially noted for the natural arrangement of specimens. Instead of a hodge-podge of all the things that could be brought into a museum,

Hunter's specimens were systematized according to a plan. He put the different groups of animals in their proper taxonomic arrangement and arranged the anatomical structures in logical order so that they could not only satisfy the curiosity of observers but could also serve as a learning device for serious students.

It was possible through this kind of a display to trace systematically different phases of life and different structural characteristics of the body. The organs and systems of the body were exhibited in their proper arrangement. Studies of comparative anatomy and comparative physiology were greatly facilitated through such a display. This set the pattern, and other museums have been organized since on much the same plan. The American Museum of Natural History in New York is now an excellent example of a museum organized for a purpose, with specimens arranged in the tradition of John Hunter to mean something.

Hunter was elected to the Royal Society of Medicine and later became a member of the Academy of Medicine at Paris. His first contribution to Philosophical Transactions was an essay on post-mortem digestion of the stomach, published in 1767. He explained digestion as resulting from the activity of gastric juice. In 1767 he joined the Surgeons Corporation and on December 9, 1768, he was elected surgeon at St. George's Hospital. He was now financially independent and much of his money and energy went into his museum. Many specimens he provided himself, through his own collecting trips and through his own dissections. He also purchased a number of articles for the museum. One of the most prized and most expensive was the skeleton of O'Bryne the Irish giant who was 7 feet 7 inches tall. Hunter arranged for this addition to his museum through payment of a large fee and some bribery that was necessary in obtaining the body of the man who hadn't particularly cared to become a museum specimen.

In spite of his fame and fortune, John never became polished in manners and behavior. He was impatient, blunt, and at times inconsiderate of others. Being a slow reader, he read comparatively little and could never adequately recall and express the information already in the literature on a given subject. He had acquired his knowledge himself and he took pride in his independence from books attaching much, perhaps too much, importance to personal observation and investigation. However, he was a true scientist at heart and did some of the finest comparative work ever accomplished.

John was a hard worker and was rigidly economical with his time. On a typical day he arose at 6:00 a. m., dissected until breakfast at 9:00 a. m., visited his patients, and performed surgery between 9:30 and 12:00 noon. In the early afternoon he held office hours and visited his hospital patients. At 4:00 p. m. he had dinner, after which he rested for an hour or so. In the evening he read, conducted experiments, and wrote notes on the day's activities. His colleagues mentioned midnight visits to his home when he was still at work.

During his lifetime he dissected and studied representatives of some 500 different species of animals, some of which he worked over repeatedly. In the course of his anatomical studies, he did pioneering work on the lymphatic system. From his experimentation he concluded that digestion did not occur in snakes and lizards during hibernation. He showed that enforced vigorous movement during hibernation was fatal to the reptiles studied. From experiments on dogs he showed that tendons will reunite after being divided and thus he prepared the way for the modern practice of cutting tendons for treatment of distorted and contracted joints. He also made critical studies of blood coagulation.

In his search for facts he was persistent, patient, and cautious. He was a careful experimenter who not only gave due attention to details but he always had a clear objective in performing an experiment. His favorite axiom was "that experiments should not be often repeated which tend merely to establish a principle already known and admitted, but that the next step should be the application of the principle to useful purposes." Some 50 volumes of notes were said to have been accumulated during his lifetime. They were not orderly but represented scattered ideas and comments put down as they occurred to him. Two of these volumes were published after his death by his brother-in-law, Everard Home. The brother-in-law, however, claimed them as his own and when he feared that the deception would be discovered he was said to have destroyed the remaining 48 volumes. The destroyed manuscript included Hunter's 86 surgical lectures and other most valuable material. This was a

serious loss to biological literature. Hunter's works that have been preserved are excellent treatises illustrated with beautiful drawings. The best series of drawings of the embryology of the chick before the 19th century was that of John Hunter. As he worked on the chick he thought how much easier it would be to study embryology if the specimens were larger. This led him to work with duck eggs and he waited 30 years for an ostrich to lay an egg for him, but found to his disappointment that the developing duck and ostrich are no larger than the developing chick.

Among the many written contributions to medicine and biology the following titles will indicate his breadth of interest: A Treatise on the Natural History of Human Teeth, Observation on Certain Parts of Animals, Directions for Preserving Animals and Parts of Animals for Anatomical Investigation, The Works of John Hunter, Observations and Reflections on Geology, Memoranda on Vegetation. There were also essays and accounts of observations on natural history, psychology, and physiology. In January 1780 John read a paper before the Royal Society on the structure of the human placenta. He claimed in this paper the discovery of certain features of the utero-placental circulation that his brother William had previously claimed. This led to a dispute that continued until William died. John had made many dissections in William's laboratory for which William received credit. In this particular case it was difficult to tell which of the brothers should have credit for the contribution. The Royal Society, however, printed the paper of John.

John Hunter's death in 1793 was due indirectly to an experiment that he had performed on himself in 1767 when he was involved in a controversy concerning the nature of the venereal diseases, syphilis and gonorrhea. He thought they were different symptoms of the same disease and in order to demonstrate the point and observe the course of the disease, he inoculated himself with the pus of a syphiletic patient. His theory was that a "virus" was responsible for the combined symptoms of both diseases; that the virus when placed on a secreting surface, that is, a mucous membrane, would produce the symptoms of gonorrhea, but when the same virus was placed on a non-secreting surface, such as the exterior of the skin, the symptoms of syphilis would occur. The causative organism in either case was believed to be the same and the manifestation of the disease would depend on the place where the organism became located in the body.

The pus with which Hunter inoculated himself evidently came from a patient with both syphilis and gonorrhea. The infection that he contracted and studied in himself was characteristic of both of these diseases. Therefore, he concluded that the two diseases were different manifestations of the same thing, as he had previously suspected. His report entitled, Treatise on the Venereal Diseases was printed in his own house in 1786. Without the aid of a bookseller it sold 1,000 copies in a year. His erroneous conclusion misdirected the study of syphilis for more than half a century after his death. Although he had made a careful study of syphilis, he did not know some of its most serious effects, for example, that it was a disease of the blood vessels as well as the epithelial tissues. He died October 22, 1793, following a dispute with a colleague at a board meeting of the Royal Society. The immediate cause of death was a heart attack; more correctly stated, the cause of death was untreated syphilis.

According to the directions of his will, the museum and collections were offered for sale to the British Government. When Pitt, the Prime Minister, was informed of the matter, he said, "What! buy preparations? Why I have not enough money to purchase gun powder." The vast collection remained locked up for 6 years under the supervision of a caretaker. Some influential people then realized the value of the collection and finally persuaded the government to purchase it. The purchase price was $75,000 which was about one-fifth of the money that John had actually spent in the collection of materials and the preparation of the museum. The museum is now maintained by the British Government at the Royal College of Surgeons in London. According to the terms of John's will, the collection must be open 4 hours in the afternoon 2 days each week for the inspection of the fellows of the College of Physicians, the Corporation of Surgeons, and persons introduced by members of these groups. A catalogue of the exhibits must be available and an official must be in attendance to explain the preparations.

John Hunter had great influence on the development of biology and particularly comparative anatomy, through his personal contributions and his students as well as through his museum. For his personal contribution, Hunter won the Copley medal and other distinguished awards. His publications brought him lasting recognition. In his conception of comparative anatomy, man was the central object and other types were compared to man. This is not true comparative anatomy. Historical relations had to be considered before further advancements could be made. In this respect some of his predecessors such as Edward Tyson were ahead of him.

Richard Owen (1804-1892), an assistant in the Hunter Museum after Hunter's death, carried on the tradition of the comparative school in anatomy, physiology, and paleontology in England. He had studied in Paris under Cuvier and later became known as the "Cuvier of England." He was director of Natural History Section of the British Museum. His great work was on the anatomy and physiology of the vertebrates. In 1859 he published a book entitled On the Classification and Geographical Distribution of the Mammalia. He was also interested in paleontology and in 1860 published the book entitled Paleontology or a Systematic Summary of Extinct Animals and Their Geological Relations. Owen was not sympathetic to the work on evolution which was presented and supported by his contemporaries Darwin, Huxley, and Hooker (Chapter 11). Although much of his work has been found since to support evolution, Owen rejected evolution and became the principal biologist of his time to take a position against evolution.

Cuvier

Comparative anatomy was founded in France during the revolutionary era of 1790-1815 with Georges Cuvier as its leader. Explorations into distant and previously unknown parts of the world had resulted in vast collections of animals that were available for study and comparison. Cuvier took advantage of the situation and worked out a systematic organization of the animal kingdom (Chapter 8). This served as the basis for natural history and comparative anatomy. From comparisons among living animals he became interested in fossils and worked out a theory of catastrophism (Chapter 11) to accommodate his religious views with his observations. He also became a distinguished leader in the field of vertebrate paleontology. In addition to his accomplishments in science, Cuvier was an eminent politician.

He fit in well as a scientist and political servant. A prodigious amount of work was turned out in good form and precise organization. To save time and facilitate his work, he fitted out a separate desk with writing material, manuscripts, and reference books for each project upon which he was working. In moving from one project to another in the course of a day's work, he could go right to work without wasting time in shuffling paper and gathering equipment. This precision and organization characterized all of his work.

Cuvier approached comparative anatomy by establishing relations between animals' form and habit or function. For example, hoofs were associated with plant-eaters and claws with flesh eaters. Distinctive shapes of bones were associated with various types of animals. Other observers had recognized connections between form and function in animals but Cuvier put the analysis on a systematic basis. Thomas Jefferson, who, like Benjamin Franklin, became closely associated with the French scientists of the period had associated a huge fossil claw (Megalonyx) with a prehistoric lion. Cuvier worked out a systematic correlation of parts with functions and identified it with an animal related to the modern sloth, but much larger and living on the ground instead of hanging upside down from limbs of trees.

A story illustrating Cuvier's confidence in his theory correlating parts with functions was told by his students. One brave student was said to have invaded the bedroom where Cuvier was sleeping dressed as the Devil and roared, "Cuvier! I've come to eat you." Cuvier opened his eyes, looked at the monster and said, "horns and hoofs, you are herbivorous and can't" whereupon he turned over and went back to sleep.

Cuvier's interest in prehistoric reptiles was stimulated when a skull with a crocodelian look was sent by French soldiers during the French revolution to the Jardin des Plantes. It had been discovered some years before in a quarry under land belonging to a Dr. Goddin, near Maastricht in the Netherlands. Cuvier identified it as the skull of a giant lizard that was later found to be a relative of the modern genus, Varanus.

Another strange fossil, described by a Florentine named Collini in the early 1800s, interested Cuvier. It had repitilian characteristics but wings. Cuvier tried to obtain the fossil for study but its owner refused. Collini's published drawing enabled Cuvier to identify it as a flying reptile which he named pterodactyl (Greek--pteron, wing; daktylos, finger). Cuvier brought his observations and theories concerning fossils together in a book Research on Fossil Bones (1825) that formed the foundation of paleontology. He did not realize the great lengths of the geological time periods and his view of catastrophism was not compatible with evolution (Chapter 11) but he was the leader of the period in the fields of comparative anatomy and vertebrate paleontology.

Cuvier was ahead of John Hunter and Richard Owen in his philosophical viewpoint because he had a more natural plan of creation and a natural explanation for fossils. His premature hypothesis of catastrophism established before the evolution concept was widely accepted was better than no hypothesis at all. It is unfortunate that through his great influence and brilliance as an orator, writer, and illustrator his mistakes were perpetuated for generations after he was dead. Cuvier was so thoroughly convinced of his theory of correlation of parts that he thought a single bone was sufficient to indicate what the animal was like. He concluded that certain kinds of teeth were always correlated (on the same animal) with hoofs. One whole group of extinct animals (chalicotheres) is now known to have teeth of the type which must (according to Cuvier) be associated with hoofs but the animals actually had large claws rather than hoofs.

REFERENCES

Ashley-Montagu, M. F. *Edward Tyson, M. D., FRS. 1650-1708 and the Rise of Human and Comparative Anatomy in England.* Philadelphia: Amer. Phil. Soc. Memoirs, Vol. 20, 1943.

Atkinson, D. T. *Magic Myth and Medicine*. Cleveland: World Publ. Co., 1956. (Chapter 19 on John Hunter).

Berry, R. J. A. *Your Brain and Its Story*. London: Oxford Univ. Press, 1939.

Bourne, G. C. *An Introduction to the Study of the Comparative Anatomy of Animals*. 2 Vol. London: G. Bell and Sons, Ltd., 1912.

Cole, F. J. *A History of Comparative Anatomy, from Aristotle to the Eighteenth Century*. London: Macmillan and Co., Ltd., 1944.

Corner, G. W. *Anatomical Texts of the Earlier Middle Ages*. Washington, D. C.: Carn. Inst. Wash. Publ. No. 364, 1927.

Guerlac, H. Some Aspects of Science during the French Revolution. *Sci. Monthly* 80:93-101, 1955.

Jones, F. W. *Hallmarks of Mankind*. Baltimore: Williams and Wilkins Co., 1948.

Kingsley, J. S. *Comparative Anatomy of Vertebrates*. Philadelphia: P. Blakiston's Son and Co., 1912.

Lassek, A. M. *Human Dissection, Its Drama and Struggle*. Springfield, Ill.: Charles C. Thomas Co., 1958.

Meyer, A. W. *The Rise of Embryology*. Stanford: Stanford Univ. Press, 1939.

Oppenheimer, J. M. *New Aspects of John and William Hunter*. New York: Henry Schuman, 1946.

Sarton, G. *Six Wings: Men of Science in the Renaissance*. Bloomington: Indiana Univ. Press, 1957.

Shearer, E. M. *Manual of Human Dissection*. Philadelphia: P. Blakiston's Son and Co., 1937.

Simpson, G. G. *Life of the Past*. New Haven: Yale Univ. Press, 1953.

The 18th century world had been enlarged through the discovery of America, the opening of the Orient to travel, and the discovery of Australia and the islands in the south seas. Early biological explorers such as Ray, Tournefort, and Linnaeus had demonstrated the values in experience and accomplishment that could come from travels in near and more distant places. More expeditions were undertaken for the purpose of observing living things in their native habitats and making collections of animals and plants. Some exploring projects were supported by academies and other institutions and some were undertaken by individuals, at their own expense, for scientific purposes and adventure. Stories of exciting experience, valuable collections, of animals

Chapter 10

BIOLOGICAL EXPLORATIONS

and plants, and further evidence of scientific accomplishment stimulated increasingly more excursions.

In the latter part of the 18th and continuing into the 19th century several well organized expeditions were dispatched to various parts of the world by governments, particularly the British government, to draw maps and make observations. Most important for their biological accomplishments were the voyages of the Endeavour, the Investigator, the Beagle, and the Challenger. Naturalists on these and other less well-known explorations did much to describe the fauna and flora in different parts of the world, including the ocean at different depths and the bottom. One important accomplishment was the development of the naturalists who participated such as Joseph Banks, Robert Brown,

Charles Darwin, and Charles W. Thompson. They received through their travels training and enthusiasm for natural history that influenced their later accomplishments.

In November, 1767, the Royal Society of London sent a memorandum to the King calling attention to a significant astronomical phenomenon which was to occur on June 3, 1769; on that day the planet Venus would pass over the disc of the sun. Information of value to navigation could be obtained by observing this event from an appropriate place near Tahiti. The King was interested and placed 4,000 pounds at the disposal of the Royal Society for a trip to the appropriate place requesting that the Admirability and the Royal Society work together in making preparations for the expedition. A 308 ton vessel three years and nine months old was purchased and renamed the The Endeavour Bark. After much consideration, James Cook, a warrant officer, was commissioned a lieutenant and appointed commander of the expedition. Cook and an astronomer were then officially appointed by the Royal Society to make the observation of the transit of Venus.

The Royal Society granted the request of one of its wealthy young fellows, Joseph Banks (1743-1820), to go along on the expedition as naturalist and to take seven naturalists and technicians to assist him in making biological studies. Later, two others were added making a total of ten in the biology section. Equipment for biological studies including a library, was provided personally by Banks at a cost of some 10,000 pounds. The Endeavour was the best equipped ship sent out up to that time for the purpose of natural history studies.

Banks already had training in botany and experience as an explorer. On his own initiative while attending school at Eton he had hired women who collected flowers for sale to druggists to teach him the names of the flowers and the places and seasons where they could be found. During one vacation period from Eton he discovered at his home a battered copy of Gerard's Herball which he studied thoroughly and carried back to school. Soon he was able to teach the women much more than they could teach him about flowers. When 17 years old Banks entered Christ Church College at Oxford but found to his disappointment that the Professor of Botany did no teaching. He was said to have given only one lecture in 35 years. Through Banks' influence and insistence, a young botanist was found at Cambridge and employed to teach at Oxford.

Three years after completing his schooling at Oxford, in April 1766, Banks was engaged on his first expedition as a naturalist. A Fishery Protection vessel was dispatched to the shores of Labrador and Newfoundland on a 7 months' voyage. Here Banks with an Oxford friend, who was also a member of the party, took excursions inland where observations were made and plants were collected. On the return trip to England the ship stopped at Lisbon where Banks added more plants to his collection. Soon after his return from this expedition he made a tour of the western part of England. He was elected a fellow in the Royal Society and when the members began talking about the projected expedition to the South Seas to observe the transit of Venus Banks saw an opportunity for further botanical studies in a new and unexplored territory and requested permission to go on the expedition.

The Endeavour sailed from Plymouth, England in August 1768. Explorations were made in the South Sea islands, mainly Tahiti, New Zealand, New Guinea, and Australia. Many landmarks (Fig. 10-1) in these areas now bear names that date back to this exploring party. Cook's Reef, a part of the Great Barrier Reef some distance off the eastern shore of Australia, is a hazard to ships at the present time. The discovery of Endeavour Strait, between Australia and New Guinea, proved the separateness of Australia and New Guinea. Botany Bay yielded many specimens to the naturalists. The name New South Wales was first used by Cook for southeastern Australia.

One of the favorable aspects of the expedition was the high quality of leadership provided by Captain Cook. Discipline was excellent, there was little illness or dissention, in spite of cramped quarters and poor living conditions, and a great deal was accomplished. Other attempts had been made previously to explore the uncharted South Seas but in most cases the men had become ill with scurvy and home-

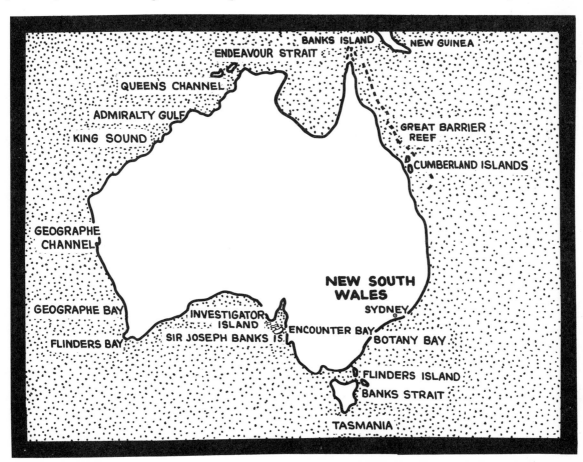

Fig. 10-1. Map of Australia showing landmarks
of early expeditions

sickness before they arrived at the place designated for study. Because of the difficulties encountered on previous expeditions, the British Government was reluctant to finance more expeditions and yet the navy depended on maps, charts, and weather data. Captain Cook recognized the significance of good health on the part of crew members and insisted on sanitation and proper nutrition. He provided sauerkraut in the rations when fresh fruit and vegetables were not available.

Another great advantage enjoyed by Cook that had not been available to his predecessors was a satisfactory method of determining longitude. It had been possible for a long time to determine the north-south position or latitude of a ship at sea, but there was no method for determining the east-west position. A table, worked out by an astronomer to determine longitude from the position of the stars was used for the first time on the voyage of the Endeavour. It was thus possible for Cook and his crew to determine their position at all times, and they were able to prepare an accurate account of their route and a detailed record of the coastlines visited. Development of new instruments and a series of circumstances not only made the voyage of the Endeavour possible but contributed greatly to its success.

Extensive notes were compiled by Cook, Banks, Daniel Solander, one of the naturalists on board who had been a student of Linnaeus, and other members of the party. Most of the notes along with the collections of plants were eventually deposited in the British Museum where they are still preserved. Interesting descriptions of strange animals, such as the kangaroo, are included in the notes. Banks demonstrated skill and leadership during the three years in the South Seas. When he returned to England in 1771 with volumes of notes and vast collections of plants and animals, he was immediately famous. The collections grew in later years through additions made by Banks himself and others. A year after the return of the Endeavour (1772) Banks and Solander made a voyage to Iceland where they gathered more plants and wrote volumes of notes in their own handwriting that are now in the British Museum.

Two years after the return of the Endeavour (1773) Banks was appointed by King George III as Royal Scientific Adviser. Among other responsibilities, Banks was placed in charge of the Royal

Botanical Garden at Kew which was developed into an exchange place where plants from the entire British Empire were studied and tested. Rare and little known plants from all over the world were gathered and subjected to observation and experimentation. When plants were found which could have practical values in particular climates or special growing conditions, they were carried to these places and tried out on a large scale. The distinguished botanists Solander, Dryander, Robert Brown, and many in humbler station were employed at Kew.

Subsidiary botanical gardens were developed in Jamaica and other parts of the British Empire to carry out the ambitious testing program directed by Banks. Expeditions were then dispatched to little known areas of the world to discover new plants for study and testing in different locations. Many exploring parties were organized for this purpose through the influence of Banks. The most significant was the voyage of the Investigator commanded by Matthew Flinders that carried Banks' young friend Robert Brown as chief naturalist.

When Banks was 35 years old he was elected President of the Royal Society and he remained in office for some 42 years. This was a difficult period for the Society because men who were not scientists but were only interested in prestige and political favor had gained control. Some society projects initiated by these men were unworthy of a great scientific organization. At times there was confusion and too often outright dissension. Banks was firm when necessary but met situations that required sympathy and tact with great understanding. He was good humored and liberal in his relations with others, and lavish in his hospitality to follow members and guests.

Investigator

Matthew Flinders had already made successful explorations in the South Seas. He had succeeded in sailing around Tasmania and thus proving that it was an island not connected with Australia. As his next project he had proposed to sail around Australia and map the coast lines. Sir Joseph Banks was approached by Flinders with this proposal and he was at once interested and sympathetic with the plan. Banks began to make arrangements for such a trip by persuading the First Lord of the Admiralty to fit out a ship for the voyage under the command of Flinders. A 334 ton ship was chosen and renamed the Investigator.

Visualizing an expedition of biological discovery similar to his own voyage on the Endeavour, Banks arranged, at his own expense, for the young Scottish botanist, Robert Brown (1773-1858), and a draughtsman, Ferdinand Bauer, to go with Flinders. Assistants were also provided and equipment and supplies for botanical work were prepared. Biological work, however, represented a secondary objective on this expedition. The first objective and excuse for the voyage, as far as the Admiralty was concerned, was the exploration of the coast of Australia. Brown was given no specific instructions but was left to make his own decisions as to how he would proceed with his natural history investigations.

The Investigator sailed from England in 1801. When only a short distance out at sea the ship developed leaks causing trouble and anxiety for the members of the party. Through sheer persistence on the part of the crew members the ship reached its destination. New territory was charted along the south coast of Australia and the continuity of the Australian coast line was demonstrated. Many places were named after familiar English locations. The name of Flinders was added to those of Cook and Banks for names of geographical features such as Flinder's Bay and Flinder's Island. Main streets in several cities in Australia are now named after Flinders who was first to use the name Australia for the great island continent. The Investigator Islands, south of Australia, were named after the leaky ship that caused the party so much trouble.

Because of the ship's dilapidated condition and the lack of facilities to make repairs, the ship was abandoned after two years. Flinders packed the maps, notes, and some biological specimens, and took passage in 1803 on another boat for England. When his ship was a week out from Australia, it crashed on a reef and was wrecked. At the risk of his life, Flinders made his way back to Australia in a row boat and arranged for the rescue of the survivors who at the time of the rescue had been marooned on a sandbar for 5 weeks. Most of the maps and notes were saved, but the plant and animal specimens were lost.

In a small ship, the Cumberland, that assisted in making the rescue, Flinders continued his journey to Europe. At Mauritius, the Cumberland stopped for repairs and Flinders became a prisoner of the French who were, unbeknown to him, at war with England. Flinders, carrying maps and messages from Australia, was considered a spy and held as a prisoner until 1810. His health was broken and he died 4 years later. The published account of his explorations entitled Voyage to Terra Australis appeared when he was ill and unable to read the finished work.

Brown and Bauer had not completed their projects so they remained in Australia until 1805 when they returned to England with great stores of herbarium specimens and seeds to be planted in the garden at Kew. Funds were not available from the Admiralty in these troubled war years to publish the complete botanical report of Brown. The large volume of material was eventually condensed and presented as an appendix to Flinders' Voyage to Terra Australis.

Robert Brown grew in stature as a botanist while on the expedition and when he returned to England, he was recognized as the leading botanist of his time. Immediately he became the librarian of the Linnean Society, a position which he held until 1822 when he was elected a Fellow in the Linnean Society. He also became librarian to Banks and had charge of Bank's vast collection of specimens, books, and manuscripts. In 1811 he was elected a fellow in the Royal Society. When Banks died, he bequeathed the collection to Brown with the stipulation that it should go to the British Museum when Brown was through with it. Seven years after Bank's death in 1827, the collection was turned over to the British Museum and Brown went with it as the first caretaker. Brown received the title as First Keeper of the Botany Department of the British Museum. He served as President of the Royal Society from 1849-1853.

Brown did not publish books as some predecessors and contemporaries had done, but he published a long series of scientific papers of great value. His work on the flora of Australia is a classic. No new system of classification was developed but he followed the pattern of others, mostly that of Linnaeus.

Several orders and families of plants were analyzed and revised. He made a special study of the adaptations of members of some families to different climates and other environmental conditions. His associates recognized him as a keen observer and critical scientist. Among the special contributions to his credit are the discovery of the cell nucleus, an analysis of the sexual process in higher plants, and the observation and preliminary explanation of the dancing motion of particles suspended in a fluid medium (Brownian movement) now known to be due to the bombardment of molecules.

Beagle

The Beagle voyage (1831-1836) was dispatched by Great Britain to sail around South America drawing maps and making measurements and to circumnavigate the world. It was said to be organized entirely for scientific purposes, particularly those that were of practical concern to the British Navy. Specific areas to be given most attention were Patagonia, that is, the southern part of South America, and Tierra del Fuego, the islands off the end of South America below Chili and Argentina. Surveys were also to be made along the shores of Chili and Peru in South America and among the islands in the Pacific and Atlantic. Biological interest in this voyage is centered around the naturalist on board, Charles Darwin (1809-1882 Fig. 10-2). A sketch of his life and work is given here in connection with his voyage on the Beagle and as an introduction for his later work on evolution considered in the next chapter.

Charles Robert Darwin was the son of a successful doctor Robert Darwin at Shrewsbury in England. His mother, Susannah Wedgwood eldest daughter of the famous potter Josiah Wedgwood, died when Charles was 8 years old. His grandfather, Erasmus Darwin, was a well-known 18th century doctor and writer. Darwin's youth in no way suggested his forthcoming greatness. He attended a boarding school which was located a mile or so from his home for 7 years and moved back and forth between home and school.

At 16, young Darwin went to study medicine at Edinburgh where he developed a distaste for chemistry and a horror for the sight of blood. He later characterized medicine as a "beastly profession". Lectures on geology and zoology were termed by him as "incredibly dull", but they were more pleasant than those in some other subjects. At Edinburgh, Darwin acquired much valuable knowledge, if not from the lectures, at least from personal observations. He became friendly with some fishermen and accompanied them when they trawled for oysters. In leisure hours on the sea shore, he observed living things and made a small discovery concerning a sea-worm that he reported before a learned society. He loved hunting and learned how to stuff birds. His vacations were spent with his Wedgwood cousins in North Wales, hiking and shooting.

Dr. Darwin observing that his son would not become a physician but was becoming "an idle sporting man," proposed that Charles leave the study of medicine and study to become a clergyman. Charles was agreeable and in his 20th year he began the study for the ministry at Christs College, Cambridge. Here his school work was again neglected while he collected butterflies, rode horses, shot birds, and led a gay social life. The Reverend John Henslow became acquainted with Darwin and through sympathy and understanding he influenced Darwin a great deal. As they become more intimate and Darwin's admiration for Henslow increased, Henslow suggested books for Darwin to read. One with which Darwin was particularly impressed was the work of Alexander von Humboldt (1769-

Fig. 10-2. Charles Darwin

1859) <u>Personal Narrative of Travels to the Equinoxial Regions of America During the Years 1799-1804</u> giving a glowing account of scientific exploration in South America. After passing his B. A. examinations, Darwin stayed on at Cambridge for two more terms planning to complete the work for the ministry. Through Henslow, Darwin became acquainted with the geologist, Adam Sedgwick with whom he later studied geology.

While on a geological field trip in Wales on August 29, 1831, Darwin received a letter from Professor Henslow informing him that a certain Captain Robert Fitz-Roy was looking for a young man to serve without pay as a naturalist on the <u>H. M. S. Beagle</u>, an Admiralty vessel scheduled to undertake a five-year survey around South America and other more distant parts of the world. Darwin had mixed feelings about such an adventure but went home to discuss the prospect with his folks. The entire family seemed at first to oppose the notion, his father and sisters mentioned the poor living conditions, wild places, and wild company, and they were concerned about the effects of such experience on his position with the clergy. Charles himself had doubts but the anticipation of high adventure encouraged him to go.

His father, still unconvinced, agreed to arbitrate, and Charles' Uncle Joe (Wedgwood) was called in to settle the matter. To everyone's surprise, Uncle Joe thought it a good opportunity for young Charles. He claimed that inasmuch as Charles was not applying himself to his studies at this time, the voyage, through the necessary application and responsibility, would prove more beneficial than harmful. Weary of the argument, the father finally consented. Charles purchased 12 shirts, slippers, Spanish language books, 2 pistols, a rifle, and a new microscope, placed these items in a carpet bag, and set out for Plymouth where the ship was being prepared. With this meager equipment, plus a few other books particularly Lyell's <u>Principles of Geology</u>, Volume I, (1830), Milton's poems and a Greek testament, Charles was ready to set out on a long journey to do original work in natural history.

The <u>Beagle</u> was a solidly built vessel of 242 tons, rigged as a barque and carrying two whale boats. She belonged to an old type vessel and was called a "coffin" because of the tendency for ships of this type to sink. A total of 76 people were signed on board including crew, marines, specialists, and artists. Captain Fitz-Roy, only 4 years older than Darwin, proved to be a good navigator and commander. Darwin was interested in the preparations of the voyage and wandered around Plymouth indulging in dreams and speculations while final arrangements were made. The most wonderful thing was that he was to see the world of which he had read so much in von Humboldt's exciting narrative of travels in South America.

After a few false starts, the <u>Beagle</u> put out to sea in December 1831. Charles had heard of seasickness, but he had never dreamed that he would be sea sick. Certainly he had no foreboding that it would last for 5 continuous years. He was pleased that he felt so well during the first day on board while the ship was in the harbor but with the effects of the open sea, he retired to his hammock. He was intermittently ill for the rest of the voyage, causing Fitz-Roy at times to consider returning him to England for the sake of his health. The enforced idleness during periods of illness gave him time for reflection and enabled him to correlate facts he had observed, in their proper perspective.

Darwin had planned to use his idle time to repay his inattention to studies at the university by excessive work on languages, mathematics, and classics. However, prescribed courses were as distasteful as ever, and he spent increasing amounts of time doing other things, particularly geological studies. His devotion to geology, incited partly by his enthusiasm for Lyell's <u>Principles of Geology</u>, caused him at first to neglect botanical and zoological observations. Though he collected industriously, his ignorance of anatomy and classification left him with woefully inadequate and incomplete collections. Some of his collections were so worthless that upon his return to England he could find no institution that would accept them. He was far from systematic in making collections and was forced at times to borrow specimens from Fitz-Roy's private collections to make his own appear respectable.

At St. Jago Island, his first acquaintance with tropical lands, he observed and collected enthusiastically considering everything to be important, but he still emphasized marine zoology and geology at the expense of the other fields. In his <u>Geological Observations</u>

published later he described the rock formation and speculated on the formation of this volcanic island. Continuing the voyage to South America, Charles, when his health allowed, worked industriously, occupying his time with notes and specimens. He dragged a net behind the ship, and although he obtained some unique specimens of marine life, he also incurred the displeasure of the officers and men whose job it was to keep the decks clean and free from the sort of messes that he was always causing. During this period he discovered that the "dust at sea", a phenomenon discussed by many previous, voyagers, was in reality the bodies of small infusoria, wafted about by the winds.

On February 17, 1832, the <u>Beagle</u> crossed the equator. On the last day of February, the <u>Beagle</u> landed at Bahia in central Brazil. Here Charles was free and on his own resources, and he observed and collected along the shore. When he moved inland he encountered a squabble over his passport but was finally allowed to go into the interior where he observed parasol ants and spiders and was fortunate in being able to observe a vampire bat in the act of feeding upon a goat. Darwin recorded his observations of slavery and his feeling of revulsion that led to a later argument with Captain Fitz-Roy over the treatment of slaves. He also observed numerous fossils and strange living animals of South America and indulged in speculation as to whether a tree large enough to hold a prehistoric gigantic sloth had ever existed.

The <u>Beagle</u> continued its voyage to Patagonia where Darwin went on land and joined General Rosas in an expedition into the interior to put down a native revolt by extermination. He was shocked and distressed by the poverty of the natives and the cruelty of the soldiery but he was impressed by the adeptness of the natives, particularly in the art of tracking. In Patagonia he observed some of the better known venemous reptiles and had leisure enough to attend several bullfights and operas. He also became acquainted with the native herdsmen of the pampus country called gauchos. When they gave him puma meat to eat, he became psychologically ill because he thought it was unborn calf, that he had heard was a delicacy of the gauchos.

At the southern tip of South America, the ship paused to let off three Tierra del Fuegians that Fitz-Roy had collected some years before as children on the voyage of the <u>Adventurer</u>. The purpose for taking

them aboard was to train them as interpreters. The children had learned to wear clothes and had gone to England and attended school. They were now being returned to their homes. The Beagle stopped here a year later and Fitz-Roy located one of the children (Jimmie Button) who had gone native again in spite of his English education and experience in the civilized way of life. Darwin commented on the degenerate condition of the natives and he wondered if they had remained in this state since the creation of the world.

The trip around the horn left Darwin so ill that he did not care to see anyone or anything but he was revived by an earthquake at Conception. Seeing "geology in the act" and obtaining confirmation of his theory concerning the importance of earthquakes in the rise and fall of land levels had a soothing effect on his stomach.

On September 15, 1835, the <u>Beagle</u> arrived at the Galapagos Islands. Darwin did not at this time attach much importance to the animal life on these islands but his work and observations here later became the foundation for his theories on evolution. When introduced to Lawson, the governor of the settlement, Darwin conversed with him concerning the possibilities of finding a live volcano on the islands. In the course of the conversation, Lawson stated that if animals from different islands were lined up before him, he could tell at a glance from which island in the group each animal had come. The importance of this did not strike Darwin at first. He went on, collecting blindly and mixing specimens from various islands in the same sack. He was finally awakened to the potentialities of the situation by the specific differences in the garden thrush. Why, he wondered, are islands that are formed of the same rocks, and of equal height, and nearly identical climate so differently tenated?

By this time four years had been spent in traveling around South America and the mission of mapping the coastline had been accomplished. The <u>Beagle</u> now proceeded on the second part of its assignment, a cruise to the south seas and around the world. When the <u>Beagle</u> stopped at Tahiti, in the Society Islands, Darwin relapsed into his theological background, by arguing with Fitz-Roy over the moral condition of the natives, Fitz-Roy contending that the missionaries were too strict. In Australia Darwin noted the effects of food supply on human and animal populations. He observed the wide differences in appearance between animals such as the platypus in Australia and animals that inhabited other parts of the world. A study of coral reef structure in the vicinity of Australia gave him material to later write a monograph on the structure of coral reefs and atols. A brief stop at St. Helena was made on the return trip to Bahia.

During the sea voyage and on land expeditions, Darwin collected more specimens than he could carry conveniently on the ship. From time to time he sent home in care of Professor Henslow cases of specimens including rocks, snails, fossil bones, spiders, and barnacles. He also sent long letters describing his scientific observations which Professor Henslow read before various academic societies. Darwin noted that Lyell's book, Principles of Geology, put forward the theory that great geological changes had occurred on the earth and that the present agencies for change were responsible for those changes that had occurred in the past. This book did much to help Darwin comprehend the vast periods of time involved in the history of the earth.

After almost five years at sea the Beagle returned to England on October 2, 1836. Charles Darwin was wealthy with the fruits of his collecting and much to his surprise, well known in scientific circles. The next few months were busy ones. Darwin took lodgings at Cambridge for a short time while he had his specimens further examined. Now 27 years old and a recognized naturalist, he settled down to his life's work, a changed man from the indifferent student of five years before.

He distributed his collections to the various museums, and supervised the publication of the official Voyage of H. M. S. Beagle. Although Darwin was busy with his work he took time in 1839 to court and marry his cousin, Emma Wedgwood. With the coming of a settled home life he again turned to his scientific labors, but soon his health began to suffer. He wrote to a friend that it was a bitter mortification for him to digest the fact that "the race is for the strong". Seeking the solitude of the country, Charles Darwin took his wife and family to the little village of Downe in Kent where he made his home for the rest of his life.

Darwin soon acquired a name as an author when he published A Naturalist's Voyage Round the World, compiled from his Beagle notes. He had also investigated coral reef formation and published his observations in Coral Reefs, that was a classic example of the use of the scientific method. He wondered why coral reefs rose so steeply from the ocean floor, and why they remained only a few feet above the waves. Their conical shape led Darwin to surmise that they were built on submerged volcanic peaks, but on investigation he found that coral could not live below a depth of 150 feet. Here was a problem; how was the gap to be bridged? Darwin showed that the foundation upon which the coral built must have been near the surface at an earlier time and that it sank gradually while the creatures worked, always keeping near the surface of the water, until the coral layer was several hundred feet thick and extended into the depths of the ocean. The work demonstrated Darwin's curiosity and restless pursuit of facts. Actually the theory does not apply to all coral formation; but it has permanently affected the science of geology. Further geological interests were presented in two publications: Volcanic Islands and Geological Observations upon South America.

Challenger

The high point of organized scientific exploration and discovery was reached in the expedition of the Challenger (1872-76). This was organized to study oceanography, meteorology, and natural history. The ship was a sailing vessel equipped with steam. It carried special apparatus for sounding, dredging, and studying the ocean at different depths, particularly the bottom. Chemistry and biology laboratories were established on the ship. The purpose of the expedition was to study the physical and biological aspects of the Atlantic and Pacific Oceans, the islands, and shorelines of the continents. Six naturalists were on board who worked under the supervision of Charles W. Thompson.

During the four years of the expedition, vast collections of plants and animals were made. These were studied and classified by a whole army of investigators under the leadership of John Murray. Results, published by the British Government in 50 folio volumes, demonstrated the importance of the physical world in relation to living things. Protozoans, particularly Foraminifera and Globigerina, were found in the ocean and thick deposits at the bottom of the oceans represented the remains of such organisms that had lived in past periods of biological history.

The plankton or living community at the surface of the ocean was given special attention and numerous organisms were found living at the surface. In the Sargasso Sea where sea weeds have become established in a wide area of the open water, all sorts of organisms were found. Shrimps and crabs were well concealed because they had become yellow like the sea weeds in their environment.

Exploration by Individuals

In addition to the well organized expeditions that made massive contributions to biology, many individuals explored, collected specimens, and wrote of their adventures. Alfred Russel Wallace (1823-1913) will be cited because of his contributions as an explorer, and as an introduction to a man who made great contributions in the areas of evolution and geographical distribution of animals.

At the age of 14, Alfred joined his brother William in London and set out to learn surveying. The following year he started an apprenticeship as a watchmaker, but before this was completed he returned to surveying and formed a partnership with his brother. While traveling on surveying projects, Wallace became interested in botany and studied plant taxonomy. He was also interested in astronomy and agriculture. In 1843, surveying was not going well enough to occupy the full time of the two Wallaces so Alfred began writing in his spare time. In 1844, he became a school master in Leicester. It was here that he met Henry Walter Bates (1825-1892), the naturalist, who stimulated in him an interest in entomology. Wallace read the thesis of Thomas Robert Maltnus (1766-1834) on population during this period and found it interesting and suggestive of basic biological relations.

Wallace and Bates decided to go on a collecting trip to the Amazon region and planned to sell the specimens they collected to defray the costs of the trip. They sailed from England in April 1848. The following year Wallace's younger brother, Herbert, joined them in South America but he died a year later with yellow fever. Bates remained in South America for 7 years but Wallace returned to England in 1852. On his way home misfortune struck again, the ship burned and most of the specimens and notes that he had collected for his own use and to sell, were lost. Material loss was great but the impressions of the Amazon region remained with him. The majesty and variety of the equatorial forest, the beauty and strangeness of the butterflies and birds, and particularly the impressions he obtained following his contacts with savage human beings were so vivid that he began to write about them. During the next few years Wallace settled in London and worked on the notes and collections he had left and wrote books entitled Travels on the Amazon and Palm Trees of the Amazon.

The trip to the Amazon had stimulated Wallace's interest in further travel and explorations and in 1854, he decided to visit the Malay Archipelago. This region, he believed, offered the richest possible field to the biological collector. He remained in the Archipelago for 12 years, studying the animals on every important island of the group. Differences in animal life were observed between the eastern and the western parts. The division line was a narrow but deep strait between Borneo and Celebes, and between Bali and Lomboc, now known as Wallace's Line. East of Wallace's Line are the Australian type animals and to the west are the Oriental type animals.

In 1855, Wallace wrote an essay entitled On the Law Which Has Regulated the Introduction of New Species. The theme of this essay was that every species has come into existence coincident both in time and space with a pre-existing, closely allied species. During the next three years Wallace pondered over the problem as to how such changes could have been brought about and in 1858 he made a great contribution to the theory of evolution that is discussed in the next chapter.

Early in the year 1862 Wallace left the Archipelago and returned to England. He took with him many specimens, some were living but most were preserved. Again he settled in London, worked on his collection and wrote about his travels and observations. Wallace did not have a position with any institution but made his living and paid the expenses of his travels by selling specimens, giving lectures, and writing books and popular articles. Although he sold many of the specimens that he brought back to London, he kept a large collection for his own investigations. Much of his early work was in taxonomy, but as he grew older his interest turned more to problems of evolution and geographical distribution. In 1859 his book on the Malay Archipelago was published with many illustrations of natural history as well as vivid accounts of his travels.

At the age of 46 Wallace married and settled down in London to a life of study and writing. About this time he was awarded the Royal Medal by the Royal Society. In 1870 Wallace wrote his mature views on evolution in a book entitled Contributions to the Theory of Natural Selection.

The book entitled Geographical Distribution of Animals published in 1876 established Wallace as the leader in this field of biology. The land masses of the world were divided into six zoogeographical regions on the basis of geography and mammal inhabitants. The six realms are as follows: (1) Palearctic, all of Europe, and most of Asia, that is quite similar to the (2) Nearctic, North America, in which such animals as the elk, fox, and bear are found, (These two realms are usually listed as subdivisions of the Holarctic) (3) Etheopian, South Africa, the home of the gorilla, giraffe, lion, and hypopotamus, (4) Oriental, South Asia, inhabited by the orangutan, Indian elephant, and flying fox, (5) Australian, the continent of Australia and surrounding islands, where marsupials are found, and (6) Neotropical, South America, the home of the tapirs, sloths, monkeys with tails, and vampire bats. Other plants and animals in addition to the mammals are distinct in these major geographical areas.

In 1878, Wallace published Island Life, and in 1881, Land Nationalization. During these later years, many short collecting journeys were taken on the continent of Europe, especially to Switzerland. Wallace spent the year 1886 lecturing in the United States and on his return to England, he wrote Darwinism (1889). He also wrote Studies, Scientific and Social (1900), Man's Place in the Universe (1903) and a two volume autobiography that was published under the title My Life (1905).

REFERENCES

Barlow, N. ed. *Charles Darwin and the Voyage of the Beagle.* London: Pilot Press, Ltd., 1945.

Barlow, N. *The Autobiography of Charles Darwin.* New York: Harcourt, Brace and Co., 1958.

Bates, H. W. *The Naturalist on the River Amazon.* New York: D. Appleton and Co., 1892.

Bates, M. and P. S. Humphrey eds. *The Darwin Reader.* New York: Schribner's Sons, 1956.

Cameron, H. C. *Sir Joseph Banks.* London: The Batchworth Press, 1952.

Cutright, P. R. *The Great Naturalists Explore South America.* New York: The Macmillan Co., 1940.

Darwin, C. *The Structure and Distribution of Coral Reefs.* London: Smith, Elder and Co., 1842.

Darwin, C. *Geological Observations of the Volcanic Islands and Parts of South America Visited During the Voyage of H.M.S. "Beagle".* London: Smith, Elder and Co., 1844.

Darwin, C. *Journal of Researches into Natural History and Geology of Countries Visited During Voyage of H.M.S. Beagle.* New ed. New York: D. Appleton and Co., 1896. (Later ed. of Vol. 3 of *Narrative of the Surveying Voyages of His Majesty's Ships Adventure and Beagle* describing only the Beagle voyage.)

Darwin, C. *Voyage of a Naturalist Around the World*. London: Oxford Univ. Press, 1930.

Darwin, C. *The Voyage of the Beagle*. New York: Bantam Books, 1958.

Darwin, C. *Origin of Species*. New York: The New American Library, 1958. (Original date of publication 1859. Several other copies prepared by different publishers are available.)

Darwin, F. ed. *The Life and Letters of Charles Darwin*. 2 vol. New York: D. Appleton and Co., 1896.

Darwin, F. *Charles Darwin's Autobiography*. New York: Henry Schuman, 1950.

Eisely, L. C. Alfred Russel Wallace. *Sci. Amer.* 200:60-84, 1954.

Fitz-Roy, R. and C. Darwin, eds. *Narrative of the Surveying Voyages of His Majesty's Ships Adventure and Beagle Between the Years 1826 and 1836.* 3 vols. London: Henry Colburn, 1839.

Hagen, V. W. von, *South America Called Them*. New York: A. A. Knopf, 1945.

Hoff, R. and H. de Terra. *They Explored*. New York: Henry Z. Walck, Inc., 1959. (Chapter 1 Von Humboldt.)

Holmyard, E. J., *British Scientists*. London: London Phil. Library, 1951.

Moore, R., *Charles Darwin, A Great Life in Brief*. New York: A. A. Knopf, 1955.

Niles, B., *Journeys in Time*. New York: Coward-McCann, 1946.

Pekin, L. B., *Darwin*. New York: Stackpole Sons, 1938.

Sears, P. B., *Charles Darwin, The Naturalist as a Cultural Force*. New York: C. Scribner's Sons, 1950.

Wallace, A. R., *The Geographical Distribution of Animals*. New York: Harper and Bros., 1876.

Wallace, A. R., *Island Life*. London: Macmillan & Co., 1895.

West, G., *Charles Darwin*. New Haven: Yale Univ. Press, 1938.

Evolution, like many theses of modern science, originated in philosophy. With the coming of the Ionian Greek philosophers (Chapter 2), the concept of change in nature began to take form. Empedocles brought together the ideas of his predecessors and developed a number of concepts that might be interpreted now as consistent with the modern theory of evolution. He believed in spontaneous generation of lower forms, which could explain the origin of elementary life, but his spontaneous generation concept did not include the origin of higher forms; he considered their development to be slow and gradual.

Plants, the first living things to appear on the earth, were visualized as being pushed up from the earth slime by internal fire. From the plants, animals were produced. This transition, like other major developments, was not rapid but was in progress for ages and came about through the fortuitous acts of the two great forces love and hate acting upon the four elements fire, air, water, and earth. Thus higher animals were not produced directly as such, but were at first strange and awkward monsters, most of which could not adapt themselves to their environment and therefore perished. After innumerable trials, nature found some combinations that resulted in animals capable of living and reproducing their kind. Most of the concepts of Empedocles were crude and primitive, but he hit upon a number of truths that have been verified in present day biology: (1) higher forms developed gradually, (2) plants evolved before animals, (3) imperfect forms were replaced by more perfect forms, that is, less perfect forms became extinct and more perfect forms lived and reproduced their kind.

Aristotle believed in the slime origin for lower forms of life, but higher forms he thought represented a progressive series, depending on the degree of Psyche they contained. Plants and plant-like animals such as sponges had only a vegetable soul, lower animals had an animal soul, higher animals a rational soul, and the highest type of human beings had an intellectual soul. A broad phylogenetic sequence was thus postulated. He believed in a great plan which governed the universe and all living things. The plan was so designed, however, that change and progress could occur. Necessity brought about change in nature. This idea led to a belief in prenatal influences and the inheritance of acquired characteristics. Aristotle was more interested in experi-

ment and induction than his predecessors, contemporaries, and most of those who followed. He was unable, however, to use these methods in the broad study of evolution and arrived at his ideas in a philosophical manner. In spite of the weaknesses of Aristotle's work on evolution, it was not materially improved for some 2000 years. Today most of Aristotle's theories bearing on evolution have been either discarded or revised but he holds a position among the great philosophers of all time.

Some theologians of the Christian era commented on the subject of evolution. St. Augustine (353-430 A.D.), for example, favored an allegorical interpretation of the book of Genesis in the Bible and openly

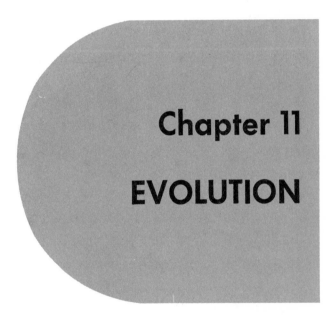

Chapter 11

EVOLUTION

promoted an evolutionary concept as opposed to special creation. The six-day creation plan was interpreted as a "series of causes" long enough for those things that were in the mind of God to be brought to their completion. St. Augustine took a position half way between abiogenesis and biogenesis in his discussions on creation. From the first, he said, there had been two types of germs present on earth: (1) the visible, associated with the bodies of plants and animals and (2) the invisible, that under proper conditions would grow into living organisms without the cooperation of other living organisms. Not only did he apply this idea to all living things but to inorganic matter as well; thus, the moon, sun, and earth were at first germs. As this process, once established, was self-perpetuating, continued change was inevitable.

Pre-Darwinian Evolutionists

From the time of the early Greek philosophers until the first part of the Christian era, evolution was discussed freely and fairly by at least a nucleus of scholars. The more liberal church fathers were not shocked by it, and some considered it as a valid alternative theory to special creation and not inconsistent with the scriptures. During the Middle Ages there was little interest in such subjects. The Renaissance was marked by sporadic developments in biology. Few contributors of that period were deeply enough involved in philosophical subjects to consider evolution seriously. The 17th and 18th centuries were dominated by the systematists who attempted to classify natural objects, including plants and animals, in fixed and rigid systems (Chapter 8). The fixity of species became firmly established by Linnaeus and his followers. With this background, evolution was crowded out of the scene. Only a few biologists of that period gave any attention to the subject.

The French naturalist, politician, writer, Buffon (Fig. 11-1) discussed evolution extensively but he took different positions on this subject at different times

believed 1st in fixity of species but later in their changeability

Warsu 293

Fig. 11-1. Comte de Buffon, French naturalist

in his life. During his early life, he took an extreme view in favor of special creation, much like that of his contemporary, Linnaeus. He did not, however, agree with Linnaeus in other respects. Linnean classification was depicted as trifling and artificial. Buffon considered nature as a whole and looked for large likenesses rather than trivial differences. This led him to a consideration of broad natural relations and evolution.

Later in life Buffon developed an extreme view on the inheritance of acquired characters. The factors that he visualized as influencing evolutionary change were: (1) direct influences of the environment, (2) migration, (3) geographical isolation, and (4) overcrowding and struggle for existence. These factors would be expected to result in a gradual development of new forms of life rather than abrupt changes. When he was more involved in politics at a later stage in his career, he adopted a more liberal, middle of the road position and wavered between the extremes of his earlier views. He compromised the position of special creation and evolution with a number of wild speculations. The pig, for example, was described as a compound of other animals, the ass was a degenerate horse, and the ape a degenerate man. Buffon was a prolific writer and an interpreter of contemporary thought but he was not an original investigator. He had broad interests in mathematics, physical science, and biology and wrote a Natural History that was intended to embrace all scientific knowledge. Some 44 volumes were actually published, some by an assistant after his death.

Erasmus Darwin (1731-1802), English philosopher and free thinker, was somewhat clearer than Buffon on the subject of evolution. The name of the best known book, Zoonomia (1794), was coined to represent the laws of organic life. In this book Darwin developed the theme of the inheritance of acquired characters. The age of the earth was described in millions of years and life was considered to have originated from a primordial protoplasmic mass. The struggle for existence that was elaborated by Charles Darwin, grandson of Erasmus, was suggested in Zoonomia.

In the preface to Zoonomia Erasmus Darwin wrote, "The Great Creator of all things has infinitely diversified the works of his hands but has at the same time stamped a certain similitude on the features of nature, that demonstrates to us that the whole is one family of one parent. On this similitude is founded all rational analogy." Erasmus Darwin independently concluded that species descend from common ancestors. He speculated on the variations in animals, the reproduction of the strongest, as well as the struggle for existence. It is now evident that Charles Darwin received more from his grandfather than was previously supposed. For every volume written by Charles, there was a corresponding chapter by Erasmus. Charles, in one of his written treatises expressed his disappointment in finding Zoonomia more speculative than scientific.

Lamarck

The most important of the 18th century evolutionists was Lamarck (Fig. 11-2).

Fig. 11-2. Jean Baptiste Lamarck, French biologist and pre-Darwinian evolutionist. "Reprinted with permission from Gardner, Principles of Genetics, 1960, John Wiley & Sons, Inc."

When his father died he was 16 years old (the youngest of 11 children) and was enrolled in a Jesuit college. Since it was no longer possible to remain in school, he joined the French Army in the Seven Years War and was stationed in Monaco. He injured his neck while scuffling with a friend and was returned to France for treatment. A lymphatic gland was affected and he never fully recovered, even after surgery. When Lamarck was sufficiently strong, he entered the study of medicine and botany at Paris and sup-

ported himself with part-time work in a banker's office. Here he came under the influence of the well established botanist, Jussieu. In the years 1781-82 Lamarck traveled across Europe studying plants and taking notes for his Dictionary of Botany. Later he wrote Flora of France, published by the French government. Through the assistance of Buffon, he obtained a job in the museum of natural history where he contributed further to botanical literature.

During the French revolution, when he was becoming a good botanist, he changed his field to invertebrate zoology, and over a period of years he prepared a 7 volume systematic study of the invertebrates. His best known written work was Philosophical Zoology, (1809). He was married four times, had many children, was always poor, and in his later life he was blind. When death came at the age of 85, he was alone and unremembered.

Lamarck's contributions to systematics, botany, and comparative anatomy have already been mentioned. His contribution to evolution was a substantial one, even though it has not always been fully appreciated. Lamarck described the animal kingdom as a graded series from simple to complex forms. In his view, no group became extinct through abrupt catastrophies as Cuvier contended, but one form changed into another. Lamarck was not as well trained and disciplined as Cuvier and Buffon but he gave the first detailed defense of evolution. When he came to an explanation of the mechanics of evolution, he made use of the theory of inheritance of acquired characters that had come from the Greeks and had been developed by Erasmus Darwin and Buffon. Lamarck made bold speculations and carried the subject to great detail, and, even though he did not originate the view, his name has become associated with the inheritance of acquired characteristics. Briefly, he held that: (1) the environment modifies plants and animals, (2) new needs modify old organs and bring new ones into use, (3) use and disuse modify development, and (4) these modifications are inherited.

Lamarck made other contributions to evolution that are more sound but are not as well remembered as his speculation on the inheritance of acquired characters. He appreciated the factor of isolation in forming new species, recognized the influence of proximity in destroying differences between varieties within species, saw unity existing in nature, provided the first diagram of an evolutionary tree and understood, at least in a general way, the physiological balance maintained in nature. Lamarck was first to use the word "species" correctly, as a term to describe a natural unit of related animals or plants. Aristotle had used the term, and in the years that followed the word was used extensively in logic. It was applied to groups of animals and plants by Ray and other early systematists but Lamarck gave the word its modern usage.

Cuvier and St. Hilaire

Cuvier has already been cited for his contributions in systematics (Chapter 8), comparative anatomy, and paleontology (Chapter 9). Although he greatly perfected the geological time table and possessed the fundamental knowledge on which evolution is now based, his personal influence on evolution was negative. He openly opposed evolution and supported the alternative view of fixity of species. His theory of catastrophism and successive new creations was popularized at the expense of the alternative theory of gradual change supported by Lamarck. Cuvier belittled Lamarck and was largely responsible for the unpopularity of Lamarck in later life.

Geoffrey St. Hilaire (1772-1844), a contemporary and colleague of Cuvier opposed Cuvier's views and defended evolution. He advocated the direct effect of environment as Buffon and Lamarck had done to explain small variations, recognized the evolutionary effects of isolation, and visualized physiological as well as geographical isolation as a factor in species formation.

A well known incident of this period arose from a controversy between Cuvier and St. Hilaire concerning the origin of the squid. Instead of discussing the matter privately and objectively, a public debate was announced and widely publicized, making the issue more emotional than scientific. St. Hilaire, who had an idea of evolution, but only meager and crude observations, was right in principle but poorly prepared and perhaps wrong in detail. Cuvier explained the origin of the squid on the basis of special creation. He was wrong in general principle but well prepared with supporting details and won the debate by a better argument and a dramatic show. The effect was to re-

tard the study of evolution for several generations.

C. Darwin

During the five years on the Beagle, Charles Darwin observed and collected plants, animals, and fossils in different parts of the world (Chapter 10). On the Galapagus Islands he was impressed with the gigantic tortoises and large crabs that were not like those on the shores of the mainland some 600 miles away. Darwin noted the diversity of the finches. Freed from competition on isolated islands, these birds had become specialized to occupy ecological niches they could not have filled on the mainland. Associated with their ecological specialization were adaptive structural changes as in the size and shape of the beak. To Darwin this indicated that a single ancestor or a few ancestral forms had arrived on these islands, the descendants of which had moved into different habitats and formed new species. These observations were of great significance in the formation of his concept of evolution by natural selection.

Among the armored animals Darwin noted transitional forms from island to island. Different islands sometimes had entirely different species. He kept notes on all these observations and pondered over the strange relations. As his observations were accumulated, his faith in the fixity of species was shaken. On his return to England, he published the Journal of Researches and took care of other matters of immediate importance. When these tasks were completed, he returned to his notes on species formation and took time to reflect on the significance of his observations.

The problem to be solved was, do species of living creatures really change or become modified? and if so, how? The general belief of the day was that plant and animal species were originally created essentially as they are at any given time. A few observers had postulated that existing species were descended from other species and had gradually become modified in the process. But why should modification occur? It was common knowledge that man could "select" certain types of domestic animals and alter the characteristic of a breed. But how selection could be applied to organisms living in nature was a mystery.

At first Darwin was merely collecting and classifying facts. Then a theory dawned on him, and he began working with a purpose. The key to the problem apparently came to him in 1838 when he read an essay by Thomas Robert Malthus entitled An Essay on the Principle of Population; or a view of its Past and Present Effects on Human Happiness. Briefly, the theme of the essay was that man multiplies more readily than does his supply of food; therefore, competition occurs for the requirements of existence. The prize for which the competitors struggled was life itself and the success of one meant the failure of others. Darwin pondered over the problem and decided that if he could demonstrate that favorable variations tend to be preserved in living populations and unfavorable ones destroyed, he could show how new species came into being. The harder he worked the more encompassing the subject became.

Darwin spent some 20 years working over his theory. In the early part of this period (1842), he prepared a small paper outlining the theory, which he sent to his biologist friends for criticism. With the help they provided, he strengthened each point and improved the theory. He read, discussed, observed, and spared no effort in making the case as clear and well documented as possible. A book was planned in which all of his data would be presented. In the meantime, while the great book was taking form, he undertook the writing of an abstract. This was about half written when Darwin suffered a shattering blow. He received for review a short manuscript written by the explorer-naturalist, Alfred Russel Wallace, entitled On the Tendency of Varieties to Depart Indefinitely from the Original Type. So closely did it agree with his own theory, he commented later, that it might have been an abstract of his work. Twenty years of work and thought had apparently been wasted. Darwin generously recognized the contribution of his then obscure, young colleague and suggested that Wallace's paper be published immediately. Friends of Darwin, Charles Lyell and J. D. Hooker, who knew of his work, intervened and suggested a joint publication by the two pioneers, summarizing the new theory of evolution. This seemed a fair solution for the problem of priority. A joint paper entitled, On the Tendency of Species to Form Varieties; and on the Perpetuation of Varieties and Species by Natural Means of Selection was read by Lyell and Hooker before the Linnean Society on July 1, 1858. The joint paper by Darwin and Wallace was published in the Journal of the Proceedings of the Linnean Society for August 20, 1858. When the paper was read there was interest but little discussion. The reaction that followed was tremendous.

The two authors of the evolution theory arrived at their conclusions through different paths. Darwin had pondered the matter for some 20 years and collected volumes of data. Although Wallace had undoubtedly given the general subject considerable thought during the preceding 3 or 4 years, he apparently arrived at the conclusion in a single flash. In February, 1858, during an attack of yellow fever, Wallace had time and inclination to think about the problem of how living populations have arrived at their present status. He remembered the thesis of Malthus on population which he had read many years before and hit upon the idea of "survival of the fittest" as it applied to animals and plants. He thought out the theory in a few hours and by the evening of the same day had prepared a rough outline of the idea. Two days later he had written the paper which was later sent to Darwin.

The great book which Darwin had planned was never written. He moved into high gear on his abstract and completed it in 13 months. It was published on November 24, 1859 under the title, On the Origin of Species by Means of Natural Selection, or the Preservation of Favored Races in the Struggle for Life. Every copy of the first edition was sold on the day of publication.

Darwin was not the first evolutionist, as shown in the first part of this chapter. Much of his theory may have come from his grandfather, Erasmus Darwin. Some recent reviewers have contended that Charles Darwin has received too much credit but, on the other hand, even though his work may not have been entirely original, he deserves much credit for refusing to accept the unproductive hints, guesses, and hypotheses that had gone before him. When the Beagle sailed, no leading scientist took any interest in evolution. So far as known, when Darwin puzzled over the facts collected in his notebooks, he was the only man in the world who seriously considered the possibility that one species could be modified to form another.

Darwinism, or the theory of natural selection, was Darwin's own invention, although perhaps based on the work of Erasmus Darwin. The theory may be outlined as follows: All living creatures multiply so fast that unless the greater part of each generation perished without leaving offspring, the world would rapidly become overpopulated, but the facts prove that the size of animal and plant populations remains roughly stationary. There must be competition between species and within species for a means of life; and the penalty for defeat is death. It follows that if any member of a species differs from its fellows in a way that gives it an advantage in competition, it is more likely to survive. Subsequently, it is more likely to have offspring, that may inherit the advantage.

Darwin was puzzled concerning the origin of variations and he recognized it as one of the unsolved problems when the Origin of Species was published in 1859. When the book, The Variation of Animals and Plants under Domestication was completed in 1868, Darwin had arrived at an explanation for the ultimate source of variation (i. e. pangenesis) based on a modified form of the inheritance of acquired characters. Immediate selection, however, was based on inherent properties rather than direct environmental influence. An old and much discussed example of evolutionary change was the development of the giraffe's long neck. Lamarck thought that the extended neck was the result of each generation of giraffes stretching more and more for the top branches of the trees. The Darwinian theory stated that the giraffes that had inherited qualities for long necks had less chance of starving than those that inherited shorter necks. If there were too many giraffes for the food supply, those with shorter necks must starve when all the lower branches of the trees were stripped of leaves. Those with the longest necks would be most likely to grow to sexual maturity and leave long-necked descendants. Thus giraffes would develop longer necks, generation after generation, until there was no further advantage in this trend. Darwin was puzzled about the ultimate origin of variation but considered it to be inherited although influenced in some way by the environment.

In his proof for natural selection, Darwin showed that: (1) new forms can be developed by man's artificial selection; (2) that the conditions in nature are sufficient to exert a similar selection in the natural world; and (3) the wide variety of existing forms over the world can be explained by this means. The suggestion was that all animals are related and have a common ancestor. A great controversy developed on this question, particularly among laymen.

While the controversy over evolution raged Darwin worked quietly, gathering support for his theory and resolving other biological problems. He spent much time in botanical research. In 1862 he published his observations on the fertilization of orchids under the title, On the Various Contrivances by which British and Foreign Orchids are Fertilized by Insects and on the Good Effects of Intercrossing. This title seemed harmless enough on the surface but the content of the book was related to the earlier work on the origin of species. In commenting on this book Darwin said, "My chief interest in the orchid has been that it was a "flank movement on the enemy". During this period the orchid represented a stronghold of the anti-Darwinians. Of all of Nature's creations, these delicately beautiful flowers were held to be a conspicuous instance of botanic art for art's sake. Darwin quietly undermined the old argument for special creation by showing that the apparently meaningless ridges and horns of the orchid draw insects that pollinate the flowers. The intricate structures of trap doors and spring mechanisms have evolved from simpler forms and serve a vital function in the life of the plant.

Two years later (1864) he produced, The Movements and Habits of Climbing Plants. It was published first in the Journal of the Linnean Society and expanded into a book in 1875. The first enlargement of the evolution theory came in 1868, with The Variation of Animals and Plants under Domestication. From this publication he went to the Descent of Man and Selection in Relation to Sex (1871). In this book he included mankind in the animal kingdom in which evolution applied. He also developed theories of sexual selection to explain the mechanics of evolutionary change. In 1872 Darwin made a further contribution in The Expression of the Emotions in Man and Animals. His later writings were devoted mainly to botanical subjects.

Darwin's real importance lies in something that cannot be simply related to an account of his life or a review of his contributions. He was a good-living man, an undefatigable naturalist, and an honest thinker; but goodness, tirelessness, and honesty are qualities that often come together and fail to produce the effect that this man's life produced. Darwin was a man who amounted to much more than the sum of his parts. He was the pioneer through which a revolution in human thought was brought about. His influence upon the age was enormously powerful.

In some of his last writings, Darwin said modestly that he regretted that he had not done more direct good to his fellow creatures. His kindly character is revealed in his comment on his favorite mode of relaxation which was novel reading in which he "blessed all novelists," provided they wrote books with happy endings. His own ending came on April 19, 1882, in his 74th year, and science mourned the loss of the thinker who had changed man's conception of the world. Charles Darwin was buried in Westminster Abbey, a few feet away from the grave of Issac Newton.

T. H. Huxley

Thomas H. Huxley (1825-1895) was the foremost of Darwin's defenders. At an early age he showed a talent for art which served him well throughout his life. He had an inquiring mind and a tendency for metaphysical speculations. By the time he was 12 years of age, he had read most of the books in his father's large library but his formal instruction was scanty because of the poor quality of the public schools at that time in the location where he lived in England. His first introduction to higher education was at Sydenham College, where he did preparatory work for the university. In 1845 he received the M. B. degree at the London University and two years later, he completed the required medical studies but was too young to qualify for the College of Surgeons.

He joined the medical service of the British Navy and was assigned to the ship, Victory. After 7 months on this ship he transferred to the Rattlesnake that was leaving England on a four-year cruise, mostly in Australian waters. During this voyage Huxley was busy making notes, that included detailed accounts of observations on biological subjects. When he returned to England the work was so voluminous that no private publisher would accept it. A choice had to be made between summarizing the data briefly enough to be acceptable to a commercial publisher or financing the production by some other

means. The manuscript was presented to the British government for publication, but the Admiralty was also reluctant to publish such a large work. The Royal Society of London had sufficient funds from a grant and undertook the publication in 1854, under the title Oceanic Hydrozoa. This momentous work established Huxley in the scientific world and he was soon in the front ranks as a naturalist.

When Darwin's work that resulted in the Origin of Species was in progress, Huxley acted as his adviser and agent. He talked with influential men and persuaded them toward the view of natural selection. In November, 1859, when the Origin of Species was published, Huxley began a vigorous campaign in support of the work. The year after publication (1860) a meeting was held at Oxford in which the controversial issue of special creation versus evolution was debated. Bishop Wilberforce, a teacher of mathematics, took the side of special creation and Huxley defended evolution. It was in this manner that Huxley obtained the nickname "Darwin's bulldog." He was called upon many times to champion the cause of evolution. Opportunities were provided for public debates as well as individual discussions with laymen of importance in biological circles.

In later life Huxley was recognized as one of the great naturalists of his day. He published many papers on different biological subjects. Much of his time was taken up by public addresses. He traveled widely and obtained a broad knowledge of biology. In the course of his 70 years he lectured and published on all areas of biological science. Some of his best known works are textbooks on physiology, comparative anatomy, and paleontology.

Evolution Today

Much discussion has been centered around the theory of evolution since the publication of the Origin of Species in 1859. Supporting material for the theory was greatly altered and improved by Darwin himself to meet the difficulties that he recognized and those suggested to him by friends and critics. Later editions of the Origin of Species were so different from the first that questions have arisen as to what Darwin actually said on certain topics. On the whole the theory has been well received by biologists almost universally.

Modern developments have brought refinements in many aspects of the problem. With the development of the new science of genetics, it has been possible to explain some of the mechanics involved in the process. Four cornerstones have been recognized that help to explain the mechanics of evolution. They are (1) mutation, the original source of variation, (2) recombination of genes, a more effective source of variation than mutation for immediate population change in species with sexual reproduction, (3) selection, the main directing force in evolution and (4) isolation, the factor accounting for barriers that make speciation possible.

Obviously, it is impossible to reconstruct the evolutionary process of living things and watch it occur. It has taken millions of years for its accomplishment. The life span, during which a human being may make observations is too short to expect to see much of it happen. Substantial evidence for the fact of evolution has been obtained from the fossil record, geographic distribution, comparative anatomy, embryology, and virtually all of the other biological sciences. The science of genetics, concerned with the mechanics of evolution, is particularly useful for determining how evolution works. Darwinism is more firmly established now than ever before because of the contribution of genetics.

It is assumed that the same processes that occurred over long periods of time and were responsible for evolutionary change in the past are in operation today. Some of these are being explored experimentally. Although many details remain to be explained, the broad principles are now well established on the basis of the hereditary process and the influence of the physical environment. Problems that have been considered more recently and those now being resolved are: (1) sources of variation in natural populations, (2) establishment of new variations in populations, (3) directing forces of evolution, and (4) isolating mechanisms through which new species can be separated from related breeding populations.

REFERENCES

American Philosophical Society Proceedings 103: (2) 1959. Commemoration of the Centennial of the Publication of the *Origin of Species*.

Barnett, S. A. ed. *A Century of Darwin*. Cambridge: Harvard Univ. Press, 1958.

Barzun, J. *Darwin, Marx, Wagner, Critique of a Heritage*. Boston: Little Brown and Co., 1941. (Part I on Darwin and *Origin of Species*.)

Bates, M., and P. S. Humphrey eds. *The Darwin Reader*. New York: C. Scribner's Sons. 1956.

Blinderman, C. S. Thomas Huxley. *Sci. Monthly* 84:171-188, 1957.

Boyd, W. C. *Genetics and the Races of Man*. Boston: Little, Brown and Co., 1950.

Carter, G. S. *A Hundred Years of Evolution*. New York: The Macmillan Co., 1957.

Clark, J. D. Early Man in Africa. *Sci. Amer*. 199: (1)76-83, 1958.

Daniel, G. E. The Idea of Man's Antiquity. *Sci. Amer*. 201:(5) 167-176,1959.

Darlington, C. D. The Origin of Darwinism. *Sci. Amer*. 200:(5) 60-66, 1959.

Darwin, C. *On the Origin of Species by Means of Natural Selection, or the Preservation of Favoured Races in the Struggle for Life*.
London: John Murray, 1859. (Numerous revisions and reprints have been made since original publication. Now available in paper-back edition by Mentor Book Co., New York.)

Darwin, C. *On the Various Contrivances by which British and Foreign Orchids are Fertilized by Insects, and on the Good Effects of Intercrossing.* London: John Murray, 1862.

Darwin, C. *The Variation of Animals and Plants under Domestication.* 2 vol. London: John Murray, 1868.

Darwin, C. *The Descent of Man, and Selection in Relation to Sex.* 2 vol. London: John Murray, 1871.

Darwin, C. *The Expression of the Emotions in Man and Animals.* London: John Murray, 1872.

Darwin, C. *Insectivorous Plants.* London: John Murray, 1875.

Darwin, C. *The Movements and Habits of Climbing Plants.* London: John Murray, 1875.

Darwin, C. *The Effects of Cross and Self Fertilization in the Vegetable Kingdom.* London: John Murray, 1876.

Darwin, C. *The Different Forms of Flowers on Plants of the Same Species.* London: John Murray, 1877.

Darwin, C. *The Power of Movement in Plants.* London: John Murray, 1880.

Darwin, C. *The Formation of Vegetable Mould, through the Action of Worms, with Observations on their Habits.* London: John Murray, 1881.

Darwin, C. *Charles Darwin's Autobiography.* ed. F. Darwin. New York: Dover Publ. Inc., 1950.

Darwin, C. and A. R. Wallace. On the Tendency of Species to form Varieties; and on the Perpetuation of Varieties and Species by Natural Means of Selection. *Proc. Linnean Soc.* Aug. 20, 1858.

Darwin, F. ed. *The Life and Letters of Charles Darwin.* 2 vol. New York: D. Appleton and Co., 1896.

Dobzhansky, T. *Genetics and the Origin of Species.* 3rd ed. New York: Columbia Univ. Press, 1951.

Dobzhansky, T. *Evolution, Genetics and Man.* New York: John Wiley and Sons, Inc., 1955.

Drachman, J. M. *Studies in the Literature of Natural Science.* New York: The Macmillan Co., 1930.

Dupree, A. H. *Asa Gray.* Cambridge: Harvard Univ. Press, 1959.

Eiseley, L. C. Charles Lyell. *Sci. Amer.* 201:(2) 98-106, 1959.

Gillispie, C. C. Lamarck and Darwin in the History of Science. *Amer. Sci.* 46:388-409, 1958.

Glass, B., O. Temkin, and W. L. Straus, Jr. eds. *Forerunners of Darwin: 1745-1859.* Baltimore: The Johns Hopkins Press, 1959.

Greene, J. C.   *The Death of Adam*. Ames, Iowa. Iowa State Univ. Press, 1959.

Hooton, E. A.   *Up From the Apes*.   New York: The Macmillan Co., 1946.

Huxley, F. Reappraisals of Charles Darwin: Life and Habit.   *Amer. Scholar* Autumn, 1959 pp. 489-499; Winter, 1959 pp. 85-93.

Huxley, J.   *Evolution, the Modern Synthesis*.   New York: Harper and Bros., 1943.

Huxley, J.   *Evolution in Action*.   New York: Mentor, 1953.

Huxley, J.   *The Living Thoughts of Darwin*.   New York: Longmans, 1939, (Also Greenwish, Conn: Fawcett Publ., 1959.)

Huxley, L.   *The Life and Letters of Thomas H. Huxley*.   2 vol. New York: D. Appleton and Co., 1901.

Huxley, T. H.   *Darwiniana*.   New York: D. Appleton and Co., 1896.

Huxley, T. H.   *Evidence as to Man's Place in Nature*.   London: Williams and Norgate, 1863.

Huxley, T. H.   *Evolution and Ethics and Other Essays*.   New York: D. Appleton and Co., 1896.

Huxley, T. H.   *Autobiography and Selected Essays*.   Boston: Houghton Mifflin Co., 1909.

Irvine, W.   *Apes, Angels and Victorians*.   New York: McGraw Hill Book Co., 1955.

Kettlewell, H. B. D.   Darwin's Missing Evidence.   *Sci. Amer.*   200:(3) 48-53, 1959.

Krause, E.   *Life of Erasmus Darwin*.   New York: D. Appleton and Co., 1880.

Lamarck, J. B. de M.   *Zoological Philosophy*   trans. H. Elliot. London: Macmillan and Co., 1914.

Loewenberg, B. J.   *Darwin, Wallace, and the Theory of Natural Selection*. Cambridge, Mass.: Arlington Books, 1959.

Lyell, C.   *Principles of Geology, being an attempt to Explain the Former Changes of the Earth's Surface by Reference to Causes now in Operation*. Vol. 1 London: John Murray, 1830.

Malthus, T. R.   *An Essay on the Principle of Population; or a View of Past and Present Effects on Human Happiness*.   London: J. Johnson, 1798.

Mayr, E.   *The Species Problem*.   Washington D. C.: A.A.A.S. Publ., 1957.

Newman, H. H.   *Evolution Yesterday and Today*.   Baltimore: Williams and Wilkins, 1932.

Oparin, A. I.   *The Origin of Life on the Earth*.   3rd ed. New York: Academic Press, 1957.

Osborn, H. F.   *From the Greeks to Darwin*.   New York: The Macmillan Co., 1894.

Packard, A. S. *Lamarck, His Life and Work.* New York: Longmans, Green and Co., 1901.

Prosser, C. L. The "Origin" After a Century; Prospects for the Future. *Amer. Sci.* 47:536-550, 1959.

Radl, E. *The History of Biological Theories.* trans. from German E. J. Hatfield. London: Oxford Univ. Press, 1930.

Sears, P. B. *Charles Darwin, the Naturalist as a Cultural Force.* New York: C. Scribner's Sons, 1950.

Senet, A. *Man in Search of His Ancestors.* New York: McGraw Hill Book Co., 1955.

Smith, H. W. *From Fish to Philosopher.* Boston: Little, Brown and Co., 1953.

Stauffer, R. C. On the Origin of Species, an Unpublished Version. *Science* 130:1449-1452, 1959.

Tax, S. ed. *Evolution after Darwin.* 3 vol. Chicago: Univ. Chicago Press, 1960.

Wendt, H. *In Search of Adam.* Boston: Houghton Mifflin Co., 1956.

One of the most fundamental developments in biology was the recognition of a plan of organization in the bodies of animals and plants based on small units called **cells.** This development required microscopic observation that in turn depended on microscopes sufficiently powerful to resolve the minute structures, and microscopists sufficiently keen and efficient to recognize the units and interpret what they saw. This was not all; theorizers were necessary to suggest the broad significance of isolated observations and to postulate a unity in all living things with reference to their fundamental organization. Finally, it was necessary for numerous investigators to test the generalization and to extend the theory and thus to recognize the

developed in the 17th century. The classical microscopists of that period made critical observations and prepared sketches showing that they had actually seen minute structural units in the bodies of living things. Malpighi observed tiny sacs or "utricles" in plant bodies. Grew observed similar bags that he called "bladders" and noted that they were filled with fluid. Leeuwenhoek saw structures that would now be identified as cells but did not use a particular name for them. Swammerdam was also aware of such structural units as he made his minute anatomical dissections and critical observations. It will be remembered that these men were observers and not theorizers. It was left to the investigators of the 19th century to put things together and develop the cell theory.

Background of the Cell Theory

Observation 18 in Hooke's <u>Micrographia</u> was an illustrated study of the minute structure of cork. Open spaces surrounded by heavy walls were observed and described as little boxes or "cellulae." It was the open space and the honeycomb appearance of the boxes that impressed Hooke and for which he chose the Latin root <u>cella</u> meaning "a little room." The term had been used to describe confined spaces such as prisoner's cells and compartments occupied by monks in monasteries. This word gained priority as a term to describe the structural unit of living things. Now that the "cell" has come to represent more than the dead, empty box that Hooke observed, the term is generally considered to be a poor one. The living content is now the important aspect and many people have suggested that the name should be changed. Such terms as "protoplast" have been suggested but the word "cell" is firmly interwoven in the literature of biology and it is doubtful that a change will be seriously considered.

Chapter 12

THE CELL THEORY

cell as a unit of function, that is, metabolism, a unit of reproduction, a unit of growth and differentiation, and a unit of inheritance, as well as a unit of structure.

Although the cell theory was not precisely stated until the middle of the 19th century, the evidence on which it was based began to accumulate at a much earlier period of biological history. Aristotle, Galen, and other philosophers of the remote past had suggested that complex organisms must be composed of elementary parts. Undoubtedly the elementary parts referred to were the roots, stems, leaves, and flowers of plants and the segments, organs, and other parts of animals visible to the unaided eye. Tools were not available to observe the more minute parts until the microscope was

Between the 17th and the 19th centuries there were speculations and indirect suggestions that might now be considered to anticipate the cell theory. Some of these were associated with developments in embryology and physiology and the suggestions about cells were incidental to the main objectives of the investigations. Others were not supported by observation. Lamarck called attention to little masses of gelatinous matter into which living bodies were organized in his Philosophical Zoology (1809). He did not however, consider the cell as an individual unit. In the same year, the French botanist C. F. Mirbel concluded that the plant is composed of a continuous cell membrane. Lorenz Oken (1779-1851) as early as 1805 stated that "all organic beings come from vessicles or cells". He used the word "Urschleim" or primitive slime to describe the living substance, that is, protoplasm, from which the cells in living things are composed. Oken was a philosopher and not an observer, but he arrived at an important generalization that influenced later contributors. In the early part of the 19th century there were many observations suggesting that minute structures were constantly present in animal and plant bodies. Henri J. Dutrochet (1776-1847), in 1824, expressed the idea of individuality of cells. Their universal distribution and significance as units of structure were not appreciated until later.

The two main structural parts of the cell, the nucleus and cytoplasm, were described before the statement of the cell theory was formulated. In 1831 Robert Brown, while working with plants that he had collected in Australia, observed constant structures in the cells of the epidermal layers. He illustrated these structures and used the word "nucleus" to identify them. Later he found similar structures in pollen grains and in the ovules and stigmas of different plants. The cytoplasmic part of the cell had been described by several investigators. Wolff in his embryological studies had observed living cells and obtained evidence against the preformation theory. He concluded that the egg cell had no organized or preformed structures. Felix Dujardin (1801-1862), in 1836, described cytoplasm which he called "sarcode" in living amebae. He found the living substance to be homogenous, elastic, contractile, and transparent. It refracted light a little more than water and much less than oil. He could not distinguish any organization. This description referred to the basic living substance without suspended elements.

Brown had also described the cytoplasmic parts of cells in his paper entitled, "Microscopic Observations on the Pollen of Plants" (1828). He had observed the dancing movement of particles in the protoplasm now called, in his honor, "Brownian movement". At first he thought the particles were alive and that the movement was a property of living things. Later he learned that it was a physical process that could occur in non-living suspensions as well. The phenomenon was described in the present century as the result of the bombardment of molecules on the suspended particles in a fluid medium. One important contribution of these early observers was the demonstration that the living substance was a fluid. Recent developments in colloidal chemistry have clarified the physical properties of such substances in both living and non-living systems. The characteristics of the living substance can be explained to a large extent by the principles of colloidal chemistry.

Statement of Cell Theory

Two German biologists, M. J. Schleiden (1804-1881) and Theodor Schwann (1810-1882 Fig. 12-1), finally made the generalization that animals and plants are composed of cells. Even though these two men are listed as co-authors of the theory, a current evaluation would not give them equal credit.

Fig. 12-1. Theodor Schwann who developed the cell theory

Schleiden was first to arrive at the conclusion from studies on plant cells, published in 1838. Schwann published his results from observations on animal cells a year later, in 1839. His work was much more comprehensive and was founded on a better biological foundation than that of Schleiden. Schwann entered into the broader considerations of cells and provided better support for the theory than did his colleague. Therefore Schwann should receive the larger share of credit for the accomplishment.

Schleiden was trained as a lawyer but deserted his law practice at the age of 27 and returned to the university to study medicine. He specialized in botany and later became professor of botany at the University of Jena. In 1837 he began a series of studies on plant organization and development in which he followed the preliminary work of Robert Brown in showing that the nucleus must be important in development. His background in basic science was weak and he made serious errors in his observations and conclusions. The most conspicuous mistake was an erroneous idea of cell propogation based on physical processes of crystalization. He visualized the nucleolus as the starting point of the cell. A form of crystalization was described in the formation of a nucleus around the nucleolus. Bubbles observed on the side of the nucleus were supposed to represent a sort of budding process from which the new cell developed. Cell reproduction was thus initiated by the nucleolus, a nucleus was next crystalized around the nucleolus and finally the cytoplasmic part developed around the nucleus.

Schleiden made few if any original observations in support of the cell theory. By capitalizing on the work of others he succeeded in arriving at a sweeping generalization that placed cells in a basic position as units of organization in living things. "Each cell leads a double life," he wrote, "one independent, pertaining to its own development alone; the other incidental, as an integral part of a plant."

Schwann was a student of the German physiologist, Johannes Müller (1801-1858). He was a thoughtful and persistent investigator. For many years at the University of Würzburg and the University of Berlin he had done microscopic research on plant and animal cells and had classified tissues. In 1839 he published a report of his observations in a paper entitled, "Microscopical Researches on the Similarity in Structure and Growth of Animals and Plants". The minute anatomy of cells and tissues of animal and plant materials was described and compared. Cells and cell parts were illustrated in full detail. Schwann promoted the generalization already stated by Schleiden, that living things are composed of cells, but he was able to support it with data from his own observations. Shortly after the publication of his work on the cell theory, Schwann received a professorship at the University of Louvain in Belgium.

In studying connective tissues in animals, Schwann found it necessary to add a phrase to the original statement of the cell theory. Some parts of living organisms were found not to be composed of cells. Analysis showed that the matrix of bone and connective tissue was acellular but represented a cell product. Therefore, he amended the theory to read, "all living things are composed of cells and cell products." Like Schleiden, he described cells as having an independent life, but he also observed that cells are subjected to the control of the organism. Schwann used the word "cytoblastema" to describe the living material which has since been called protoplasm. He coined the word "metabolism" to describe all chemical processes carried on in the cell. The cell was described as the structural unit of living organisms. Indeed, Schwann referred to the cell as the unit of life.

Corrections and Extensions

Both Schleiden and Schwann emphasized the structural unit or box when they spoke about cells. They attached importance to the living processes that must go on in cells, particularly in development, but the cell contents were either unknown or unappreciated. The next step was to identify cell parts and to determine their functional significance in the activities of cells.

The first important error to be corrected was Schleiden's misconception of the behavior of the cell and nucleus in cell reproduction, a point which Schwann had passively accepted. In 1841 Robert Remak (1815-1865) studied the frog egg and followed the early developmental stages. He discovered that cells came from preexisting cells. Karl Nägeli (1817-1891) followed this work in 1844 with a general description of cell division. He did not observe the details of mitosis but showed that Schleiden's idea was incorrect. Nägeli made chemical analyses of cells and found that different cell structures were made of different chemical materials. Some cell parts such as the nucleus contained nitrogenous material whereas the cell wall was made of carbohydrate. Bodies were found in the cytoplasm that were entirely made up of starch, that is, starch grains.

In 1846 Hugo von Mohl (1805-1872) coined the word "protoplasm" to describe the living substance. He studied the contents of living plant cells and observed the streaming of cytoplasm around the central vacuole. Soon a group of investigators working with protozoa found that ciliary movement reflected a fundamental property of living things. Instead of movement confined to the inside of the cell, as in streaming protoplasm, a special organization of structures made it possible for the entire cell to move. This basic principle has been extended to muscular action. It can now be shown that the complex activities dependent on muscular action in higher animals is a refinement of the streaming movement that can be observed in generalized cells.

Albrecht Kölliker (1817-1905), another student of Johannes Müller, applied the cell theory to embryology and histology. He showed that the egg is a single cell and that the nucleus is the most constant cell part with great significance in cell reproduction. Nuclear division was found to precede cell reproduction. Remak and other cytologists supported and clarified this view and the cell theory was extended to make the cell a unit of development. Kölliker also visualized the cell as the carrier of hereditary determiners long before definitive data on this point were available. He conducted investigations on complex nerve-fibers in the central nervous system and found that they are cellular structures with greatly extended processes. Involuntary muscles were examined and found to be composed of cells. Again the cell theory was extended to include a large group of animal structures not specifically included before. Valuable text books in embryology and histology were written by Kölliker.

A further extension in the cell theory was made by the German pathologist, Rudolf Virchow (1821-1902). In 1856 Virchow opened his laboratory for studies in cytology and pathology. He followed his predecessors in the observation that all cells must come from other cells. Detailed microscopic observations of bone and connective tissue were made in healthy and diseased animals. Abnormal or pathological events in the body were found to depend on cells. His first cellular paper was entitled "On the Evolution of Cancer" and a long series of studies on malignant tumors followed. With the publication in 1858 of Virchow's Cellular Pathology, the cell theory was applied to pathology and the new concept of "cellular pathology" developed. Before Virchow, humoral pathology was the main theme; after Virchow, cellular pathology took precedence. In spite of his great interest and early accomplishment in cellular pathology he was able to shift in later life to a consideration of the body as a whole and the influence of infectious agents. In addition to his investigations and technical writings, accomplished independently and in connection with his professorship at the University of Berlin, he was an anthropologist, sanitarian, and statesman of considerable importance. His work in public health resulted in a great saving of human life. For some 55 years he was editor of the German periodical, Archives for Pathology.

Max Schultze in 1865 recognized the trend that had occurred in the 200 years since Hooke's publication, Micrographia and placed emphasis on the contents of the cell. It was now a living, functioning unit instead of a dead, empty box. Schultze defined the cell as a "mass of cytoplasm with a nucleus." This definition is more concise than some others but it recognizes the essential living unit and serves well as a brief definition.

The next major contribution was the detailed description of cell division. Eduard Strasburger (1844-1912), Professor of Botany at Bonn, followed in 1875, the mitotic process in plant material and illustrated the details of cell division. Four years later he demonstrated that nuclei arise only from pre-existing nuclei. Living materials were used in these studies and there was no doubt that the structures observed existed in live cells. Walther Flemming (1843-1915), Professor at Prague and later at Kiel, followed the process of mitosis in animal cells. His reports appeared in 1879, 1882, and in the 10 years that followed. Flemming used modern methods of fixation and staining on tissues from amphibian larvae, and worked with killed instead of living material. More precise stages were observed and a detailed and accurate account of the process was made possible even though there was always some question as to whether the structures observed were present in the living cells or artifacts resulting from the treatment. Flemming coined terms still used to describe structures and stages in the process including such useful terms as: mitosis, aster, chromatin, prophase, metaphase, anaphase, and telophase. He observed the longitudinal division of structures that originated in the nucleus during cell division and disappeared when the division was completed. These structures, visible only during the division stages of the cell, were named "chromosomes," by W. Waldeyer (1836-1921) in 1888.

Theodor Boveri (1862-1915), Professor at Würzburg, described, in 1888, the cytoplasmic structures associated with spindle formation in the mitotic division of animal cells and gave them the name "centrosomes." It soon was observed that plant cells do not have such structures. The cytoplasm of plant cells can apparently accomplish the same function in division that the centrosomes accomplish in the division of animal cells. Plastids in the cytoplasm of plant cells were described by Nathaniel Pringsheim (1823-1894) and Julius Sachs (1832-1897). No single discoverers are known for other cytoplasmic structures such as chondriosomes and vacuoles.

With the work of the great investigators of the last quarter of the 19th century, the study of cells developed to a point where it justified recognition as a separate biological science "Cytology." The book by Oscar Hertwig (1849-1922) entitled Cell and Tissue which was published in 1893 was a landmark in the early development of the new science.

Modern techniques have facilitated the study of cells. Ross Harrison (1870-1959) at Johns Hopkins University developed a tissue culture technique that made it possible to raise embryonic cells outside of the body and watch their activity under the microscope. Alexis Carrel of the Rockefeller Institute and Charles Lindberg improved the technique. It has since been adapted for the study of growth and differentiation in normal cells and also for the study of abnormal growth in cancer cells. The phase contrast microscope has brought a rebirth in studies of living cells. This instrument makes it possible to distinguish cells and parts of cells and watch cell division and other cell processes without killing or staining the material. The electron microscope has been useful in describing minute structural parts of killed cells.

Problems and Criticisms of Cell Theory

Many problems have arisen in the interpretation of the cell theory as it ap-

plies to various groups of organisms. When bacteria were found to occupy an important place in the living world a question arose concerning their relation to the cell theory. They did not seem to fit the definition of Schultze because no formed nucleus could at first be identified but they were known to contain nuclear material. It now seems evident that bacteria, have a type of sexual reproduction. Evidence is suggestive of a nuclear organization much like that in higher forms.

Then came the discovery of viruses. Are they cells? They lack some of the properties of cells such as semipermeable membranes to control the diffusion of materials in and out of the unit. The same chemical materials found in the nuclei of higher organisms are also present in viruses. They have the properties of mutation and recombination that are associated with genes. Viruses are not cells in the usual sense but they have some properties of cells.

Some structures of organisms and some whole organisms are not divided into cells in the usual way. Molds of the genus Mucor are coenocytes, that is, they have nuclei suspended in the hyphae, but they are not partitioned off into compartments. Likewise some muscles such as the heart muscle are not divided into discrete cells. Schultze's definition would apply very well in these cases. Even though there are no partitions to separate units, there are nuclei surrounded by cytoplasm. The boundary around the unit was not important, but only the essential unit of protoplasm with a nucleus. Some protozoans that were considered to be single celled organisms were found to have more than a single nucleus. Examples were found with two nuclei and some with many nuclei. Again these are exceptions to the separateness of cells, now considered to be only a superficial characteristic.

Are complex protozoans one-celled animals as they are often identified in elementary texts? The malaria organism is a one-celled organism at one stage of its cycle but it goes through a process of sporulation and in one type 16 cells are formed. The sixteen-celled organism then breaks down to form 16 independent merozoites. Therefore the answer to the question depends on the stage in the cycle of the organism. Higher animals, including man, are one-celled animals in one stage of their cycle. Some of the protozoans such as Euplotes are much more complex and highly organized than some metazoans. The distinction between protozoa and metazoa as one-celled and many-celled organisms is superficial and subject to criticism.

Finally, is the cell or the organism the unit of life? Schwann said that the functions of life reside not in the organism but in separate elementary units or cells. This was interpreted to indicate that cells are independent units of life. Indeed, some cells of higher animals do remain alive for hours or days after the organism as a whole is dead. However, the organism is more important than the individual cells.

Organismal Theory

The organismal view is that the whole animal or plant is the unit and the cells are only divisions in its organization. This view is supported by the philosophical concept of synergism, that the organism is not merely the sum of its parts but represents something more, that is, the product of interaction. More precisely in biological terms, an individual is more than a bundle of genes; profound interactions occur in development. The relative significance of the cell and organism is a fundamental problem that does not have a clear-cut answer at the present time. From investigations designed to discover how life might have originated on the earth and developed to its present stage of complexity data

may come to resolve this point. It seems possible that the cell as a unit represents one important stage in development of living things. Further developments in higher forms have made the organism as a whole the center of organization.

The organismal theory provides a foundation for ecology. Organisms become remarkably well adjusted to their environments. This adaptation must occur over long periods of time. Complicated and continuing interrelations make it necessary to regard the organism not merely as the sum of its cells but as a new pattern resulting from the interactions of parts. Development of such organisms with such adaptations must represent a process of integration rather than summation. This point of view has broad implications in the fields of education and medicine. It suggests the education of the whole child, rather than particular academic disciplines or faculties of the child. Likewise in medicine it favors the treatment of the patient rather than the disease.

If the cell theory is interpreted to mean that the cell is an independent unit of life, it must be modified to fit present biological thinking. The theory has been quite properly expanded to place the cell in the position as structural, functional, embryological, and perhaps the genetic unit of higher organisms. There is some question as to whether it is actually the unit of life. Life can exist in precellular forms but organization into cells has been an important advancement in those organisms higher up in the scale of living things.

REFERENCES

Ackerknecht, E. H. *Rudolph Virchow, Doctor, Statesman, Anthropologist.* Madison: Univ. Wis. Press, 1953.

Brown, R. Observations on the Organs and Mode of Fecundation in Orchideae. *Trans. Linn. Soc.,* 1831.

Cattell, J. ed. *Biological Symposia.* Vol. 1. Lancaster, Pa.: The Jaques Cattell Press, 1940.

Conklin, E. G. Predecessors of Schleiden and Schwann. *Amer. Nat.* 73: 538-546, 1939.

'Espinasse, M. *Robert Hooke.* Berkeley: Univ. Calif. Press, 1956.

Gerould, J. H. The Dawn of the Cell Theory. *Sci. Monthly* 14:268-277, 1922.

Hertwig, O. *The Cell.* London: Swan Sonnenschein and Co., 1895.

Hughes, H. *A History of Cytology.* New York: Abelard-Schuman, 1959.

Moulton, F. R. ed. *The Cell and Protoplasm.* Publ. of A.A.A.S. No. 14 Washington, D. C.: The Science Press, 1940.

Rudnick, D. ed. *Cell, Organism and Milieu.* New York: The Ronald Press Co., 1959.

Sachs, J. von *History of Botany.* English trans., London: Oxford Univ. Press, 1890.

Wilson, E. B. *The Cell in Development and Heredity.* New York: The Macmillan Co., 1928.

Physiological aspects of biology have developed more slowly than morphological. One reason is that the human mind grasps tangible, observable, structural characteristics more readily than intangible functional relations that must be approached by experimental procedures. A second reason is that physiology depends on the physical sciences, particularly chemistry, physics, and mathematics. These were slow in their development and only recently have they attained the stature necessary to lend themselves effectively to the explanation of biological phenomena. The early history of some branches of physiology such as reproduction and development have already been mentioned in other connections and will be treated further in later chapters. For this discussion, the history of plant nutrition, vital activity, that is the nervous and muscular systems, and circulation of the blood will be considered. The life and contributions of two great physiologist of the 19th century, Johannes Müller and Claude Bernard, will be reviewed.

Plant Nutrition

Plant physiology was less advanced than animal physiology during the Renaissance. The Greeks considered plants to be the lowest forms of life, capable of arising by spontaneous generation, and there was little incentive for making critical observations concerning their nature and nutrition. Aristotle thought the soil was a reservoir for preformed food that could be carried through the root system into the plant where a sort of digestion process took place. Cesalpino likened plants to animals with respect to their nutrition and described a circulatory system with a heart and blood vessels in plants. He did not follow the Aristotelian view that preformed food was provided in the soil but visualized more elementary materials in the soil from which food was made. In the heart of the plant, presumably the crown where the roots meet the part above the ground, simple materials were supposed to be changed to usable food. Cesalpino also attempted to explain, by physical laws, how water is taken up in a plant. A blotter-like material was postulated in the plant as an agent for absorbing the water.

Jung suggested that tiny openings in the roots were capable of selecting out from the soil materials needed in the plant for making food. These openings also had the ability to reject constituents of the soil that were not needed by the plant. Jung also suggested that waste materials resulting from chemical activities in the plant might be released into the air. No mention was made at that time of the importance of air in the nutrition of the plant. J. B. Van Helmont (1577-1644) introduced the experimental technique in plant physiology. He raised a tree in an earthen vessel and measured the water that was added during the period of growth. The weight of the grown tree was comparable with that of the water added. Therefore, he concluded, that water was the only requirement for growth. His measurements were not critical enough to detect some two ounces of material from the soil that was involved in nutrition and he, like his predecessors, did not realize the importance of the air.

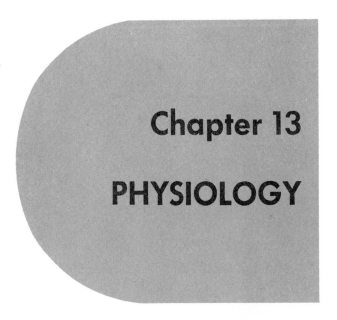

Chapter 13

PHYSIOLOGY

Edme' Mariotte (1620-1684), a French physicist, performed significant experiments on plant nutrition and in 1676 read a paper entitled, On the Vegetation of Plants, before the French Academy of Sciences. He observed the movement of sap upward in trees under pressure. Therefore, he reasoned, there must be something in plants that permits the entrance but prevents the exit of fluids. He took a position against the idea of preformed foods from the soil. Instead, he described a chemical process through which the plant could manufacture its own food from common materials available to all plants, particularly air and water. He concluded that plants do not take preformed food directly from the soil but only elementary materials that they can build into food. The mechanism through which air could be taken into the plant was suggested by the Italian microscopist, Malpighi, who observed minute openings in the surface of plant leaves, (stomata), and traced the plant vessels that carry fluids. Malpighi also speculated on the functions of leaves and suggested that the leaf elaborates food.

Stephen Hales (1677-1761), English physiologist, carried on the experimental procedure and succeeded in showing that something important in plant nutrition is taken from the air. Hales received his training in mathematics and physical science at Cambridge and was well prepared for critical experiments. He became interested in plants through his study of Ray's work, particularly the descriptions of the plants in the vicinity of Cambridge. As his interest in plants developed, he performed a number of simple but ingenious experiments the results of which were published in 1727 under the title Vegetable Staticks. In one series of studies he measured the amount of water taken up by the roots and the amount given off by the leaves. In another series calculations were made of the relation between the moisture in the earth and that taken up by the plant. He also studied the rate at which water rises in the plant and showed a relation with the intake through the roots and outgo from the leaves. Physical models were constructed to show the absorption of water through fine pores and the movement of water in capillary tubes. The activities of plants were thus explained on the basis of physical forces. For the present discussion, his most significant discovery was the one showing that the air contains a factor important in plant nutrition.

The separate gases in the air were not distinguished at the time the early observations and speculations on plant nutrition were made. Something necessary for burning, however, was known to be present in air. Georg Ernest Stahl (1660-1734), a German chemist, named the substance "phlogiston" and proposed the theory that every combustible substance is a compound of phlogiston. When a substance burned phlogiston was supposed to leave whereas the other constituents of the burned material remained behind as ash. Coal was considered to be almost pure phlogiston and sulfur contained a high proportion.

Joseph Priestley (1733-1804), English chemist, demonstrated in 1772 that plants emersed in water give off a gas (oxygen) and that this gas is required by animals. The French chemist, Antoine Lavoisier (1743-1794), studied animal respiration and demonstrated the significance of oxygen, carbon dioxide, and water in breathing. The phlogiston theory was replaced by the description of oxidation, and combustion was defined as the combining of oxygen with the substance being burned.

Jan Ingenhousz (1730-1799), Dutch physician and naturalist, developed the "balance of life" concept in his publication, Experiments upon Vegetables, Discovering Their Great Power of Purifying the Common Air in the Sunshine and of Injuring it in the Shade and at Night (1779). He demonstrated that green plants take in carbon dioxide from the atmosphere in the daylight but give off some carbon dioxide at night. In the daytime carbon dioxide is used as the carbon source for nutrition and at night it is the product of respiration. Animals also have a place in the carbon cycle in nature. They are dependent on plants for food and they release carbon dioxide into the air through respiration and decay of their bodies. The ability to build carbon dioxide into compounds is a most fundamental property of plants and an important phase of the carbon cycle that is significant in the conservation of nature.

The next major steps in the understanding of plant nutrition were the discoveries of the enzyme system and energy source for the nutrition process, that is, photosynthesis. The green substance in plants had already been described and named "chlorophyll." Henri J. Dutrochet (1776-1847), a French experimenter, found in 1837, that only cells carrying the green substance could combine or fix carbon dioxide with other substances to form nutrient material and chlorophyll was found to be the enzyme required in photosynthesis. Experiments with plants had now reached the stage of complexity where special laboratory facilities were required. The first laboratory for the study of plant physiology was established in 1824 by J. E. Purkinje (1787-1869), in a room of his own home. In 1844 the Prussian Government furnished Purkinje with a physiology institute. Julius Sachs, a student of Purkinje, carried on the tradition of experimental plant physiology and became one of the most influential teachers of botany during this period.

Sachs, in 1862, performed an experiment by coating parts of live plant leaves with wax and exposing them to

sunlight.   He found that starch was produced only in the uncoated parts.   The
importance of sunlight was thus demonstrated in the photosynthesis process.
These studies led Sachs and Nathaniel
Pringsheim (1823-94) to observe and
describe chloroplastids as the structural
carrier of chlorophyll in green plants.
The green substance was not distributed
freely in cells and tissues as earlier investigators had supposed but was restricted to cytoplasmic structures.   The
major steps in plant nutrition were thus
discovered in the last century.   More recent developments have been in the direction of working out the chemical steps
involved in photosynthesis.   Technical
aspects of starch production and storage
are also being resolved at the present
time.

Chemists of the 19th century such as
Justus von Liebig (1802-1873), Professor
of Chemistry at Heidelberg, and Karl
Nägeli, German Botanist, found that nitro-
genous materials as well as carbohydrates
were necessary to build up plant bodies.
Liebig in his textbook entitled, Organic
Chemistry Applied to Agriculture and
Physiology, (1840) showed that ammonia

as well as carbon dioxide and water was
needed for plant growth.   The same three
materials that are required by the growing plant, that is, carbon dioxide, water,
and ammonia, are released by decom-
position when the plant is dead.   The
French chemist, Jean B. Boussingault
(1802-1887) showed that plants get nitrogen from the soil in the form of nitrates.
Bacteria were found to fix nitrogen and
form nitrates which the plant could use.
Some plants, the Leguminosae such as
peas and beans, have a symbiotic relation with bacteria that live in nodules on
their roots and fix nitrogen from the atmosphere.   The nitrogen cycle includes
several steps, as illustrated in Fig. 13-1.
Nitrates are taken up by plants and formed
into plant proteins, plants are eaten by
animals, and the plant protein is transformed to animal protein.   Either plant
or animal protein may be broken down in
the metabolic processes to form urea and
other residues.   Bacteria reduce the
waste products of metabolism and the
bodies of dead plants and animals into
ammonia that may be used directly by
plants.   Ammonia may also be transformed with the aid of certain bacteria,
to nitrites which may in turn be changed

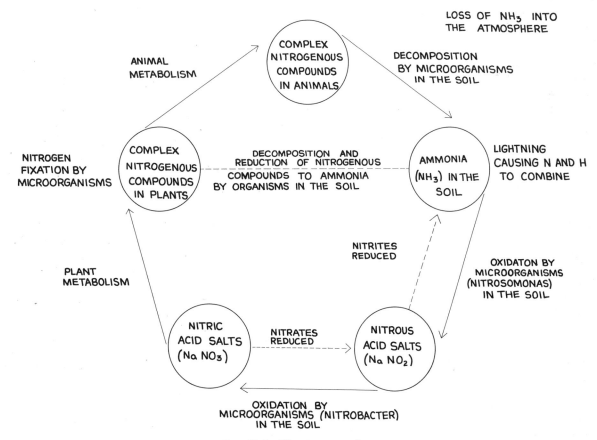

Fig. 13-1. The nitrogen cycle

by other bacteria to nitrates that the plant can use.

Vital Activity

Among thinking people there has always been interest in the nature of life and the mechanism of vital activities in the living body. In early biological history the word "soul" was used to represent a directing force in at least the higher forms of life. Early philosophers gave it physical dimensions and speculated as to where it was located in the body. The early Chinese considered the liver to be the important center of the body. Homer, the Greek poet, placed the soul in the diaphragm. Empedocles, the Greek philosopher who developed the humoral explanation for physical and biological relationships, located the soul in the blood. Aristotle gave attention to the basic properties of life and considered the seat of the soul to be in the heart because the heart gives noticeable indications of emotion.

Among the early philosophers, some placed the seat of the soul in the brain. Alcmaeon (500 B. C.), a Greek from Croton in Southern Italy, was one of the earliest to locate the powers of thought in the brain. He also described the nerves of the eye and the tube from the ear to the mouth that is now called the Eustachian tube. Plato also considered the seat of the soul to be in the brain. Hippocrates was an adherent of the humoral theory and gave the blood great importance in the living system but at times he recognized the brain as an important coordinating center. The French physiologist, Descartes, was one of the first to revive the theme in a more modern setting during the 17th century. He developed a mechanistic view of the nature of life, similar in general to the one prevalent among most biologists at the present time. The soul in his system was merely the part of the structure that directs the machine. Descartes located this function erroneously in the pineal body near the center of the brain. Although he had many other interests, particularly in philosophy, he did much to establish a foundation for a modern approach to physiology.

Descartes

When Descartes was ten years old, he was sent by his father to a Jesuit college where he proved to be a good student but was soon identified as a nonconformist.

Conflicts arose in his mind when discrepancies occurred in the material presented by the teacher as compared with that in various books. At times he detected inconsistencies when comparing the material presented by different teachers on similar subjects. He enjoyed mathematics because of its stability and exactness. In later life he classified the subjects other than mathematics that he had taken, as being either merely entertainment or worthless. When he was 17 years old he went to Paris to continue his education at the University. After a short introduction to the social life of Paris he retired from society and spent most of his time in solitude and study. When he was 21 he entered the military service and was stationed for 2 years at a garrison in Breda. It was while in the service that he wrote his first treatise entitled On Music.

In 1622 when he was 33 years of age he divorced himself entirely from society and concentrated on independent study. He traveled to Holland to find a retreat where he could develop his ideas concerning man's relation with nature, even though they might be contrary to accepted doctrines of the church. During the next 10 years in Holland he studied conscientiously his main interests in mathematics, optics, mechanics, and acoustics but he experimented in anatomy. He was particularly interested in Harvey's theory on the circulation of the blood. Although he spent most of his life in seclusion, he carried on a correspondence with Princess Elizabeth and won her admiration for his intellectual accomplishment.

Christina, Queen of Sweden, heard of Descartes and his scholarly work and, in 1647, sent for him to come to her court. He considered this invitation for a long time, hesitating mainly because of a chest condition that he feared would be more serious in the cold climate of Sweden. Finally he was persuaded by the offer of an appointment in the Swedish court and a title with an estate. He remained in Sweden for 3 years, until his death in 1650. During the severe winter of 1649 one of Descartes' friends was ill with an inflamation of the lungs, probably tuberculosis. After his daily work in the court of the Queen, Descartes walked a long distance in the cold, wet weather to his friend's house and frequently remained there through the night to care for him. This went on for months and no doubt contributed to the illness that resulted in the death of Descartes. On February 2, 1650,

Descartes became ill with the same symptoms and died 8 days later.

Descartes' Discourse on Method is only a small book consisting of 6 essays. A 7th was prepared but was not published with the other 6. In the first essay the author told the story of his school days and of his resolution to abandon book learning and study independently. Second, he described his experience during a winter while he served with the army. In this essay he set forth the rules of his method of study and told how the method occurred to him. Descartes' method included 4 requirements: (1) never accept anything that is not clearly known to be true; (2) divide each of the difficulties under examination into as many parts as possible and attempt solution of one part at a time, that is, "divide and conquer;" (3) conduct the thinking processes in such order that the simplest and easiest parts might be approached first, that is, a step-by-step build-up will resolve even the more complex problems; (4) make enumerations so complete and reviews so general that no significant part of the analysis can be omitted. The 3rd essay is a code of morals and the 4th is an account of the mental steps leading to the concept that is translated "I think, therefore I am." This topic is found expanded in his later work entitled Meditations. The 5th essay was a sketch of his theory concerning the essence and mutual relations of mind and body and the 6th included a statement of his reasons for not publishing this work at an earlier date. The 7th was a philosophical and physiological essay not in harmony with generally accepted religious doctrine and, therefore, was not published with the other essays. It was published 12 years later (1662) in Latin and 14 years later (1664) in French.

In the 7th essay Descartes presented a thoroughly materialistic account of a variety of physiological functions and issues of the mid 17th century period. He used scientific facts as far as they were available to him and from there on he speculated as to the mechanism of various functions of the body. In this process fact and fancy became intermixed and it is difficult to determine which of his comments were based on fact and which came from his imagination. Scientifically, the essay is significant in being the first frank attempt to explain organic functions on a materialistic basis. Philosophically, it is significant in having established the famous Cartesian (Cartesius is Latin for Descartes) duelism of matter versus mind.

Descartes' supreme achievement was the perception that mathematics is necessary in science. He saw nature as a machine operating according to the laws of mathematics. His weakness was in the attempt to interpret nature out of his mind as a mathematician does his theorems, without paying due respect to observation. Descartes was one of the inventors of analytical geometry that led to the calculus of Newton. He was also successful in theoretical optics. Some of his work in physics is quite modern and some is absurd. Among biological interests, he was most successful in physiology but here he made many factual errors because he did not make observations. For example, Descartes developed a mechanistic explanation for the operation of the nervous system to explain how single sensations influence bilateral organs. To make an ideal plan Descartes envisioned the pineal body as an organizing and coordinating center. Nerves were imagined to be hollow tubes through which fluids from the pineal body could flow. Valves in the pineal body were visualized as regulators of the flow of fluids. They were controlled directly by stimuli entering from external sources. This was an efficient mechanical devise. The defect was that it was not true. Most of the Cartesian views that applied to biology were superficial because they were not based on observation and they were soon replaced with other theories that had a more substantial foundation.

Nerve and Muscle Mechanics

G. A. Borelli (1608-79), a student of Galileo at Pisa, followed the mechanistic approach of Descartes but he was more interested in muscular mechanics and attempted to explain the action of muscles according to mathematical laws. His formulas involving statics and dynamics of muscles were sound in theory but like those of Descartes they were not based on observation of activities in real living systems. Weights, fulcrums, and energy sources were used in developing models of muscular activity. Attempts were made on the basis of mechanical models to explain the flight of birds, swimming of fish, and walking of land animals. Borelli predicted that contraction of muscles would eventually be explained on the basis of chemical and physiological processes.

Albrecht von Haller (1708-1777), a Swiss physiologist, provided an early description of the action of the nervous system in which he featured living material as being sensitive or irritable. Some parts of the body, he found, were specialized to carry impulses and some were capable of contracting and thus moving arms and legs and other structures. The properties of irritability and contractility were inherent in all living materials but some parts had become especially efficient in these functions and were thus enabled to serve the entire organism. Nerve channels carried messages from the receptors to the appropriate centers associated with sensations in the brain. In response to impulses sent out from the brain, muscles were brought into activity. Haller had a modern and rational view of nerve and muscle action but the scientific background at the time was not sufficient for an explanation of the detailed mechanics involved.

The English comparative anatomist and embryologist, John Hunter (Chapter 9) was not as specific as Haller in following the mechanics of nerve and muscle activity but he was equally interested in the fundamental properties of living materials. He recognized a living substance (protoplasm) which had general properties of living things and was not present in dead objects. The most obvious characteristic of life that he observed was heat. This "latent heat of life" was always associated with living activities and was released when death occurred.

Animal electricity was discovered in 1786 by the Italian investigator, Luigi Galvani (1737-1798) who showed that a nerve could be stimulated by an electric current. In an experimental animal, a particular nerve could be stimulated and a particular muscle would contract. It was shown further by sensitive instruments built by Galvani (galvanometers) that active nerves carry a small current of electricity called an action current. This observation lead to the modern theories of transmission of the nerve impulse. Hermann Helmholtz (1821-1894), German physiologist, followed the work of Galvani and investigated further the electric current associated with nervous activity. He found that the rate of conduction in the leg of a frog is only about 30 meters per second which is much slower than the movement of electricity in a copper wire. Since 1915, theories have been developed that involve chemical reactions as well as the electric current.

The mechanism of the non-voluntary responses of the body were considered and speculated upon by the early physiologists. The term "reflex action" was first used in 1833 by the English physiologist, Marshall Hall (1790-1857). Lloyd Morgan (1852-1936) attempted to simplify the nervous response and reduce the nervous system to the lowest possible unit. This was called a "reflex arc" which in its simplest form consisted of only three nerve cells or neurons; one to carry an impulse into the nervous system, one to make the transfer in the spinal cord, and one to carry the message for response to a muscle.

H. S. Jennings (1868-1947) studied protozoa and lower plants and showed that they follow simple physio-chemical rules in their response to stimuli. The word "tropism," used earlier by T. A. Knight (1759-1838) to identify responses of plants to external stimuli, was applied to the responses of protozoa (response to chemicals was called chemotropism to light, phototropism). Jacques Loeb (1859-1924) extended the work of Jennings to higher invertebrate animals and showed that many actions are controlled by physical conditions.

Circulation of Blood

The circulatory system was studied by Greek, Alexandrian, and Roman physicians. Aristotle summarized the work of the Greeks and added his own refinements, probably from actual dissections of animals. He identified the heart as the central organ controlling circulation, the seat of vital activity, and the place where the blood received its animal heat. From the lungs came pneuma or spirits. Pulsation was described as a boiling process in the heart that occurred when the blood and pneuma came together. A description of blood vessels is also included in Aristotle's writings. Herophilus, anatomist of Alexandria, counted the pulsations and worked out a rhythm and rate of heart beat. He also described the function of the valves in the heart. Erasistratus, physiologist of Alexandria, elaborated on the pneuma as the cause of heart beat and the source of body heat. He distinguished between the different kinds of spirits that controlled the functions of the body. The vascular system he considered to carry "vital spirits" whereas the nervous system carried "animal spirits."

Galen summarized the work of his predecessors and supplemented their findings with his own observations on such animals as sheep, dogs, swine, and apes. He described the aorta, and the main veins (Fig. 3-3). The valves of the heart were known to him but he regarded them as "fireplaces" for heating the blood. A reaction occurring with the mixing process in the heart provided the motion for moving the blood out of the heart. Galen's plan of body physiology was complicated. Food entered the stomach, underwent "coction," (boiling), and proceeded to the liver where it was changed to blood. From the liver it was carried to the right heart where a portion entered the pulmonary artery and went to the lungs. There was no return; the blood was used up in the lungs. A smaller portion of blood passed through the imaginary pores of the septum into the left heart where it was mixed with pneuma that entered the heart separately from the lungs through the pulmonary veins. A mixture of blood and pneuma was expelled through the aorta and carried out by the blood vessels to nourish the body.

Galen's description of circulation, like his anatomical work, was considered infallible for some 14 centuries until Harvey succeeded in demonstrating continuous circulation. Harvey's predecessor, Vesalius, had corrected many of Galen's errors in human anatomy but Vesalius did not find this correction in circulation. Vesalius was puzzled when he dissected the heart and found no pores between the right and left heart but he had no microscope and assumed that the pores were invisible. It was left for Fabricius and his student Harvey to apply modern experimental methods and to arrive at a description of continuous circulation. Harvey is one of the great founders of physiology. His life and contributions will be presented in more detail.

Although Harvey's contribution on the circulation of the blood is well known, little has been recorded concerning his life and his other contributions. William Harvey (1578-1657 Fig. 13-2) was born at Kent, England, the son of Thomas Harvey, a successful businessman. There were 7 sons in the family, 5 were turkey merchants in London, one was employed at the court of James I, and one, William, became a medical pioneer and scholar.

Harvey's early schooling was obtained at Kings School in Canterbury. At the age of 16 he entered Caius College at Cambridge and received the B. A. degree 3 years later, in 1597. From Caius, Harvey went to northern Italy and enrolled at the University of Padua, one of the most famous universities of this period. A link had been established between the two schools since 1539 when John Caius was a student of Vesalius at Padua. At Padua, Harvey studied under the faculties of physics and medicine and became associated with the Fabricius, who was the most eminent anatomist of his day in all Europe. The academic lineage of Harvey's teacher was of the highest order. Fabricius was a student of Fallopius, who was a student of Vesalius, who in turn had studied under Sylvius. Fabricius had observed the valves in the blood veins and had an idea that circulation was continuous. Harvey became interested in the problem and was encouraged by Fabricius to go on with the study.

Harvey received the degree, Doctor of Physics, in 1602 at Padua, returned immediately to Cambridge and the same year was awarded the M. D. degree from that University. Two years later he was admitted to the College of Physicians in London and was elected a Fellow in 1607. At that time he became a physician at St. Bartholomew's Hospital, a position he

Fig. 13-2. William Harvey, English anatomist who discovered continuous circulation of the blood

held for 36 years until advanced age made it impossible for him to carry out his duties at the hospital.

In 1618 he was appointed physician extraordinary to King James I and this was followed in 1631 by his appointment as physician to Charles I. During these years, Harvey carried on a private practice among people of wealth and distinction. Besides all of his professional activities, he found time to continue his studies of human anatomy and he also became well versed in comparative anatomy. His studies ranged from insects through every major group in the animal kingdom and included some 60 species of mammals. The demonstration of the circulation of the blood so overshadowed his other contributions in importance that most other studies are usually overlooked.

Two books were left as evidence for his research, De Motu Cordis (Movement of the Heart and Blood in Animals) (1628) and De Generatione Animalium, (The Development of Animals) (Chapter 16). The first book was short, having only about 72 pages, but it demonstrated a clear understanding of the circulation of the blood that Harvey had gained in 12 years of investigation. Harvey was familiar with the writings of Aristotle and had first hand knowledge of the work of Fabricius. He quoted them repeatedly and also cited the work of Aldrovandi, Descartes, and Parisanus. Some other Greek and Roman writers, including Galen, were also mentioned in Harvey's work.

When Harvey began his experimentation on the heart and circulation he found the problem complex and difficult. He almost believed with Fracastorius that the heart was meant to be understood by God alone. With great care and persistence he was able to observe the heart action in a variety of animals. This provided accurate information on the motions and functions of the heart and the arteries, and led to his discovery of circulation. He measured the amount of blood flowing out from the heart and concluded that it would be impossible for the body to produce that much blood. Next he succeeded in demonstrating that blood was being returned to the heart through the veins. He did not see the capillaries but postulated that there must be connections between the arteries and the veins. It remained for the microscopists in the latter part of the century to observe the capillaries.

Harvey's ideas were ridiculed in public by those who did not understand or appreciate the kind of observations he was making. In the book De Motu Cordis Harvey countered with the statement, "A path is open for others starting here to progress more fortunately and more correctly under a more propitious genius." Harvey's work was not only the starting point in the modern science of mammalian physiology, but it was also the first milestone on the road to the modern rationalization of biological thought. In announcing his great discovery Harvey modestly suggested that it was merely a return to Aristotle.

Harvey was recognized as a leader in medical circles as well as a physician and he held many responsible positions. In 1613 he became the censor for the medical profession in London and was responsible for safeguarding the practice of medicine from the inroads of quacks. In 1627 he was one of the 8 elect examiners in the profession whose duty it was to examine those desiring to practice medicine in any part of Great Britain. In 1628 he was appointed treasurer of the College of Physicians. He could advance only one step higher, to the Presidency. This office was offered him in 1654, but he declined because of advanced age and infirmities. In 1651 when he was 73 years of age he gave the college a building at Amen corner for a library and museum. The college appropriately placed a statue of Harvey in the entrance. The great fire in 1666 destroyed Harvey's library building, his statue and most of his books and specimens.

Müller

Johannes Müller was one of the great German physiologists of the 19th century. He studied medicine in his early life, became professor of anatomy and physiology at the University of Bonn, and later was widely known for his Handbook of Physiology (1840) that was used extensively as a text and reference. In the beginning stages of physiology as a science he was a leader, not only through his book, but also through his effective teaching and his original investigations. In the course of his work he correlated comparative anatomy, chemistry, and physics and showed their relation to physiological problems. This represented an important development and had much to do with the future of physiology. His main interest was in the mechanisms of the sense organs and the production of sensations. Color sensations were investigated by appropriate experimental procedures, some of which were originally devised by Müller. The anatomy and functioning of the voice organs were studied and relations between the organs and various sounds were established. The structure of the inner ear was also investigated along with the mechanism by which impulses received by the ear are transmitted to the brain.

Müller is known for the formulation of the "doctrine of specific nerve energies." This doctrine states that impulses originate in particular sense organs and are carried over certain tracts to the central nervous system. It was shown experimentally that the kind of stimulus is not as important in determining the response as the particular tract over which the stimulus is carried. External events initiate specific action of certain nerves that in turn carry the impulses to the brain where sensations are interpreted.

In his later life Müller became interested in the broader aspects of biology such as morphology and embryology as well as physiology. He worked out the microscopic anatomy of glandular and connective tissues. Not the least of his accomplishments was the training of several excellent students who carried on in various aspects of anatomy and physiology. Among his more famous students were Theodor Schwann, Rudolf Virchow, and Hermann Helmholtz.

A German colleague of Müller and another great teacher of physiology was Karl Ludwig (1816-95). In addition to his great skill as a teacher and investigator, he invented several ingenious devices for studying physiology. The mechanically rotating drum or kymograph used to record the heart beat, muscular activity, and movements involved in breathing was worked out by Ludwig. He studied secretions and provided physical and chemical explanations for activities in the animal body.

Bernard

Claude Bernard (1813-78) was the leading French physiologist of the last century who made more basic contributions to the science of physiology than any other one person. He began his education when he was 8 years old, under the supervision of a parish priest, mastering Latin and other classical subjects in his early years. Later he went to a Jesuit school and in his free time taught language and mathematics to private students in his own home.

In 1832, when he was 18 years of age, his folks could no longer support him in school and he went to a neighboring town where he became an apprentice to a druggist, M. Millet. His main responsibilities were the routine and menial tasks necessary in the drugstore. Among other duties he swept the floors, washed bottles, made paper corks, and delivered prescriptions. A veterinary school was located a short distance from the drugstore and Claude frequently had the opportunity to carry drugs to the school. He sometimes lingered and watched the operations that were being performed on live animals. Vivisection experiments made a deep impression on him and he frequently discussed his observations with his employer. Eventually Claude was given the opportunity to make simple preparations. He took great pride in his first product, shoe polish, and said later, "Now I could make something; I was a man."

Bernard was interested in the theater and on his night off from the drugstore he often attended a comedy or a vaudeville. After attending numerous performances, he thought he could write as well as some authors whose plays were being presented, and decided to try it. His first attempt was a small play entitled "LaRose du Rhone." This was a farce-comedy based on a popular medicine of that day called "theriac." Theriac was a complex mixture of about 60 different drugs, including opium, squills, spikenard, honey, and wine. In addition to all the regular constituents that were in the recipe, druggists made a practice of adding all the spoiled products and prescriptions that were not called for. No one knew exactly what was contained after all the extras had been added to the usual formula. Obviously no two batches of theriac were the same, and it was impossible to duplicate a particular batch if it should be found to give good results for some particular illness. Theriac took the place of the "pink pills" that some doctors are said to prescribe nowadays for ill-defined complaints. Bernard's play was a story of strange experiences that followed the use of theriac. The play sold for a hundred franks and had some success in a small theater at Lyons.

The success of this play made Bernard overconfident. Next he attempted a larger 5-act play, but it was not successful. This time he chose a historical theme based on a 12th century incident concerning King John and his nephew who was heir to the throne. It was a tragedy in more ways than one. So much time was devoted to the play that Bernard was unable to take proper care of the responsibilities at the drugstore. M. Millet wrote to his home explaining that after a year and a half as an apprentice, Claude had lost interest in rolling pills and could no longer remain at the drugstore. Claude went to Paris with his unfinished play under his arm. His ambition to write plays was discouraged considerably by a critic, Saint-Marc Girardin at the Sorbonne, who advised him to learn a profession and write plays only in his spare time. Claude followed the advice and in 1832 entered medical school.

The results of his examination for internship in 1839 were not impressive. He was ranked number 26 in a total of 29 students taking the examination. He had been indifferent to his work and his fellow students considered him to be lazy. At the college of France, however, he was observed by the physiologist, Francois Magendie, to have considerable skill as a dissector. Magendie took him into his laboratory as an assistant and there Bernard had the opportunity to work intimately with one of the great physiologists of the time. Although Magendie was well recognized in his field, he was skeptical, intolerant, and sarcastic, with little patience for his students and assistants. He was, however, interested in original research and made it a practice to teach by doing actual dissecting along with his students.

Bernard thrived in this environment and stayed with Magendie as an assistant for many years. When he was 35 years old he was still an assistant. Several times he had tried to obtain a university appointment but was not successful. Although he was a good thinker and an excellent technician, he was a poor speaker. In 1854 he became Professor of General Physiology at the Sorbonne and in 1858 replaced Magendie as Professor of Medicine at the College of France. Only 2 years after the latter appointment when Bernard was 47 years of age, he became ill with tuberculosis and retired to his birthplace in southern France to regain his health. He never practiced medicine but continued his research and writing when his health would permit.

In 20 years of research, Bernard had learned many facts in the field of physiology. He had also provided an excellent example of the effective use of the scientific method in physiology. Bernard had great respect for natural law in the organic as well as in the inorganic world. Not the least of his accomplishments came from his great influence on other physiologists of his own time and on the teaching of philosophy, medicine, and literature. He wrote one important book, Introduction to Experimental Medicine, while he was ill. It was the first excellent attempt to formulate the basic laws of experimental physiology and medicine.

In his first research publication Bernard reported a study of the chorda tympani nerve that supplies the taste buds of the anterior two-thirds of the tongue and the submaxillary gland. This nerve was traced to the 7th cranial nerve. In this study Bernard demonstrated his excellent facility for dissection as well as the patience and skill necessary in tracing a tiny nerve over a long distance. Many papers followed. In 1843 he wrote his thesis on gastric juice and its role in digestion. In this study he traced the digestion of different foods in the alimentary canal. The next paper described the spinal accessory nerve and demonstrated its relation with the vagus nerve. Later papers appeared on the pancreas and the sympathetic nervous system. His most valuable discoveries may be classified under the following 5 subjects:

(1) Pancreatic digestion. This study was initiated when he noticed that the urine of rabbits was clear when the animals were fed meat, but cloudy when they were fed herbs. Therefore, he reasoned that different chemical processes must be involved in the digestion of animal food as compared with that of plant food. He followed the course of digestion and discovered the enzyme steapsin. Furthermore he found that pancreatic juice contained more than a single enzyme. Enzymes that act on proteins, carbohydrates, and fats were identified in pancreatic fluid.

(2) Glycogenic function of the liver. Bernard performed careful experiments over a period of 12 years and showed that carbohydrates are stored as glycogen in the liver. This contribution became important in understanding and treating diabetes but even more significant in demon-

strating that the animal body can build up as well as break down complex chemical materials, that is, it performs synthetic as well as analytical functions.

(3) The vaso-motor nerves. The vaso-constrictors and vaso-dilators that control the size of the blood vessels were observed in the ear of a rabbit and were found to be innervated by the sympathetic system. Various chemicals in the blood were found to activate these nerves and thus to influence blood pressure.

(4) The action of drugs or poisons on the body. Curare was one of the drugs to be investigated by Bernard. It was used by Indians in America to poison arrows many years before its physiological properties were known.

Now it is used in physiology laboratories to block nerves while dissections of living animals are in progress. Bernard made careful studies of the effects of curare and found that it was effective at the point where the nerve enters the muscle. He also studied carbon monoxide poisoning and found that this substance could displace oxygen in the blood by forming a more stable combination than oxyhemoglobin and thus destroy the oxygen carrying capacity of the blood. The serious effect from carbon monoxide poisoning was due to suffocation for want of oxygen.

(5) The endocrine system. Bernard showed by chemical methods that the liver could release sugar directly into the blood, and described this function as "internal secretion".

REFERENCES

Bernard, C. *An Introduction to the Study of Experimental Medicine.* New York: Henry Schuman, 1949.

Chauvois, L. *William Harvey.* New York: Philosophical Library, 1957.

Clark-Kennedy, A. E. *Stephen Hales.* Cambridge: The Univ. Press, 1929.

Clark-Kennedy, A. E. *The Art of Medicine in Relation to the Progress of Thought.* Cambridge: Cambridge Univ. Press, 1945.

Crombie, A. C. Descartes. *Sci. Amer.* 201:(4) 160-173, 1959.

Foster, M. *Lectures on the History of Physiology.* Cambridge: The Univ. Press, 1901.

Green, J. R. *A History of Botany.* Oxford: The Clarendon Press, 1909.

Gruber, H. and V. Gruber, Hermann von Helmholtz: Nineteenth-Century Polymorph. *Sci. Monthly* 83:92-99, 1956.

Harvey, W. *Movement of the Heart and Blood in Animals.* Oxford: Blackwell Sci. Publ., 1957.

Harvey, W. *Exercitatio Anatomica De Motu Cordis Et Sanguinis in Animalibus.* trans. C. D. Leake, Springfield, Ill.: Charles C. Thomas, 1958.

Keynes, J. *The Personality of William Harvey.* Cambridge: Cambridge Univ. Press, 1949.

Lowndes, R. *René Descartes; His Life and Meditations.* London: F. Norgate, 1878.

122

Mahaffy, J. P. *Descartes*. Philadelphia: J. B. Lippincott and Co., 1881.

Maritain, J. *The Dream of Descartes*. trans. M. L. Anderson. New York: New York Philosophical Library, 1944.

Meyer, A. W. *The Analysis of the De Generatione Animalium of William Harvey*. Stanford: Stanford Univ. Press, 1936.

Olmsted, J. M. D. *Claude Bernard, Physiologist*. New York: Harper Bros., 1938.

Olmsted, J. M. D. *Francois Magendie, Pioneer in Experimental Physiology*. New York: Henry Schuman, 1944.

Olmsted, J. M. D. and E. Harris, *Claude Bernard and the Experimental Method in Medicine*. New York: Henry Schuman, 1952.

Roth, L. *Descartes' Discourse on Method*. Oxford: Clarendon Press, 1937.

Scott, J. F. *The Scientific Work of Rene' Descartes*. London: Taylor and Francis, 1952.

Singer, C. *A Short History of Anatomy and Physiology from the Greeks to Harvey*. New York: Dover Publ., 1958.

Stevenson, L. *Sir Frederick Banting*. Toronto: The Ryerson Press, 1946.

Valery, P. *The Living Thoughts of Descartes*. Philadelphia: David McKay Co., 1947.

Microbiology is one of the newer fields of biological science which has developed almost entirely since the year 1860. Before this time bacteria and other microorganisms had been observed and some of their activities, for example, fermentation, had been suggested but the body of facts was too fragmentary to be considered a science. The ground work was laid by Pasteur, Koch, Ehrlich, and their associates between 1860 and 1890. Since 1890 this area has developed rapidly and has now become one of the most practical fields of biology. Four main reasons for the slow development of microbiology before the end of the last century and the rapid progress since that time are: (1) the development of the microscope, (2) the long and heated controversy over spontaneous generation, (3) the establishment of the germ theory of fermentation, and (4) the germ theory disease.

The importance of the microscope in microbiology is obvious and needs no further discussion. Morphological studies of minute organisms require a tool that can produce an enlarged image of an object and make it possible to distinguish critically the fine details. As shown in Chapter 7, the microscope has served this purpose.

Throughout the history of biology there has been much interest in the origin of life. Of the theories advanced, the most widely discussed among biologists has been that of spontaneous generation. This implies an origin of living things by processes other than the reproduction of parent organisms. A favorable combination of non-living materials was considered sufficient to account for the origin of living things. Spontaneous generation was a common explanation from the earliest periods of biological history until the middle of the last century. Aristotle, like many of his contemporaries, considered flies and frogs to be formed spontaneously from the mud in the bottom of streams and pools. He was able to observe other animals such as the cuttlefish and octopus engaged in the reproductive process. These he recognized as being formed from eggs produced by the female and activated by the "milt" from the male. Higher organisms were considered by Aristotle to develop from eggs even though they had not been observed, but lower organisms whose reproduction was entirely unknown, were believed to arise spontaneously.

From the time of Aristotle through the Middle Ages, many people expressed themselves favorably toward spontaneous generation. This belief survived the rebirth of inquiry and persisted without serious question until the 18th century. J. B. van Helmont, Belgian alchemist, physician, and philosopher, was outspoken in promoting this explanation for the origin of life. He was specific in prescribing a technique for producing mice. It was only necessary, he said, to place moist, soiled rags in a dark attic and surround them with kernels of wheat or pieces of cheese. Within a reasonable time mice would invariably appear and there seemed to be no doubt that they were actually produced spontaneously. Many

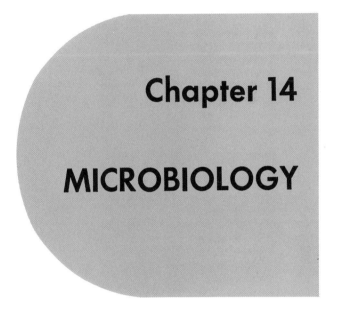

Chapter 14

MICROBIOLOGY

authors described the spontaneous origin of frogs, eels, and snakes from the mud in river bottoms.

Redi's Experiments on Flies

One of the first men to question the spontaneous origin of living things was the Italian physician and naturalist Francesco Redi (1626-1697). After studying medicine at the University of Pisa, he became court physician to Ferdinand Medici, Grand Duke of Tuscany, and a member of the famous Academy of Experiments that was organized in 1657 at Florence, Italy.

Redi set out to determine by experimentation whether flies could be developed spontaneously. His procedure followed a precise pattern and represents an example of the use of the experimental method. He began by killing 3 snakes and placing them in an open box where they were allowed to decay. Maggots appeared on the decaying flesh, fed on the meat, and grew rapidly. During the growth process they were observed critically day after day. Following the period of rapid and continuous growth the maggots became dormant (pupated) and after a few days emerged into flies. Several varieties of pupae were identified by size, shape, and color and each was observed to give rise to a particular type of adult fly.

Redi continued his experiments, testing different kinds of flesh both raw and cooked. He used the meat of oxen, deer, buffalo, lion, tiger, duck, lamb, kid, rabbit, goose, chicken, and swallow and also studied several kinds of fish, including sword fish, tuna, eel, and sole. Particular types of maggots developed on the meat and emerged in due course to become particular types of adult flies. Sometimes the maggots were all of the same type and Redi observed that only one type of fly emerged whereas in other cases several different types were identified. Each type of maggot was later isolated and found to give rise only to a particular kind of fly. Adult flies of the same kinds that emerged from the maggots were observed to hover over the decaying meat and Redi noticed that the flies dropped tiny objects on the meat. Some flies would remain quiet on the meat and deposit several units in one place while others would deposit single objects while hovering above the decaying meat. Redi theorized that the flies might be developed from the objects dropped by the adult flies on the putrifying meat.

An experiment was carefully designed to test this hypothesis. Portions of fish and eel were placed in flasks, the openings of some were completely sealed off and the meat was observed through the glass as it underwent decay, but other comparable flasks prepared in the same way were left uncovered. Flies were soon attracted to the opened flasks and in a few days maggots appeared on the meat. Similar flies were also observed hovering over the sealed flasks but no maggots developed on the meat inside. Occasionally maggots appeared on the top of the sealed flasks. They would wriggle on the surface and appear to be trying to get through the glass to the putrifying meat inside. This indicated that the maggots were developed

from the elements dropped from the adult flies and were not derived spontaneously on the decaying meat.

Even though the results seemed conclusive, Redi was not content with these experiments. He tried variations of different kinds to see if the results could be repeated. The experiments were repeated at different seasons of the year with various kinds of vessels and different kinds of meat. He even buried meat underground and observed that no maggots were developed in the covered meat, but at the same time maggots appeared and emerged into flies on meat that was exposed to the air. There was one difficulty with the experiments; the sealed containers and the soil covering could exclude some vital force necessary for the spontaneous generation of life. To obviate this uncertainty, Redi designed a further experiment in which air was permitted to enter but flies were excluded.

For this experiment Redi covered glass containers with a fine veil that allowed air to enter but through which flies were unable to reach the decaying meat. He found that the covered meat would not produce maggots but the unprotected containers provided as the controls were well supplied with maggots and in due time with adult flies. Thus, he had demonstrated that under conditions in which air was not excluded but the flies were merely prevented from laying their eggs on the meat, no life was created. Redi observed carefully the activities of flies during the different phases of the experiment. Flies were attracted to the meat as soon as it showed the first signs of decay and laid eggs on the outside surface of the unprotected meat. Some eggs were deposited on the veil and the larvae that emerged would have wriggled their way through the mesh work and entered the containers but Redi removed them as fast as they appeared. He observed closely the method of egg deposition and noted that in a few cases active young were deposited by adult flies. The eggs had apparently hatched in the body of the mother. Some adults would remain quiet on the surface and deposit several eggs at one time while others would drop single eggs or larvae from the air without lighting.

Redi, through these simple but ingenious experiments, was able to demonstrate that flies do not develop spontaneously on putrifying meat but that they must come from other flies through the medium of eggs. In his book, Experiments on the Generation of Insects, published in 1668, Redi recorded the results of his experiments that disproved spontaneous generation as it applied to animals as complex as flies. However, with the advent of microbiology, the whole controversy flared up again and required further and more critical experiments. In dealing with minute organisms that could not be readily observed, more elaborate tools and refined techniques were necessary.

Experiments on Microorganisms

One of the earliest experiments on microorganisms that produced evidence against spontaneous generation was performed by the French microscopist, Louis Joblot (1645-1723). He observed in 1710, as did Leeuwenhoek in an earlier period, that hay when infused in water and allowed to stand for a few days gave rise to countless microorganisms that were called "infusoria." According to present day taxonomic arrangements the organisms included in a hay infusion would mostly fall into the groups of bacteria and protozoa. Only a small portion would represent the class of protozoa, now known as infusoria.

Joblot's contemporaries, and many who followed, considered the presence of microorganisms in a hay infusion as conclusive evidence for spontaneous generation but he was critical of this interpretation and carried out an experiment to test the prevalent idea. He boiled the fluid to be used for a hay infusion and divided the boiled material into two parts. One was placed in a container that was sealed off completely and thus protected from air whereas the other was left open. The open container soon had numerous microorganisms but the material in the closed container was free from all living things. By this experiment, Joblot showed that the boiled infusion alone was not capable of producing life anew. Something in the air was required for organisms to become established in the originally sterile infusion.

In 1745 a report on a similar study, but with different results, was published by John T. Needham (1713-1781), an English Catholic priest who was interested in science. In his experiments, organisms developed in the heated and closed hay infusions as well as in those left open, supporting spontaneous generation. Obviously. there were technical differences in the way the two experiments were conducted

by the two investigators. Hay is now known to carry resistant spores that are not killed by ordinary boiling. Needham apparently did not heat his cultures to a temperature sufficiently high to kill the spores.

On the strength of his contribution, Needham was elected a member of the Royal Society of London and later he became one of the 8 foreign associates of the French Academy of Science. One of the main reasons for the wide recognition accorded Needham's results was the support and systematic treatment provided by Buffon. In his enthusiasm for Needham's work, Buffon gave it considerable space in his own publication and added his own comments favoring spontaneous generation. Needham was invited to Paris as the guest of Buffon and he collaborated with Buffon on the 2nd volume of Buffon's encyclopedia of scientific knowledge. The distinguished London churchman and the famous French encyclopedist thus formed a strong team favoring spontaneous generation.

At this same time, a slightly different idea concerning the origin of life was presented by another distinguished French naturalist, Charles Bonnet (1720-1793) who spoke of a pre-existence of germs. This idea was speculative, like many others of that period, but it supported the existence of microorganisms and the stability of the living processes. The pre-existence of organisms was never demonstrated and the idea suffered for want of experimental support. A heated discussion, however, followed the presentation of Bonnet's speculation. It has since been shown that neither the view of Bonnet nor that of Needham and Buffon were correct.

Another scientist entered the controversy at this point and added an impressive chapter to the history of spontaneous generation. This was the Italian physiologist Lazaro Spallanzani (1729-1799). Spallanzani was an experimenter who recognized the problem of spontaneous generation as one lending itself to the experimental procedure. The actual experiments of Spallanzani were similar to those of Needham but he designed and conducted them with greater care. Several different media were used, including urine and beef broth as well as hay infusion. He boiled the media for an hour or so and hermetically sealed the containers while they were still hot completely removing all organisms.

Spallanzani considered the matter closed when he published his results in 1765 in Italian.

In 1769, the work of Spallanzani was translated into French and published with accompanying notes written by Needham who found a different explanation for most of Spallanzani's results and conclusions. The result that seemed to Spallanzani most conclusive, that is, the absence of microorganisms in boiled and sealed cultures, was attacked by Needham on the basis of the extreme and prolonged heating that Spallanzani had applied to his cultures. High temperatures and prolonged heating were considered by Needham to be sufficient to destroy the "vegetative force" that he thought was necessary for the development of any life. He accused Spallanzani of torturing the vegetative infusions to the point where the vital material was weakened or destroyed. Furthermore, argued Needham, the air remaining in the empty part of the vessels was completely spoiled by the heat treatment.

Needham then suggested a type of treatment by which supposed foreign organisms could be removed and the vegetative force uninjured. These provisions were considered by Spallanzani not sufficient to remove all the organisms from the culture, but he was challenged to take up his experiments again. He found that, in order to destroy all microorganisms, it was necessary to boil the medium for at least three quarters of an hour. The argument between the two adversaries then faced an insurmountable difficulty. Needham insisted on a treatment that would not destroy the presumed "vegetative force", whereas Spallanzani insisted that the treatment prescribed by Needham was not sufficient to destroy the foreign organisms present in the cultures.

The problem was further confused by an observation of the eminent French chemist, Gay-Lussac (1778-1850) who analyzed the air in the sealed containers in which meat and grape juice had been boiled and found no oxygen. Therefore, he concluded that preserved foods could be kept only in the absence of oxygen, which he considered to be the life giving property of the medium. Needham's objections were now more readily justified since oxygen was considered to be removed by the treatment performed by Spallanzani. Even though the Italian experimenter felt secure in his earlier position, there was some doubt raised in his own mind by the objections of Needham and Gay-Lussac.

Another development came with the entrance of the German physician and physiologist, Theodor Schwann, into the controversy. Schwann reported in 1837 an experiment in which a preparation of lean meat in a glass flask was sealed off in a flame and the entire preparation was boiled. The material was allowed to cool in the sealed flask and no organisms appeared. To test the objections made previously concerning this type of experiment, Schwann modified his experimental procedure in such a way that air could be added continuously to the culture by a system of tubes. When the air coming in was heated no growth occurred in the medium. It was shown further that air could be heated and then cooled before it was introduced, and still no contamination would occur in the meat juice. This experiment reinforced Spallanzani's view and was contrary to Needham's observation. It contradicted, in part at least, Needham's objection that a vegetative force had been destroyed and disproved Gay-Lussac's hypothesis that preservation could be accomplished only in the absence of oxygen.

However, a further problem arose when Schwann prepared 4 flasks with a solution of cane sugar. Some were opened to permit ordinary air to enter whereas others were closed off and only heated air was allowed to enter through appropriate tubes. At the end of this experiment, organisms were present in the flasks that had been exposed to ordinary air, but those in which only heated air was allowed to enter were completely free from organisms and no fermentation was detected. When these experiments were repeated, some of the flasks open to ordinary air did not show fermentation. Schwann concluded that it was not oxygen, or at least not oxygen alone, in the atmosphere that was responsible for alcoholic fermentation but a principle sometimes present and sometimes absent in ordinary air, that Schwann considered to be a living organism. Although Schwann's experiments yielded strong evidence in support of a living principle involved in alcoholic fermentation, that could be carried in the air, the conclusion was not widely accepted. There was still uncertainty in the minds of most investigators as to whether living organisms were introduced with air or whether some chemical alteration of air such as the removal of oxygen or some other vital material was responsible for the origin of living organisms in the medium.

Frantz F. Schulze (1815-1873), a Berlin agricultural chemist, added another step to the experimental procedure when he devised an experiment similar to that of Schwann, but instead of calcining (heating) the air, he passed it through concentrated solutions of potassium hydroxide or sulfuric acid. His results were similar to those of Schwann. The question of the effect of the heat on the air was resolved by this method but the fundamental objection was not overcome. It was possible that sulfuric acid and potassium hydroxide as well as heat could destroy the vegetative force or the "germs of life."

Two other German scientists, Heinrich G. F. Schröder (1810-1885) and Theodor von Dusch (1824-1890), devised a method of filtering air through cotton-wool. This did nothing to the air that could be construed to destroy any force it contained or alter in any way its fundamental properties but microorganisms were successfully filtered from the air as the air was passed through the cotton. The original method used by Schröder and von Dusch was an elaborate procedure making use of a complex system of flasks and glass tubes. A plug of cotton-wool was placed in the glass tube that entered the flask containing nutrient medium and a pump was arranged to force the air through the cotton, along the tubes, and into the flask. Every precaution was taken in the preparation and heating procedure to make sure that all of the organisms were removed from the original material and air was introduced only through the cotton plug.

Different kinds of media, such as meat juice, beer must, and milk were used in the experiments. Some of these were shown to behave differently. Meat juice and beer must remained free from organisms and without physical change after the treatment. Milk, however, curdled and spoiled as readily in the tubes through which the air was filtered as in the tubes through which ordinary air was introduced. Different kinds of changes were thus associated with the different kinds of material. In milk, a putrifaction was occurring that required only oxygen, whereas in meat juice and beer must, factors from the air were required before alcoholic fermentation could proceed. In their publications of 1854 and 1859, these authors concluded that some agency carried by the air was required for alcoholic fermentation. Furthermore, they demonstrated that this agency could be filtered out from air by the use of ordinary cotton, appropriately arranged in the tubes.

The cotton plug has since been developed to simple and practical usefulness in bacteriology. Flasks and test tubes containing sterile media or cultures of microorganisms are commonly stoppered with plugs of sterile non-absorbent cotton. As long as the plugs remain tight and dry they serve the valuable purpose of excluding the microorganisms carried on dust particles, and provide an efficient means through which the air can circulate in and out of the container.

In spite of the excellent experimental work of the investigators listed above, the controversy concerning spontaneous generation had not been resolved to the satisfaction of everyone. Recognizing the uncertainty existing on this fundamental question, the French Academy of Science offered a prize for the best dissertation on the subject "Attempts by Well-Conceived Experiments to Throw New Light on the Question of Spontaneous Generation." The main competitors for this prize were the French naturalist, Felix A. Pouchet (1800-1872), and the chemist Louis Pasteur (1822-1895). Pouchet carried out experiments in which he prepared flasks containing hay infusions, sterilized them by boiling, and sealed off the necks of the flasks. He observed no difference between the control flasks left open to the air and those sealed off, following the heat treatment that was presumed to be sufficient for the removal of the organisms. In the course of his studies, he obtained air from various places, including the edge of a glacier at 6,000 feet elevation, and found that all the containers, regardless of the source of air or the presence or absence of air, had growing organisms.

Pasteur

Louis Pasteur had been trained in chemistry and although at this time he had done some research on fermentation he was considered a chemist rather than a biologist. Pasteur's experiments were similar to those of Pouchet but he used sugared yeast water for the medium instead of hay infusion. Nineteen of Pasteur's prepared flasks were opened and then sealed in a lecture hall of the Museum of Natural History in Paris. Following incubation, 4 showed evidence of living organisms. Of the 18 which were opened outdoors under trees, 16 developed organisms. Pasteur was thus able to show that different results were obtained when air was introduced from different sources. This suggested that it was not the air itself, but something that was sometimes carried in the air and sometimes not present, that was responsible for the microorganisms.

Insufficient heat treatment was considered by Pasteur as a possible explanation for the presence of organisms in Pouchet's sealed containers. He did not know that hay infusions may carry organisms in a dormant stage (as spores) that are not destroyed by the ordinary boiling. Spores are carried in the hay itself and provide an insidious means by which living organisms can remain dormant for long periods and develop when conditions are suitable. Since yeast water had no resistant spores, the experiments of Pouchet as well as those of Pasteur yielded results that could now be repeated and explained. Unfortunately, the reason for the difference was not understood at that time. Later Pasteur became aware of the presence of resistant spores of certain bacteria in such materials as hay infusions as well as the existence of anaerobic organisms that cannot live in the presence of free oxygen.

Pouchet withdrew from the competition and Pasteur won the prize. In his detailed treatise, Pasteur described the experiments in which flasks carrying media were sterilized and sealed off; no life was found in these flasks. Some were opened in various places, incubated, and observed for the presence of organisms. Twenty were opened in the high Alps and all except one were negative whereas all of those opened in a dusty building developed living organisms. Flasks opened on the streets in downtown Paris were all contaminated. A decisive experimental treatment was thus recorded by Pasteur that not only won the prize offered by the French Academy, but also won the immediate argument against spontaneous generation.

A controversy developed between a London physician, Henry Charlton Bastian (1847-1915), and Pasteur, following the publication in 1872 of Bastian's two volume work under the title The Beginning of Life in which difficulties with Pasteur's experiments were cited. Bastian was particularly concerned with the discrepancies between the experiments of Pasteur and those of Pouchet and reemphasized the old theory of Gay-Lussac that oxygen was the only essential factor in the origin of life.

John Tyndall (1820-1893) an English physicist, had discovered in 1869 that the last portion of a breath expelled from the lungs, was remarkably free from suspended dust. The air had been filtered by the cells of the lungs. Tyndall was engaged in studies of the optical effects of dust and devised a method of identifying optically pure air, that is, a method of determining when air is free from dust, by optical means. This approach provided a more decisive method than those used by Pasteur for removing the foreign bodies in the air, without any treatment that could alter the air for example, remove the oxygen.

In the years 1876 and 1877, Tyndall presented the results of his experiments in the Philosophical Transactions of the Royal Society of London, describing a method of purifying air by allowing it to settle in closed boxes. Following the settling period he introduced light through a slit in an otherwise closed box in such a way that rays of light could be reflected from suspended particles in the air. The optical test could be used to indicate when the air was completely free from foreign bodies. When pure air was introduced into a medium capable of supporting living organisms, no organisms were in evidence. It was thus established that organisms carried in the air are responsible for contamination. These results, coupled with those of Pasteur, added the final step to the long controversy concerning spontaneous generation in bacteria.

A further contribution which prevented a recurrence of the idea of spontaneous generation for organisms as complex as bacteria was made later by Pasteur when he showed that a particular kind of organism kept in pure culture could be introduced into a medium and if the culture was protected from contamination, only the kind of organism in the original culture would be present. Other media inoculated with organisms from other types of pure cultures would produce only those particular types. This evidence was clear and decisive and showed that parent microorganisms generate their own kind.

With the controversy over spontaneous generation for bacteria closed, life histories and reproductive processes of microorganisms took on great significance. Practical applications also followed in food preservation. It was no longer hopeless to attempt to preserve foods and a great canning industry soon developed. Applications were also made in problems concerning fermentation and control of disease. Antiseptic methods were applied in hospitals and particularly in surgical procedures. In Paris at this time about one in every 19 mothers who went to hospitals to have babies, died of puerperal fever, a disease familiarly called "child-bed fever". When doctors became aware of the importance of washing their hands and sterilizing their instruments, the mortality from this disease dropped considerably.

Even more striking were the applications of antiseptic surgery pioneered by the English surgeon, Joseph Lister (1827-1912). He was interested in bacteriology and as early as 1878 had obtained pure cultures of bacteria. Following the impressive work of Pasteur and Tyndall, he devised methods of sterilizing the operating room with all its equipment, spraying 5 per cent carbolic acid over the hands of the doctors before an operation and on the immediate surroundings while operations were in progress. This was a much needed improvement at a time when most surgical treatments were complicated by infection. The legandary old Doctor Lowry, who preceded Lister, was reported to have performed 1000 operations and 3 of his patients survived.

Spontaneous generation is now being considered in another setting and different background. Modern naturalistic discussions concerning the origin of life have centered around the possibility of life developing once in the far distant past by the combination of inorganic materials present in a primordial "soup". An energy source such as lightning has been suggested for promoting the chemical synthesis. Simple amino acids and nucleic acids have been produced in the laboratory by bringing together materials probably present in the early stages of the earth's history at a favorable temperature and introducing electrical energy. To be sure, there is some distance between these crude organic materials and the complex proteins and nucleic acids that occur in the bodies of living organisms. Investigators in this field have estimated that life would be produced in the test tube by the end of the present century.

Pasteur showed that living things as complex as bacteria could not arise spontaneously in a short period of time under the conditions of his experiments. The

possibility is not excluded that much more simple organisms having the power of self duplication could have arisen by natural means in the long period of the distant past. It is not likely that this could occur now and the new living organisms could become established because of the greater amount of oxygen which would immediately oxidize an unprotected protoplasmic mass. If it could survive immediate oxidation it would surely be eaten or absorbed by some form of life that is now so abundant in any place suitable for life to originate spontaneously.

Germ Theory of Fermentation

The third important factor in the development of microbiology was the germ theory of fermentation. In the middle of the last century fermentation was considered to be a chemical process. The chemist Liebig described it as depending on a ferment, or an alterable substance that decomposes and in so doing excites chemical change, that is, fermentation in ground substance. The disintegration of a ferment was thus believed to cause a disturbance among the molecules bringing about the changes associated with fermentation. According to this view, the primary cause of fermentation was a chemical instability. Other chemists of the period, including Berzelius (1779-1848) and Bertholet (1827-1907), held similar views concerning alcoholic fermentation. Although Schwann had in 1837 described alcoholic fermentation as a process dependent on a yeast, none of the leading chemists of the time considered seriously the possibility of a living organism as the causative agent of fermentation.

Pasteur followed the approach of Schwann and became a pioneer in experimental studies on fermentation. He confirmed the observation of Schwann and showed that a living organism, a yeast, is required for the chemical change that transforms sugar into alcohol and carbonic acid. In 1857 he discovered that a different kind of organism was associated with the process by which sugars were broken down to lactic acid. These observations led Pasteur to a hypothesis that microorganisms of some kind are essential for each kind of fermentation. To obtain evidence concerning this hypothesis, Pasteur isolated microorganisms associated with fermentation and raised them in nutrient solutions. These were inoculated into appropriate natural media from which the natural organisms had been removed and fermentation was produced experimentally. A temperature of 30 to 50 degrees centigrade was found to be the optimum in which this process was accomplished.

Pasteur followed carefully the cycle of fermentation. He repeatedly removed the organisms from fermenting cultures, transferred them to other sterile media, and found that fermentation was always produced when the proper conditions were arranged. At the end of the experiment, Pasteur identified the materials that were produced and thus described the chemical changes involved in the transformation from sugar to lactic acid, requiring organisms to carry out the chemical processes. Organisms were observed under the microscope and their characteristics were carefully described. Lactic acid organisms were found to be similar in some ways to those associated with alcoholic fermentation, but they were also different in some characteristics. More recent studies have shown that the two kinds of organisms are not as closely related as Pasteur supposed. The lactic acid organism is a bacterium rather than a yeast. Distinctly different kinds of organisms were thus shown to be responsible for different kinds of fermentation. When brewer's yeast was added to a standard medium containing sugar, alcoholic fermentation would proceed. When lactic acid organisms were added to a similar medium, lactic acid fermentation would go on.

During the next 20 years (1857-1877), Pasteur studied a number of other fermentable materials and became an authority in the field. In 1858 he discovered that the organism associated with fermentation in ammonium tartrate was a mold. Yeasts, bacteria, and molds had now been identified with fermentation. Pasteur's memoir on alcoholic fermentation, written in 1860, remains to this day a classic on the subject.

In 1861 he investigated butyric acid fermentation and made another important discovery; that fermentation can proceed in the absence of oxygen. The rod-shaped organism associated with butyric fermentation was considered by Pasteur to be animal in character and was named vibrio. While examining a drop of fluid culture containing butyric vibrio under the microscope, Pasteur observed that the organisms in the margin of the drop where they came in contact with the air were not active, but in the center they were actively motile. He developed the hypothesis that oxygen had an inhibiting effect on the growth and activity of these organisms. To test the hypothesis, he passed a stream of oxygen through an active butyric fermenting culture and observed that all action was inhibited. Two words, aerobic and anaerobic, were used respectively to distinguish between the two kinds of organisms. Also, in 1861 Pasteur published his research on acetic acid fermentation and showed that it was accomplished by organisms of the genus Mycoderma, studied in detail in 1862. A full scale study of vinegar preparation was undertaken and the results were published in 1864 and 1868.

Pasteur was then asked by his former professor, J. B. Dumas, and personally requested by Napoleon III, to study the problem of souring wine that threatened the important French wine industry. He pursued the investigation with vigor and enthusiasm and in 1866 published a famous memoir on wine. This 264 page treatise dealt with the so-called diseases of wine which Pasteur described as being due to foreign organisms, that invaded the wine and altered its chemical and physical properties. He showed that undesirable organisms could be removed by partially sterilizing the juice from which wine was to be made at a temperature below the boiling point that was not sufficient to destroy the valuable properties of the juice. Other organisms could then be introduced from pure cultures of organisms with desirable qualities. The process, now called pasteurization, was later adapted to milk for the purpose of removing most of the natural organisms and all of the pathogens such as the tuberculosis, brucellosis, and typhoid organisms.

Germ Theory of Disease

Hieronymus Fracastorius (1485-1553) wrote a treatise in 1546 entitled "On Contagion," which was the earliest well considered exposition on the concept of contagious infection. In this treatise, he postulated seeds of disease called "seminaria" that were capable of transmitting disease from individual to individual. Fracastorius suggested several modes of transmission such as direct contact, passive transfer on clothing or other articles, and through the air by which they could be spread at a distance. As an illustration Fracastorius mentioned the transmission in the air of a substance released when onions are peeled that makes the eyes of people at few feet away smart and release water. The example was considered only as a model demonstrating how disease could be transmitted from person to person even at considerable distance. Fracastorius presented accurate descriptions of several common diseases including typhus fever, plague, rabies, and syphilis. Leeuwenhoek, in 1676, described organisms not visible to the unaided eye as being widespread in nature. These observations added considerable support to the idea of living organisms which might presumably be the causative agents for disease.

A 17th century physician, Thomas Sydenham (1624-1689), also contributed to the idea of specific causes for specific diseases. Sydenham was a famous physician who had great influence on his fellow doctors, but had no immediate successors to carry on what he taught. He insisted that disease had an infectious cause thus initiating the beginning of the end of the humoral theory of disease. Sydenham gave clear accounts of the differential characteristics of infectious diseases, such as small-pox, dysentery, plague, and scarlet fever. In order to treat the disease properly, it was necessary to understand the cause. When the cause was understood and appreciated a cure might be forthcoming. In many cases the cure would be the removal of the cause. At the time this concept was developed, few diseases were known well enough to provide a test for the hypothesis. Even now few diseases are completely known and entirely curable. Sydenham made one observation that resulted in a practical treatment for an important disease when he observed that cinchona bark, now known to contain quinine, was useful in the treatment of malaria. When he tried this remedy on other fevers he found it had no value. It was not a cure-all, but was considered to be a specific cure for a specific disease. Later it was found that quinine only arrested the disease and did not cure it.

Another practical accomplishment was made in 1796 by Edward Jenner, a brilliant London physician, who had lived and studied with John Hunter. In his practice he observed that people who had recovered from the comparatively mild disease, cowpox, did not get smallpox. This suggested the possibility of a vaccination against smallpox with the less severe cowpox. Vaccination for smallpox was accomplished before the time of Jenner, but Jenner developed it to a stage of practical usefulness. He and his contemporaries were not able to explain the

reason for the success of the vaccination and it remained for Pasteur to develop the explanation on the basis of his attenuated virus theory.

The first actual demonstration of a specific organism associated with a specific disease was made by the French pathologist, Casimir J. Davaine (1812-1882) who was led to this accomplishment through his interest in symptoms that might prove valuable for diagnostic purposes. In 1850 Davaine and Rayer noticed rod-shaped bodies in the blood of animals that had died with splenic fever or anthrax. At the time, they did not attach any significance to the observation. In 1861, after reading Pasteur's memoir on butyric acid fermentation, Davaine returned to his study and in 1863 became the first to associate a particular organism with a specific disease. The rod-shaped organism, Bacillus anthracis, was identified as the causative agent of anthrax. Robert Koch added the next step in the sequence when he succeeded in tracing the life cycle of the anthrax bacillus.

Koch

Robert Koch (1843-1910, Figure 14-1), a German physician, teacher, and bacteriologist, was closely associated with the firm establishment of the germ theory of disease. His education was

Fig. 14-1. Robert Koch, German bacteriologist

obtained at the University of Göttengen where he studied under the pathologist Jacob Henle, who in 1840 had anticipated the germ theory of diseases. Koch received the doctor of medicine degree in 1866 and during the next few years he practiced medicine, served in the Franco-Prussian War, and began research projects in the field of microbiology. In 1876 he traced the life cycle of Bacillus anthracis and developed pure cultures of the anthrax organism.

From cultures of anthrax, Koch observed the multiplication of the organisms and discovered avenues through which infection was transmitted from animal to animal. He also explained the delayed action that had puzzled earlier investigators. Cattle placed in a pasture where diseased animals had been buried months or years before contracted the disease. Koch showed that organisms buried with diseased animals could form spores and persist in the soil for long periods of time. They were brought to the surface by earthworms and thus became associated with the vegetation the animals ate. Once introduced into an animal body, the organisms became active, multiplied, and caused the symptoms of the disease. Through his careful studies of the life cycle of the organism and the effects of the organism when transmitted into new host animals, he discovered an immunizing agent in which Pasteur also became interested.

Another valuable contribution of Koch, that did much to verify the germ of disease, was the isolation, in 1882, of the tubercle bacillus, Mycobacterium tuberculosis. This represented a milestone in the history of bacteriology and epidemiology. The infectious nature of an important human disease was understood for the first time. Tuberculosis was attributed to a living organism capable of reproducing itself and thus spreading the infection from one individual to another.

In 1883 Koch discovered the cholera vibrio, Vibrio comma. Control of another important human disease, cholera, was then accomplished by improved sanitary conditions in the areas where cholera had spread in epidemics.

Koch also contributed in the development of techniques for the study of bacteriology. One was the use of solid media for bacteriological culture, developed as a means for obtaining and perpetuating pure cultures. In the early days of bacteriology, only fluid media were used. This is a common and efficient type of medium for growing most bacteria, but it is difficult to catch and study critically the individual organisms. Colony formation cannot be observed when the organisms are dispersed in an excess of fluid. Koch recognized the desirability of isolating organisms in a solid or semi-solid material in order to follow their growth and colony formation. He visualized stationary organisms, stopped like ships frozen in the ice, as ideal objects for study. If, while the organisms were localized, division could continue, colonies would appear.

The material first used as a solid medium was gelatin. It can be liquefied by heat and poured while warm into dishes. When allowed to cool it becomes solid but retains enough moisture to provide a suitable medium to support bacterial growth. This was a great advance in the technical aspect of bacteriology because colonial formations and characteristics of growing organisms in groups rather than only as individuals could now be followed. Flat glass plates were at first covered with warm gelatin and protected from air contamination with bell jars. The gelatin ran off the edges and created an untidy situation in the laboratory and Koch's assistant, Richard J. Petri (1852-1921), invented a dish with the edges turned up, called a Petri dish (Figure 14-2). A lid, loose enough to allow air to enter, was later added to protect the plate from contamination.

Another contribution of Koch was the hanging drop or depression slide method (Figure 14-2) of bacterial culture. This was accomplished by preparing a slide with a hole or depression in the center. A drop of culture containing organisms was then placed on a cover glass that was placed over the depression in such a way that the drop could hang freely into the open space. Sufficient air was provided in the surrounding space, and at the same time, the drop was protected from contamination. The slide could be placed conveniently in the incubator and held at the appropriate temperature for the development of the organisms. When it was necessary to inspect the culture, the glass depression slide could be placed on the microscope without disturbing the activities of the living organisms.

Since its original development for bacteria, the hanging drop technique has been adapted and widely used for blood studies. Another valuable application has been the adaptation of the depression slide technique for tissue culture. By this means tissue cells taken from the body of an animal are kept alive and may be studied minutely. Growth characteristics of such cells have been followed by frequent observation under the microscope and valuable contributions have been made in the study of normal as well as abnormal growth. When cells that are ordinarily rigid, such as connective tissue and bone cells, are raised in tissue culture they grow in spongy masses without restriction.

Koch also made contributions in staining techniques. He introduced methyl violet, one of his first bacteriological stains, that greatly facilitated the identification and study of microorganisms.

Another contribution, that has theoretical as well as technical implications, was the method devised by Koch to associate specific organisms with specific diseases. People were observing organisms in the vicinity of disease symptoms

PETRI DISH AND COVER

DEPRESSION SLIDE

Fig. 14-2. Petri dish for raising bacteria on a solid medium and a depression slide for culturing bacteria in a drop of fluid culture medium.

and considering, without critical evaluations, the organisms to be the cause of the disease. It was, therefore, necessary for a system to be established through which organisms could be properly identified with diseases. Perhaps it was even more important to protect those not causing the disease from being wrongly incriminated through circumstantial evidence. Koch formulated a set of postulates that required critical analysis of the organism, in association with the symptoms: (1) the organism must be associated with the disease, (2) the investigator must isolate the organism from the diseased animal and establish it in a pure culture, (3) the organisms from the pure culture must be injected into animals free from the disease which must in due time show the symptoms of the disease, and (4) the organism must be isolated from the second host. In many cases it is impossible to carry out all of the steps required by these postulates. Some organisms cannot be cultured under usual laboratory conditions. Nevertheless, the standard established by Koch was well considered and did much to eliminate the loosely drawn conclusions all too prevalent at that time.

Not the least of Koch's accomplishments was the wholesome influence that he radiated as a pioneer in the field of bacteriology. His own contributions were basic and significant but the contributions of his many students and assistants represented a vital body of knowledge in the development of the new science. One of the most original of Koch's assistants, Paul Ehrlich, carried out research similar to that of Koch on staining methods and also pioneered in the field of chemotherapy, that is, the aspect of medicine devoted to the treatment of internal diseases by chemical reagents.

Ehrlich

Paul Ehrlich (1854-1915) was born in Strehlen, upper Silesia, the son of a Jewish innkeeper. His earlier training was in chemistry but he had basic preparation in biology. He attended medical school to learn about biological processes in living systems and to search for methods through which diseases might be cured. Paul's cousin, Carl Weigert, who was 9 years older than Paul, had pioneered the field of differential staining in tissues and bacterial cultures.

The observation of Weigert, in 1878, that certain kinds of bacteria were susceptible to different stains, fascinated Ehrlich. This was followed by discoveries that certain tissues in the body were susceptible to certain chemical preparations. Ehrlich learned the art of staining from Weigert and soon was doing independent research. Methylene blue, was found, when injected into the living animal, to be taken up by the fine structures of the brain, thus providing a differential stain for specific tissues. This was developed as a tool enabling the scientist to pick out tissues that had affinities to certain stains.

A more fundamental application was also considered by Ehrlich: if different tissues have varying affinities for different stains, they may also have different affinities for drugs. It may thus be possible to introduce materials into the body that will affect invading organisms and cells differentially, for example, materials might be found to have an immediate toxic effect upon invading microorganisms without seriously affecting the tissues of the host. The idea of "magic bullets" developed from this line of reasoning. Certain problems were immediately suggested, such as: why does one tissue stain blue and another red when the same stain is employed? Why does the cell nucleus accept one stain and the cytoplasm another? Different bacteria exposed to the same dye are not all affected in the same way, some remain unchanged while others are deeply stained. More immediate and practical questions could be asked on the basis of facts then known about certain important diseases. Diphtheria toxin, for example, could be injected into a pigeon without any harm or injury to the bird. When the same quantity of toxin was placed in a child's body, great disturbance and possible death would follow. There must be a fundamental difference, therefore, between the cells of the pigeon and those of the child, with respect to their affinity to diphtheria toxin.

Ehrlich did more than postulate relations, he worked out ingenious methods and tools to test his hypotheses. Diagnostic measures were first developed to identify symptoms of diseases to be studied. Laboratory techniques were then invented to introduce chemicals into the cells of experimental animals. Throughout all of this work, Ehrlich was motivated by the idea that chemical affinities represented the keys to life's secrets. The first logical questions in his study of diphtheria was, "how does the toxin injure the cell?"

Ehrlich was largely responsible for developing the antitoxin to neutralize the effect of diphtheria toxin but he was not content with the practical application of an antitoxin; he wanted to know how the antitoxin prevents the injury that the toxin produces. Furthermore, he wanted to know how the animal body can produce an excess of antitoxins and thereby become immune. Since toxins and antitoxins must both be chemicals, he attempted to produce toxins and antitoxins in the laboratory. This was not accomplished but progress in that direction has been made since the time of Ehrlich.

Following his brilliant work on diphtheria, that was completed in 1904, Ehrlich devoted his attention to cancer chemotherapy. He searched for a chemical agent to offset abnormal growth and malignant change in different parts of the animal body. This was not realized but the pattern of Ehrlich's experiments has been continued, with some progress.

Ehrlich's crowning achievement was the discovery of salvarsan, an arsenical used for the treatment of syphilis. Shortly after the discovery of the causative agent of syphilis, Treponema pallidum, by Fritz Schaudinn in 1905, Ehrlich began experimenting with various arsenicals with the object of finding a drug that would be toxic to the spirochaete, but not seriously toxic to the individual being treated. It was in the course of this investigation that the famous "606" remedy was discovered. Ehrlich and his associates tried 605 compounds without appreciable success but number 606 gave positive results. It was found later that this chemical did not completely rid the individual of the disease producing organism, but it did largely control the disease symptoms. Salvarsan was the first great therapeutic agent to be discovered in modern times. Sydenham had, many years before, discovered a therapeutic agent, quinine, for the control of the malarial organism in the human body, but Ehrlich was first to make a systematic approach to the problem of chemotherapy. Arsenicals remained the best agents for treating syphilis until the discovery of the sulpha drugs and penicillin in the 1930's.

Pasteur's Contribution to the Germ Theory of Disease

In 1865 Pasteur's study on fermentation was interrupted by another request from Professor Dumas. A silkworm disease called pebrine was threatening the important silk industry in France and Pasteur was asked to devote his attention to this disease with the hope that it might become understood and controlled. Six years were devoted to this investigation. Pasteur began by observing diseased worms and found that a sporozoan was present in the intestinal canal of the silk-worms that had the disease. The parasite was found to spread throughout the body of the worm, eventually filling the gland in which the silk is normally spun and making the worms unable to produce silk. Pasteur discovered the mode of transmission from worm to worm and was able to find a link in the reproductive cycle that could be broken to eradicate the parasite. The organism was spread from parent worms to their offspring in the egg.

Silkworm eggs could be examined under the microscope for the detection of parasites. At first, the silkworm growers considered this method tedious and impractical, but adequate tests proved it to be both practical and convenient. By examining the eggs and destroying those in which the parasite was present, cultures free from the disease could be maintained. In this way, the disease was eradicated and the French silk producers were able to re-establish the industry. In the course of his work, Pasteur discovered that two diseases were involved instead of one. Pebrine was spread by a protozoan but the other disease, flacherie, that had previously been indistinguishable from pebrine, was caused by a bacterium.

In 1871 Pasteur returned again to his investigation of fermentation, this time devoting his attention to the fermentation of beer. The results were published in 1876 in a detailed, nearly 400 page, paper, that not only included the results of investigations on beer, but also summarized Pasteur's general knowledge of the fermentation process based on living organisms. The explanation of fermentation was again challenged, this time by Liebig, who had developed a modified version of an older theory in which enzymes were postulated to be responsible for fermentation. No enzymes could be demonstrated, however, and Pasteur's view of living organisms responsible for the process eventually won support.

Following the completion of the lengthy paper on beer production, Pasteur became interested in human infectious disease. He had already studied anthrax, which affected human beings as well as animals, and was interested in making

further observations and practical applications of the germ theory as it applied to man. In 1880 he examined cases of osteomyelitis and puerperal fever. These diseases were attributed to microorganisms and Pasteur believed that pus, transferred from one person to another on doctor's hands or instruments, would result in the spread of the disease. Following preliminary observations, Pasteur became interested in the so-called "virus diseases," such as smallpox, and was particularly impressed with the immunity established following an attack of such diseases. He had great respect for Edward Jenner's work on vaccination.

As a disease on which to study immunity experimentally, he chose a common disease in France known as fowl cholera. This disease had been identified as a bacterial infection, and the causative organisms had been cultured. Pasteur began by testing the organisms in pure culture on appropriate media and he discovered that organisms transferred from culture to culture would tend to lose their virulence, that is, their ability to infect chickens when inoculated. In 1880 Pasteur described weakened organisms produced in this way as attenuated viruses. The virulence of a culture was found to depend on the time that elapsed between successive transfers. When the cultures were allowed to remain for several months without transfer, the disease producing ability of the organisms became weak.

Quite by chance, he inoculated a group of chickens with a culture of virulent organisms after they had already been inoculated with attenuated organisms. The chickens were found to be immune to the virulent culture, presumably having been immunized from the mild attack of the disease brought on by the weakened virus. The principle of acquired immunity was interpreted from these results. Attenuated viruses when inoculated into healthy chickens would thus enable the chickens to withstand subsequent introductions of virulent strains of the fowl cholera organism. The attenuated virus was a protective agent stimulating the body to build up an immunity against the specific bacterium. Pasteur applied the principle of the attenuated virus almost immediately to anthrax and later to swine erysipelas and rabies.

The fowl cholera vaccine was soon produced on a large scale and used widely for injection into flocks of chickens. It protected them in most cases, but unfor-

136

tunate results were sometimes observed. Once in a while the inoculation itself adversely affected the chickens, and sometimes it killed them. Although criticism came from some sources, the principle of immunity through the inoculation of an attenuated virus soon became well established. In 1888 Pasteur recommended a virulent culture of pathogenic organisms for the destruction of rabbits in Australia and New Zealand. Pilot experiments were attempted, but the results were not as promising as Pasteur had anticipated.

From the studies of fowl cholera Pasteur returned to more critical investigations on anthrax. When the anthrax bacillus was cultured in broth at 42 to 43 degrees C for 8 days it lost its virulence and was not capable of producing the symptoms of the disease when injected into experimental animals, such as guinea pigs and rabbits. Sheep were also found to develop no symptoms after inoculation with the attenuated virus. Pasteur recommended the inoculation of sheep with the newly found vaccine as a protective measure against anthrax. The Agricultural Society of Melun became interested in the prospects and offered 60 animals to Pasteur for a demonstration. Pasteur accepted the challenge and the test was made in a farmyard a mile from Melun. Thanks to a correspondent of the Paris Times, M. de Blowitz, the publicity was spread throughout the world.

The experiment consisted in the inoculation on May 5, 1881, of 24 sheep, 1 goat, and 6 cows with 5 drops each of a living but attentuated strain of anthrax bacillus. At the same time 24 sheep, 1 goat and 4 cows were assembled but were not inoculated. On May 17, all of the animals that had been previously treated were reinoculated with a less attenuated culture. The crucial test was applied on May 31 by inoculating all the 31 immunized animals with a highly virulent anthrax culture. This same culture was also inoculated into the 29 unprotected animals. On June 2, when Pasteur and his assistants arrived to make their observations, all of the vaccinated sheep were well. Twenty-one unprotected sheep and the goat were dead of anthrax. Two others of the unprotected sheep died at the end of the same day. The 6 vaccinated cows were well and showed no symptoms whereas the 4 unprotected cows had swellings at the site of inoculation. On June 3, one of the vaccinated sheep died. It was pregnant and the autopsy indicated that it had died following the

death of the foetus. This demonstration won wide publicity and Pasteur's attenuated virus was soon well known and widely used throughout the world.

At the International Medical Congress, held in London a few weeks after the demonstration, Pasteur delivered an address on, "Vaccination in Relation to Chicken Cholera and Anthrax." In this address he explained the use of vaccination as a prophylactic measure and described for the first time the reason for the success of smallpox vaccination many years before.

Anthrax vaccine was used widely and soon many animals were inoculated. Results were not always successful, but in general, they were highly favorable. In 1882 Pasteur reported that 85,000 animals had been inoculated. In a report covering 79,392 sheep, the mortality from anthrax had fallen from 91.01% among the unprotected to 0.65% among the vaccinated. By 1894 three and one-half million sheep were reported to have been inoculated for anthrax. The disease has since become relatively unimportant through the efficient prophylactic measure made possible with the vaccine.

Pasteur's next project was an investigation of swine erysipelas in which he was associated with L. Thuillier. An organism was found in the blood of diseased animals, and the investigators succeeded in obtaining a pure culture. They next attempted to attenuate the virus, but were not entirely successful. Different effects of the immunization were observed on different animals and varying susceptibilities were encountered in different races of pigs. This confused the study, and made it difficult to tell the extent of immunity that was being induced by the vaccination. In the course of the experiments, it was found that the virus could be attenuated more uniformly by passage through the body of a rabbit. Large scale production began, and between 1886 and 1892, over 100,000 pigs were inoculated in France alone and many in other countries.

The last of Pasteur's great achievements was concerned with the disease rabies. This disease was not common in either animals or human beings, but it was spectacular when it occurred because the symptoms aroused the imagination of people and caused excitement and publicity whenever a case was reported. Pasteur and his collaborators,

Chamberland, Roux, and Thuillier, began a series of investigations involving the animal nervous system. After 3 years of work, it was found that the rabies virus could be attenuated for the dog, rabbit, and guinea pig by passage through a series of monkeys. Protective inoculations for the dog were then devised by the use of virus attenuated in a monkey. An incubation period was established for the virus and Pasteur reported in 1885 that dogs could be protected even after having received the virus from the bite of a mad dog. The method finally developed consisted of drying the spinal cords of rabbits that had died from the disease after having been injected with the virulent organisms. In about 2 weeks of drying, the materials taken from the cord became highly attenuated. By inoculating the attenuated virus from the dried cord, it was possible to immunize a healthy dog against the effects of the virus. The results on dogs suggested that the method might have practical application for human beings.

A case was brought to Pasteur before he was ready to test the material on human beings. On the 6th day of July 1885, a 9 year old boy, Joseph Meister, was brought from Alsace suffering from bites on the hand and legs from a mad dog. The next day, 60 hours after the bites had been inflicted, the boy was given his first injection of the attenuated rabbit material which was 14 days old. In 12 inoculations which followed, the virus was made stronger and stronger and the boy was saved from the symptoms of the disease. By October of 1886, some 2,490 persons had been inoculated. A few deaths occurred following inoculation, but for a disease that had previously been nearly 100% fatal, these few failures were not especially disturbing. It was estimated in 1905 that over 100,000 persons in the world had received treatment. The records of the Pasteur Institute showed that up to 1935, 51,057 persons had been treated in that Institute in Paris. About 150 deaths had occurred among the inoculated people, a mortality of 0.29%.

The numbers of persons who came to Pasteur's laboratory for treatment were soon much larger than could be treated with the limited facilities available, and it was suggested by a commission of the Academy of Sciences that a scientific institute be erected for providing inoculations and further scientific research. Public subscriptions were solicited and a total of 2,586,680 francs were contributed. A plot of land was purchased in Paris, and the Pasteur Institute was erected in 1888.

The inauguration on November 14, 1888, was attended by a large group of distinguished people from France and elsewhere in the world.

Pasteur died 7 years later on September 28, 1895. A memorial was erected to him in the main entrance of the Pasteur Institute in Paris. On the walls and ceiling of the sanctuary are represented in picture form the major accomplishments of Pasteur.

Insect Vectors of Disease

Further support for the germ theory of disease came from another line of investigation. Following the example of Koch, in his study on anthrax life history, studies were designed to follow the cycle of pathogenic organisms and their relations with their animal hosts. Intermediate hosts were found in some cases to be the carriers of the organism from one animal to another. In 1880 Alphonse Laveran (1845-1922) observed an organism in the blood of human beings suffering from malaria. This was a triumph in the study of one of the most important diseases of mankind. A protozoan, Plasmodium, was identified as the causative organism for malaria. Ronald Ross, in 1898, showed that the bird malaria organism, Plasmodium cathemerium, was carried by a mosquito of the genus Culex. In the same year, Grassi and Bignami discovered that the human malarial organism is transmitted by a mosquito of the genus Anopheles.

During the same period, insect transmission of other diseases was being considered. In 1893 David Bruce (1855-1931) found that African sleeping sickness was transmitted by a tsetse-fly. Walter Reed, in 1900, showed that the yellow fever virus was transmitted by a mosquito Aedes aegypti. Theobald Smith (1859-1934) and his assistant, Kilborne, followed the cycle of Texas cattle fever. Smith was the first American to distinguish himself in the field of microbiology.

In 1889 Smith and Kilborne performed a series of controlled experiments and established the fact that ticks, Boophilus annulatus, were carriers of cattle fever but the nature of the disease and its causative agent were unknown. When Smith examined the blood of infected cattle, he found little bodies within the red corpuscles that he identified in 1891 as protozoa, Babesia. He was able

138

to demonstrate that the organisms were passed from infected animals to healthy animals by the bite of the tick. His most striking discovery was that the protozoa could be introduced into cattle by the bites of young ticks that had received the infection from their mother ticks through the eggs. The report of the investigation of Texas cattle fever, in 1893, was one of the classics in the literature of bacteriology. For the first time in history, a complete cycle of transmission of an infectious disease by an insect carrier, was established.

Koch had already established the tubercle bacillis as the causative agent for tuberculosis in man. The bovine type was considered to be the same as the human type and the same organisms was believed to cause tuberculosis in man and cattle. In 1898, Smith showed that the bovine and human forms were distinct. This suggested a new avenue for the control of bovine tuberculosis, which could be transmitted to man from tuberculous cattle through raw milk. Pasturization of milk was the method devised for control of the bovine infection in man.

REFERENCES

Bullock, W. *The History of Bacteriology*. London: Oxford Univ. Press, 1938.

Burrows, W. *Textbook of Microbiology*. 17th Ed. Philadelphia: W. B. Saunders Co., 1959.

Cohen, B. A.*The Leeuwenhoek Letter*. Baltimore: Soc. Amer. Bact., 1937.

Conant, J. B. ed. *Pasteur's Study on Fermentation*. Cambridge: Harvard Univ. Press, 1952. (Harvard Case Histories in Experimental Science, Case 6. Translation of Portions of Pasteur's memoir on lactic acid fermentation and exerpts from Tyndall's lecture on the same subject arranged and supplemented by Dr. Conant.)

De Kruif, P. H. *Microbe Hunters*. New York: Harcourt, Brace and Co., 1950.

De Kruif, P. H. *Men Against Death*. New York: Harcourt, Brace and Co., 1932.

Dobell, C. *Antony Van Leeuwenhoek and his "Little Animals"*. New York: Harcourt, Brace and Co., 1932.

Dubos, R. J. *Louis Pasteur, Free-lance of Science*. Boston: Little, Brown Co., 1950.

Ford, W. W. *Bacteriology*. New York: Harper and Bros. , 1939.

Frobisher, M. , Jr. *Fundamentals of Bacteriology*. Philadelphia: W. B. Saunders Co., 1944. Chapter 1 on history.

Gage, S. H. Theobald Smith, Investigator and Man. *Science* 84:117-122, 1936.

Gladston, I. Ehrlich, Biologist of Deep and Inspiring Vision. *Sci. Monthly* 79:395-399, 1954.

Green, J. R. *A History of Botany*. Oxford; The Clarenden Press, 1909.

Guthrie, D. *From Witchcraft to Antisepsis*. Lawrence, Kansas: Univ. Kansas Press, 1953.

Metchnikoff, E.   *The Founders of Modern Medicine*.   New York: Walden Publ., 1939.

Paget, S.   *Pasteur and After Pasteur*.   London: A and C Black, 1914.

Reddish, G. F. ed.   *Antiseptics, Disinfectants, Fungicides and Sterilization*.
   Philadelphia: Lea and Febiger, 1954.

Sexton, A. N.   Theobald Smith, First Chairman of the Laboratory Section, 1900.
   Amer. Jour. of Public Health   Part II 41:125-131, 1951.

Strode, G. K. ed.   *Yellow Fever*.   New York: McGraw Hill Book Co., 1951.

Thompson, C. J. S.   *Lord Lister*.   London: John Bale, Sons and Danielsson, Ltd.,
   1934.

Vallery-Radot, R.   *The Life of Pasteur*. trans. R. L. Devonshire.   New York:
   Doubleday, Doran, 1923.

Vallery-Radot, R.   *Louis Pasteur, A Great Life in Brief*.   New York:
   A. A. Knopf, 1958.

Entomology, the study of insects, is a branch of zoology that has become important enough to justify independent status. Insects were among the first animals to be studied carefully, and some have attained great practical importance in history. The silkworm, for example, and its product, silk, have been responsible for many political and economic issues of great significance, especially in the history of the Orient (Chapter 1). Insects have also been important in a negative way through their destructive powers and their disease carrying capacities. Malaria, the disease which was largely responsible for the fall of ancient Greece and Rome and has been prevalent in many parts of the world since, is insect borne.

Chapter 15

ENTOMOLOGY

For convenience in discussion, the history of entomology will be divided into four eras: (1) the ancients, (2) microscopists, (3) systematists, and (4) the modern era. A few prominent contributors in each era will be considered to represent the era.

Ancients

Aristotle, who has many "children" represented among the biological sciences is the "father of entomology". He was first to use the term "entomology", (from Greek meaning cut into segments) and he was first to develop a system of descriptions and classification for insects. Among the 520 species of animals he described, some 60 species were arthropods, that is the phylum which includes insects, crusta-

ceans, and spiders. Aristotle believed that small insects such as fleas and lice arose spontaneously, but he observed sexual reproduction in beetles and other more conspicuous forms. In his morphological studies, he observed that some insects had straight and some coiled intestines; their wings, legs, and mouth parts also showed distinguishing differences. Metamorphosis was observed in the development of insects from stage to succeeding stage or instar to instar. Aristotle observed that only the male cicada could make sounds. He made some mistakes as might be expected, for example, he confused the drone bee with other members of the hive. Nevertheless, Aristotle's work was used, mistakes and all, and considered authoritative for some 2000 years after it was completed.

The work of Pliny, Roman authority on biology during the first century A. D., compared in popularity with that of Aristotle. Although he was less precise and less original, his writings had great influence and were widely used until the Renaissance. Pliny wrote an elaborate compendium of natural history that was made up of stories from many sources, some real and some mythical. For some 1400 years after the time of Pliny, there was little biological awakening and no significant developments occurred in entomology.

Microscopists

To represent the era of the microscopists, Aldrovandus, Redi, Leeuwenhoek, Swammerdam, Malpighi and Re'-amur will be considered. Since these men have appeared in other connections, only their specific contributions to entomology will be cited here to place them in sequence. Aldrovandus, Italian naturalist at Bologna, published the first book on entomology. It was largely a recapitulation of the works of Aristotle, but it had great influence and is still preserved in its original form. Aldrovandus arranged insects according to the medium they inhabit, thus the aquatic, terrestrial, and air (flying) insects were the main categories.

Redi made one series of simple entomological experiments (Chapter 14), reported in 1668, that dispelled the theory of spontaneous generation as it applied to blow flies. Leeuwenhoek (Chapter 7) put entomology on the map by inventing and using lenses to observe many insects and parts of insects that had not been carefully observed before. Of special significance was his study on the life history of the flea. His work on parthenogenesis in aphids was also significant.

Swammerdam was particularly interested in insects as a group and classified them according to type of metamorphosis. His work laid the foundation for modern classification and provided classical anatomical studies on the mayfly nymph, and the honey bee. Through his work in tracing the developmental steps in insects from instar to instar, the theory of preformation was supported in contrast to the theory of epigenesis developed by Harvey and Wolff. Malpighi's most important contribution to entomology was his anatomical study of the silkworm. René de Réaumur (1683-1757), French physicist and naturalist, studied entomology and wrote a six-volume work on insects.

Systematists

Six naturalists will represent the era of the systematists: Ray, Linnaeus, DeGeer, Fabricius, Latrielle, and Say. Ray and Linnaeus have been discussed in connection with classification (Chapter 8) and are mentioned here only to identify them with their work in entomology. DeGeer was a minor contributor, but deserves a place among the entomologists of the period. The last 3 have made major contributions and will be treated in some detail.

Ray was primarily a botanist but toward the end of his life he undertook the study of insects which Willughby had begun. In classifying insects, Ray combined the systems of Aristotle (descriptive) and Swammerdam (based on metamorphosis). Linnaeus brought together the good points used in classification by his predecessors and developed the binomial system to practical usefulness. His first and best work was on plants, but he also described some 4,000 species of animals, including about 300 species of beetles. Linnaeus did not recognize the difference between the crustaceans and insects. Aristotle did better on this point. He began with 4 orders of insects and developed 7 classical orders in the 12th edition of Systema Naturae.

Carl DeGeer (1720-1778), a Swedish systematist, had broad interests in the biology of insects. In addition to taxonomy, he studied the anatomy and life history of several species. He was also interested in control measures and established the beginnings of economic entomology.

John Christian Fabricius (1745-1808) (not Hieronymo Fabricius, 1537-1619, teacher of Harvey) did his undergraduate work at the University of Copenhagen. Later, he became a student of Linnaeus for 2 years at Uppsala. Although he was well trained, he was not successful immediately in finding employment in entomology. Much of his time was devoted to studies of insects, in which he was primarily interested; but he earned his living for several years teaching political science at the University of Copenhagen. Eventually, he was employed as an entomologist at Kiel.

Fabricius was a close personal friend of Linnaeus and used some of Linnaeus' methods effectively, but in his insect classification, he ignored the characteristics used in the Linnean system. He classified insects according to mouth parts rather than wings. On the whole, this system was highly artificial and of little lasting value; only one of the original 13 Fabrician orders (Odonata) has persisted. In spite of this artificiality, Fabricius built up a great reputation through his systematic work and many specimens were sent to him for identification. Therefore, a large number of genera and species from all parts of the world were described by Fabricius and bear his name.

J. B. A. Latrielle, a Frenchman and a contemporary of Lamarck, was educated as a priest but in the French Revolution he was on the losing side and was condemned to death. His fellow entomologists rescued him from the Bastile and kept him hidden until it was safe for him to be about. Latrielle redefined the insect orders established by Linnaeus and introduced the family groupings. Using the Linnean system as a framework, he built up a more natural scheme than those of Linnaeus or Fabricius based on all characters of insects instead of only the wings or mouth parts. He thus laid the foundation for the modern system and became the "father of systematic entomology".

Thomas Say (1787-1834), "father of American entomology", was born in Philadelphia, educated in a Quaker school, and later learned pharmacy under the direction of his physician father, Benjamin

Say. As he grew older, he lost interest in his father's business and spent his spare time collecting and studying insects. His love for biology was stimulated in 1812 when, at the age of 24, he became a charter member of the Academy of Natural Sciences at Philadelphia. Here he was associated with an enthusiastic group of naturalists.

In 1818 he accompanied W. M. Mac-Lure, T. R. Peale, and George Ord on an insect collecting trip to the islands off the coast of Georgia and Florida. Hostile Indians forced the party to return without accomplishing its purpose. During the years 1819-20, Say served as naturalist on Long's expedition into the far west and visited the Rocky Mountain region for the first time. In 1825, he was induced by MacLure and Robert Owen to join in a co-operative enterprise at New Harmony, Indiana, that was designed as a communistic paradise, or eutopia. The members of the group quarreled and the enterprise failed. Say was resident agent for the property and was left with the bills and the remains of the project. He stayed at New Harmony until he died, the victim of a fever, at the age of 47. Although the communistic experiment was a dismal failure it was a good thing for entomology because it provided an opportunity for Say to devote considerable time to research and writing. He was an able systematist and his early death was a great loss to entomology.

Say was a naturalist with broad interests who collected and studied birds and other groups of animals as well as insects. His specialty was the order, Coleoptera, and he described many species in this order. At the time of his death he was one of the leading entomologists in the world. He published a three-volume classic, American Entomology, and shorter articles in a number of journals. His complete work was published after his death under the heading The Complete Writing of Thomas Say on Entomology of North America.

Although Charles Darwin (Chapters 10 and 11) is not usually listed among the entomologists, he made significant studies on insects, and his Origin of Species had a great impact on the classification of insects as well as on the classification of other groups of animals and plants. Before Darwin most taxonomists were trying to fit animals and plants into an artificial preconceived plan. Their task was essentially one of "pigeonholing". Following the work of Darwin the objective of the taxonomist has been to place each animal and plant properly in the natural system based on actual relations. The position of the taxonomist has thus been elevated from a sorter of type specimens and label-writer to that of a profound biologist constantly studying natural relations.

Modern Entomology in the United States

Most of the fields of biology considered thus far have had their major development in Europe. This is also true of the older background studies of insects, but entomology is one of the younger biological areas to gain stature and it's modern phase has developed largely in the United States. The building of a professional body of entomologists and the recognition of that field through government appointments have influenced greatly the trends in the modern science. No less important was the development in the teaching of entomology, that occurred in the universities of the United States. Entomology was the first of the more practical or applied fields of biology to find a place among the traditional and classical areas in which university courses are offered. The study of insects was at first a part of natural history, later it was a part of zoology, and in some universities it has now become a separate field.

The incentive for practical and professional entomology came with an early interest in the control of certain destructive insects such as the Hessian fly, wheat midge, and plum curculio. A major factor in stimulating not only interest but action in the United States, was the spread of the Colorado potato beetle from its native habitat in the plateau region, where it fed on weeds, into the central and eastern states, where it did great damage to potatoes. The Rocky Mountain locust invaded the prairie states in the 1870's doing enormous damage and bringing renewed concern about potential damage from other destructive pests.

Modern professional entomology was established in 1854 when Asa Fitch (1809-1878) was appointed entomologist for the state of New York. In the same year Townend Glover became the first entomologist for the United States. He was first employed by the Commissioner of Patents. When the Department of Agriculture was established in 1863, he became the first official entomologist under the Commissioner of Agriculture.

Among other responsibilities, he was curator of the collections at Washington. Outside Washington, his activities took him mostly to the south where he worked on citrus and cotton pests.

The most illustrious of American entomologists of the last century was C. V. Riley (1843-1895). He was born in London, England, the son of a clergyman, and as a child he was sent to a boarding school in Dieppe, France. Later, he studied at Bonn, Germany. From childhood, he was fond of natural history and skillful in drawing. His teachers encouraged him to study art at Paris, but this seemed financially impossible and he returned to his home at the age of 17. Later, he sailed for the United States and eventually reached Illinois where he found employment on a farm. His attention was drawn to the damage being done to crops by insects, and he wrote articles for farm journals through which he soon won considerable recognition. At the age of 21 he went to Chicago and became a reporter on entomological subjects and an artist for a leading agricultural journal.

Riley's articles attracted the attention of a prominent entomologist, B. D. Walsh, and Walsh and Riley soon became associated and began the publication of the American Entomologist. Through Walsh's influence, Riley was appointed in 1868 to the newly created post of Entomologist in the state of Missouri. Riley's 9 annual reports (1868-1877) formed a foundation of entomological literature in the United States. Carefully worked out life histories illustrated with his own drawings made up a large proportion of these reports. The grasshopper invasions during the years 1873-1877 gave Riley a significant problem to attack and considerable attention was given to this problem in the reports. In 1877, Riley succeeded in persuading Congress to pass the bill creating the U. S. Entomological Commission and Riley was appointed chief, with A. S. Packard and Cyrus Thomas as members. The commission published its findings on the grasshopper studies and later the members made additional reports on cotton insects and forest insects.

In the spring of 1878, when the first report of the commission was in press, Glover retired from his position as Entomologist in the U. S. Department of Agriculture and Riley was appointed to fill the position. Riley's main contribution here was in biological control, particularly on cotton pests. At the end of the first year in office, Riley had a disagreement with the Commissioner of Agriculture and resigned. J. H. Comstock was invited to Washington from Cornell University to fill the vacancy. Two years later the political difficulty was resolved and Riley was reinstated as Federal Entomologist in the service that soon became the Division of Entomology in the Department of Agriculture. Under the able leadership of Riley, the division increased in size and importance. The annual reports were practical and yet had high scientific value. Riley had a tremendous list of publications – some 1657 individual authorships, 479 coauthorships with Walsh, and 364 coauthorships with L. O. Howard (1857-1950) his associate and successor as Chief of the Bureau of Entomology. Some of the latter coauthored articles appeared after Riley's death. Howard continued in the tradition of Riley as an entomologist and as an administrator of the Bureau. He wrote extensively and profoundly influenced the development of economic and medical entomology in America. His main work was The Insect Menace (1931).

When insect problems became more involved, special agents were appointed by the Federal Bureau of Entomology in various sections of the country to study and control insect pests. In 1902, twelve divisions were established to cover different groups of pests and distinctive phases of insect work. Refinements in the organization have been continuous since that time to meet changes in agriculture and administrative adjustments. In 1912, a Federal Horticultural Board was established for the purpose of preventing the introduction of fruit tree pests into the United States. A reorganization occurred in 1933 from which the Bureau of Entomology and Plant Quarantine emerged with L. A. Strong as chief.

The following practical applications have been made in entomology since the beginning of the modern era: (1) plant quarantine inspection stations have been set up with trained personnel to scrutinize all plants and other materials entering the United States for injurious insects. Before the inspection stations were established some serious insects such as the Hessian fly had already been introduced. Inspection stations are now established in the larger U. S. postoffices and in other places where materials are received from foreign countries. Arizona and California have state highway inspection stations where automobiles and baggage are inspected for injurious insects, particularly the pink bollworm, that is known in other parts of the United States, but not yet in Arizona and California.

(2) Biological controls. Living organisms have been introduced to control insect pests of some crops, for example, certain insects have been imported from Europe to destroy the European corn borer that is now widespread in the United States. These insects are released in infested corn fields where they seek out the corn borers and lay eggs in or on them. When the eggs hatch, the immature parasites feed on the borers and eventually destroy them.

(3) Disease resistance in bees. Because of the importance of bees for pollination in agriculture, they are being hybridized to improve strains for resistance to the disease, American foulbrood. This breeding program is carried on through artificial insemination, made possible by newly developed instruments through which the queen bee can be injected with selected sperm.

(4) Tests for effectiveness of DDT and other insecticides against fabric pests. Large scale tests have been made by United States Department of Agriculture entomologists, in cooperation with representatives of the armed services, to test the effectiveness of insecticides in preventing damage by the black carpet beetle and the cloths moth. It has been demonstrated that DDT, when properly used, is effective in preventing damage by these insects.

(5) Erradication of cattle ticks. Large scale facilities have now been developed to dip cattle in vats containing arsenicals and thus to remove ticks that live on the fur of cattle. This preventative measure has saved many millions of dollars otherwise lost through wasted food, lower production, and damaged hides.

(6) The development of more efficient insect sprays. Aerosols have been developed recently to control mosquitoes, flies, and other insects. This type of material can be sprayed as a fog in places where insect damage is serious and the insects are thus controlled.

(7) Large scale spraying devices have been developed through which DDT and other sprays can be spread over large areas under pressure and thus control forest insects that otherwise would do serious damage to forests.

The Teaching of Entomology in the United States

Parallel with the development of practical and professional entomology, university teaching programs were developed. Before formal course work became a part of the university curriculum, private courses and individual instruction were available on several university campuses. W. D. Peck and T. W. Harris gave private instruction at Harvard University intermittently when sufficient numbers of students were interested. B. F. Mudge taught a practical course at Kansas Agricultural College in 1867. Courses were offered at Michigan in 1867, Illinois in 1868, California in 1868, and Maine in 1871. The Morrill Acts of 1862 and 1890 establishing Land-Grant institutions and the Hatch Act in 1888, providing for experiment stations in the states, stimulated entomology as a practical science.

The first university Department of Entomology was established in Cornell University largely through the work of John Henry Comstock (1849-1931, Figure 15-1). He was born on a small farm at Janesville, Wisconsin, in the year of the California gold rush. As farming prospects were poor, his father left for the

Fig. 15-1. John Henry Comstock, American entomologist

west to find gold. The emigrant train in which he traveled suffered an epidemic of cholera and Ebenzer Comstock, father of young John Henry, was one of the many who died. The mother, Susan Comstock, with her son returned to New York to live among her relatives, but her own illness and hospitalization soon followed, leaving her son to be cared for by relatives. At the age of 11, John Henry began making his own way in the world at odd jobs. He was employed by Captain and Mrs. Lewis Turner, at first as an errand boy in their home and later on a schooner that sailed the Great Lakes with grain and lumber cargoes. The bargain was that John was to be employed full time, for which he would receive as pay board and clothing and an opportunity for 3 months' schooling each year. Several years were spent in this way, attending school during short winter sessions and performing duties during the rest of the year.

Growing up in the home of a captain influenced him to look toward sailing as his future occupation and as he grew older, opportunities came for more responsibilities aboard freighters on the Great Lakes. He was always equipped with books and studied diligently at odd hours and after his work was completed. Through reading, he found opportunity to follow his interest in natural history. He began with botany books, acquainting himself with the flowering plants in the Great Lakes region. When his ship was anchored on one occasion at Buffalo, he set out to find a bookstore where he might locate a book about flowerless plants. Instead he found A Treatise on Some of the Insects Injurious to Vegetation by Thaddeus William Harris, M. D. This book played a large part in determining his future. On the flyleaf of his worn copy, now one of the treasures of the Comstock Memorial in the library of Cornell University, is written the following inscription: "I purchased this book for $10.00 in Buffalo, New York, on July 2, 1870. I think it was the first entomologist book I ever saw. Before seeing it I had never given entomology a thought; from the time that I bought it, I felt that I should like to make the study of insects my life's work."

Comstock went to Cornell University to study entomology, but on arriving, found that there were no such courses offered. Dr. Burt G. Wilder, head of the Zoology Department, gave him every aid and facility to study entomology independently. After trying Comstock out as a helper in his department, he employed

him as his personal assistant. Comstock had made such progress with his studies on insects at the completion of his sophomore year, that 13 of his fellow students petitioned the faculty of the university to allow him to give them a course of lectures on entomology with university credit. It was during the 3rd term of his junior year that his first course was offered. He was assigned a small room in McGraw Hall, the second permanent building of the university, as his first entomological laboratory, and he gave a course entitled "Lectures and Field Work in Entomology". He was not content to have his students know insects only as dried specimens stuck on pins. The class went to fields for first-hand knowledge of what insects are and can do. Aspects such as the role of insects in the living world, their association with each other, and their effect on human interests were given full consideration.

Comstock made great progress on the basis of his limited experience, but he needed contact with entomologists more experienced and more eminent in the field. Dr. Wilder had watched Comstock with fatherly interest, and mainly to aid his growth, recommended that C. V. Riley, best known American entomologist and the only one devoting his time entirely to entomology, he brought to Cornell for a short course on entomology. This brief contact with Riley made Comstock more conscious of his lack of training and experience. The summer following, he had an opportunity to study with another great entomologist, Herman A. Hagen. The Museum of Comparative Zoology at Cambridge, Massachusetts, had just brought Dr. Hagen from Germany to take charge of the insect collections. Comstock became acquainted with him and from this association he learned insect morphology and the importance of collecting, and studying the life histories of insects along with their adult stages. Also, he learned how to deal with the infinity of detail that the study of insects imposes. Later, Comstock worked with Asa Fitch, Entomologist of the state of New York, who had published many reports on economic insects of New York.

During his senior year, Comstock received his first regular appointment to the teaching staff of the University. Following his graduation from Cornell in June, 1874, Riley, the Entomologist of the U. S. Department of Agriculture, asked him to investigate the depredations of the cotton leafworm of the South. He

146

spent that summer in Selma, Alabama, studying the history and habits of the destructive cotton leafworm, the first real investigation in the field of applied entomology. The study was continued until the fall of 1878 when Comstock and Riley prepared a report of the findings.

As a teaching aid, the system of keeping pinned specimens in glasstopped cases was begun and later groups of insects were pinned to movable blocks making rearrangement easier. Comstock then began to write a textbook of entomology for his classes that was built from the ground up and was based on materials that his students could see and handle. He then turned his efforts to accumulating an entomological library. To these accomplishments he added the task of building an insectary, one of the first of its kind, a building in which live insects were kept for observations. Comstock was now equipped to take advantage of the rising tide of interest in entomology.

While Professor Comstock was doing much to promote interest in entomology, Mrs. Comstock took up wood engraving, preparing herself to illustrate her husband's textbook. She made engravings for Comstock's Manual for the Study of Insects. In the depression of the nineties, Mrs. Comstock took upon herself the task of writing and illustrating nature study leaflets for rural teachers to use in their classes, with the hope of interesting future farmers in things of value and of beauty in their rural surroundings. She organized courses at Cornell University for teaching nature study, again especially designed for rural school teachers. For this work she was awarded an assistant professorship and later a full professorship in nature study at Cornell, the first woman to attain academic standing. She published, Problems of the Six Footed, How to Keep Bees (1904), Handbook of Nature Study (1911), The Pet Book (1914), Bird, Tree and Plant Notebooks (1914).

Professor Comstock retired from teaching in 1917 and devoted himself to writing. His books included: The Wings of Insects (1918), and An Introduction to Entomology (1920). He was invited to join the editorial staff of the American Naturalist as editor of the section on entomology, and he contributed articles on insects for the Standard Natural History. Others of his more important works in book form are: Elements of Insect Anatomy, edited with Kellogg in 1901, and How to Know Butterflies, published, with his wife as coauthor in 1904.

REFERENCES

Comstock, A. B.   *The Comstocks of Cornell.*   Ithaca, N. Y.: Comstock Publ. Associates, a division of Cornell Univ. Press, 1953.

Comstock, J. H.   *Insect Life.*   New York: D. Appleton and Co., 1897.

Comstock, J. H.   *An Introduction to Entomology.*   9th ed. Ithaca, N. Y.: Comstock Publ. Co., 1947.

Essig, E. O.   *A History of Entomology.*   New York: The Macmillan Co., 1931.

Howard, L. O.   *A History of Applied Entomology.*   Washington, D. C.: Smithsonian Inst. Publ. 3118, 1930.

Jaffe, B.   *Men of Science in America.*   New York: Simon and Schuster, 1944. (Chapter 6 on Thomas Say.)

Keller, L. *Directory of Organization and Field Activity of the Department of Agriculture.* Washington, D. C.: U. S. Printing Office.   USDA Misc. Publ. 640, 1948.

Knight, P.   The Development and Present Status of Entomological Courses in American Colleges and Universities, *J. Econ. Ent.*   871:77, 1928.

Le Conte, J. L.   *The Complete Writings of Thomas Say on the Entomology of North America.*   2 vol. Philadelphia: A. E. Foote, 1891.

Needham, J. G. The Lengthened Shadow of a Man and His Wife, I and II. *Sci. Monthly.* 62:140-150; 219-229, 1946.

Osborn, H. *Fragments of Entomological History.*   Columbus, Ohio: The Spahr and Glenn Co., Part I 1937, Part II 1946.

Ross, H. H.   *A Textbook of Entomology.* 2nd Ed. New York: John Wiley and Sons, Inc., 1956.

Weiss, H. B. *The Pioneer Century of American Entomology.*   New Brunswick, N. J.: (Published by author), 1936.

Weiss, H. B. and G. M. Ziegler,   *Thomas Say, Early American Naturalist.* Springfield, Ill.: Charles C. Thomas, 1931.

Embryology is the science of development. Usually it is defined in a rather restricted sense to include the stages from the fertilized egg to the birth or hatching of an animal. For the purpose of this discussion, however, the definition will be extended to include the entire developmental process, beginning with gamete formation in the parents and continuing up to the adult or mature stage of an animal or plant. The reproductive process is thus included here as a part of embryology.

The earliest description of reproduction and development were based on supernatural interpretations. A more realistic and natural approach to the problem was made by the Greek philosopher-scientists.

Chapter 16

EMBRYOLOGY

Three books (Regimen) dealing with obstetrics and gynecology originated from the Hippocratic school. In these books the 4 humors were discussed in relation to the formation of human embryos and suggestions were made concerning methods to be employed by the physician at child birth. Aristotle (Chapter 2) considered eggs to be made of undifferentiated material requiring fertilization before development could occur.

Hieronymus Fabricius wrote two treatises on embryology: On the Form of the Foetus (1600) and On the Formation of the Egg and the Chick (1621). Harvey pondered over the subject and, being unable to visualize a natural explanation for development, he followed the theme of his predecessors and applied a mystical interpretation to some aspects. Six years before his death (1651) The Development of

Animals was published. It was long and speculative and did not lead immediately to any significant advance in embryology. This was mainly because embryology demanded more advanced techniques than those available to Harvey.

The best remembered part of Harvey's book was the dictum, "all creatures come from an egg" (Ex ovo omnia). Harvey was far ahead of his time in this suggestion, but it must be noted that his conception of an egg was quite different from the modern concept. He called any embryonic mass an egg. Harvey had not seen a mammalian egg, and he did not know what an egg was, but, nevertheless, he introduced a concept that has proved to be true for all higher animals. Harvey speculated that all animals arise from eggs and that the semen has a vitalizing role in development.

Major contributions that brought the process of reproduction in animals to the stage of active investigation were made by three Dutch experimenters. First in chronological order was the Dutch physician, Regnier de Graaf (1641-1673), who in 1672 observed that the progeny of mammals express characteristics of both the mother and the father. Therefore, he reasoned, both sexes must transmit agents of heredity. In search of some physical basis for this observation, he studied sections of Mammalian ovaries prepared for microscopic examination. Fluid filled spaces large enough to be seen without magnification, now called Graafian follicles, were erroneously considered to be the eggs. In spite of this mistake, de Graaf was able to describe in general terms the process of ovulation and development of the embryo in the uterus of the mother. Even though mammalian eggs and sperm had not yet been actually observed, these beginnings in embryology prepared a foundation for the understanding of reproduction and heredity in animals. The mammalian egg was finally discovered by von Baer a century and a half later.

The next contribution after that of de Graaf came from the Dutch microscope maker, Leeuwenhoek, who in 1677 observed human sperm with his single-mounted lenses, and in the years that followed, sperm of several animals (Chapter 7). He also observed the association of sperm with eggs in frogs and fish and considered the sperm to furnish the essential lifegiving properties whereas the egg merely provided the proper en-

vironment for nutrition and development
of the embryo.   Two years later (1679)
Swammerdam, also using the microscope,
studied the development of insects.   He
observed an unfolding process from stage
to stage, or instar to instar, in the developmental sequence and visualized a simple
enlargement from a minute but preformed
animal.

Preformation

Two schools of thought emerged when
attempts were made to trace the tangible
changes that occur in development.   The
preformation idea was based on the speculation that the egg contained a miniature
individual that required only a suitable environment for growing to the adult stage.
The opposing view, called epigenesis,
held that the egg was undifferentiated, and
a step by step process resulted in succeeding stages of development.

The preformation doctrine, as a
philosophical conception, has its roots in
antiquity.   It is an essential factor in the
usual interpretation of the Biblical scheme
of creation.   Empedocles, Plato, and the
fathers of the Church, alike, regarded it
as a part of their system.   Aristotle considered the male semen to be nothing but
fluid.   He argued against the idea of the
animal existing ready-made in the semen
but lacked proof for his belief.   If he had
known of spermatozoa in the semen he
would probably have been a preformationist.

Joseph of Aromatari was probably
the first 17th century writer to claim that
the rudiment of the chick embryo was actually visible in the egg before incubation.
In a letter dated October 31, 1636, Joseph
said briefly that the chick is fashioned in
the egg before it is incubated by the hen.
Henry Power, in 1664, stated that, as
soon as the pulsating particle appears in
the chick, the microscope most distinctly
shows it to be a complete heart with both
auricles and ventricles.   He believed the
complete circulation to be fully developed
at the 2nd day of incubation but that it was
not discernible owing to the fact that the
circulating liquid is colorless and not yet
converted by the heart into red blood.   On
this latter point, Malpighi later expressed
a similar view.

Swammerdam made observations
and prepared drawings based on early frog
development from which he enterpreted a
type of preformation.   Writing in 1669,

he expressed a belief in preformation, and
used it to explain certain passages in the
Bible.   He had just discovered that the
larva of the butterfly was present in the
egg (chrysalis) and he used this as an indi-
cation that all animals are preformed.   The
French philosopher, Nicolas de Male-
branche, in 1674, developed the observation obtained by Swammerdam into a conception of an endless series of embryos,
each encased in the others like a nest of
boxes.   Swammerdam had suggested
further that the whole human race was
comprehended in the loins of Adam and
Eve and consequently that the race will be
faced with extinction when the original
supply of germs is exhausted.

Malpighi was less philosophical and
more scientific than his contemporaries.
He made accurate microscopic observations of chick embryos of various stages
and set them forth in terse descriptions
and clear sketches.   Development in general was described as occurring gradually
but Malpighi did not believe the parts were
formed gradually.   The heart, for example, was supposed to have existed fully
formed from the beginning but he observed
that it did not begin to beat until the 38-40
hour stage.   His theoretical views in some
instances seemed to be opposed to his observations.   This may be explained partly
by his inability to observe the early stages;
he saw nothing during the first 24 hours of
incubation.   On one occasion he observed
an unincubated egg (that had been in the
sun) and found an embryo already developing.   This and his lack of observations of
early stages led him to believe that the
embryo was preformed.   Malpighi's two
papers on chick embryology were entitled
On the Formation of the Chick in the Egg
(1673) and Observations on the Incubated
Egg (1689).

The preformation doctrine was generally accepted in the years following
about 1674.   Then it was only a question
of whether the miniature organism was in
the egg or in the sperm (ovism or animalculism).   It should be pointed out that
during the whole period of the controversy
on this point, little research was carried
out.   The continuance of the dispute depended directly on the absence of a microscopic investigation of the early stages of
development.

Leeuwenhoek was an animalculist.
He was the first to direct attention to the
importance of the spermatozoa in animal
development.   His views on preformation,
however, were not clear and often appear

to be inconsistent. He once pointed out that insect larvae are not insects, although insects proceed from them, and, likewise, spermatozoa are not children, although children proceed from them. He would not admit that the frog's egg contained a young frog, but said that the parts of the embryo appear gradually in the fertilized egg. The embryo, when it does appear, does not resemble a frog. He said, the frog must be locked up in the fertilized egg, but he did not say that it was locked up in the form of a miniature frog. Leeuwenhoek is sometimes, but quite wrongly, credited with having described homunculi in spermatozoa. Nevertheless, he was unquestionably a philosophical preformationist; at least he had a belief in an intangible preformation.

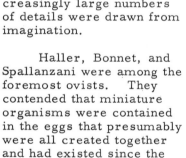

A long list of animalculists followed, basing their views largely on philosophical speculation and making a special effort, in most cases, to link their theories with theological dogma. Curious sketches and elaborate descriptions of the homunculus (Figure 16-1) were produced by numerous pseudoscientists. In practically all cases the foetus described was seen only by the author and increasingly large numbers of details were drawn from imagination.

Fig. 16-1. Sketch of homunculus, miniature individual imagined to be preformed in the sperm cell

Haller, Bonnet, and Spallanzani were among the foremost ovists. They contended that miniature organisms were contained in the eggs that presumably were all created together and had existed since the beginning of the world. Generation, in their interpretation, consisted of 2 distinct processes: (1) the production by the female under the influence of the male, of an "ethereal ferment," that reacted on the dormant and miniature foetus and prepared it for expansion; and (2) the generation process proper, or the nutrition and development of the animated foetus.

In 1758, Haller completed his work on the development of the chick. He concluded that it is now almost demonstrable that the embryo can be found in the egg, and that the mother contains in the ovary all the essentials of the foetus. According to Haller, one of the most powerful

arguments in favor of the ovist, as opposed to the animalculist theory, is the fact, first demonstrated for Aphididae by Leeuwenhoek in 1695 and afterwards confirmed in detail by Bonnet in 1745, that an egg that has not been fertilized can nevertheless reproduce and develop a perfect individual. It will be remembered that aphids are different from most insects in their ability to reproduce by parthenogenesis, that is, without fertilization.

Bonnet used his own work on parthenogenesis in aphids as definite evidence in favor of ovism. He later endeavored to explain the phenomena of regeneration on the basis of preformation. Germs of higher animals, he said, are confined to definite organs of the body, but in worms and polyps they are scattered throughout the tissue generally, and hence are able to reproduce the organism at any point, and replace lost organs. When the question was asked, "why should the animal reproduce a head at the head end only, and a tail at the tail end only?", he multiplied or reduced the germs in various localities to make his theory fit the observations and the theory became complex, indeed. The mechanism is explained by Bonnet thus: "It is well known that the eggs of virgin hens grow, and it is now demonstrable that the germs pre-exist in them. Hence the germ grows also, but it encloses others which grow with it and through it." Bonnet believed that the germs are imperishable. The resurrection of the body may be explained by assuming that it is composed of an essential, imperishable basis or framework, that is unaffected by development or by death.

Voltaire's criticism of animalculism (1767) was that of an amateur. How, he asked, could the little men that run about so nimbly in a drop of semen be expected to remain motionless for nine months in the mother's womb. He was certain, however, that reproduction was by germ cells, whichever system may ultimately prevail. In 1780 Spallanzani followed Swammerdam in contending that the embryo develops from the substance of the fertilized egg. The tadpole of the frog, he said, does not come out of the egg, but the egg is transformed into a tadpole.

Immanuel Kant (1790) was opposed to the entire preformation theory and to any mechanical conception of the origin of life. The theory of preformation, he said, "removed every individual from the formative power of nature in order to make it come immediately from the hand of the creator... as if it were not all the same whether a supernatural origin is assigned to these forms in the beginning or in the course of the world." Kant held that epigenesis had great superiority over preformation in the empirical grounds of its proof, and insofar as it regards nature as self-producing and not merely self-unfolding. Even apart from proof, he said, reason regards epigenesis with particular favor. Oken (Chapter 12) believed that the ovum is an entire animal in idea and design, but not in structure. He was therefore opposed to preformation either of the egg or sperm. Oken is an early, if not the first, author to express belief in the intracellular or more modern version of preformation.

Saint-Hilaire, (1822) incubated eggs for 3 days under normal conditions and then subjected them to abnormal treatment such as shaking, perforation, and coating the shell with varnish or wax. Monstrosities of various kinds were produced. He regarded this as experimental evidence against preformation, but it was argued by others that the organism could be preformed and still become abnormal because of injury.

Karl von Baer's celebrated work, Development of Animals, published in 1828, added the final stroke against the old preformation doctrine. He followed the actual developmental stages and showed differentiation to be a progressive process. The wealth of careful, sound observations that his work contained reduced to negligible proportions the rhetorical and argumentative methods of the preformationists of the past.

It is surprising that preformation lasted as long as it did. The school of Cuvier was deficient in embryologists. This is an important reason for the long life of the preformation doctrine in its original form. A more modern interpretation of preformation has developed recently with the gene theory which suggests that development is the expansion of a potential, but invisible, preformed organism embodied in the gene complement of the individual. It is evident, however, that organisms are more than bundles of genes. When interactions among gene products are incorporated into the theory, a more modern interpretation of preformation is possible. According to this view the germ cell is not a simple, unorganized unit but a highly complex microcosm, the architecture of which can in a measure be deduced from its reactions during development.

Epigenesis

The theory of epigenesis that developed in contrast to preformation states that the organism is entirely new. It arises gradually from unorganized or undifferentiated material in the egg. Aristotle was probably the author of epigenesis. His observations on the chick, as far as they went, indicated that preformation was not the rule but his main objection was a philosophical one. If all parts are made by the semen it is evident that no part can exist in it from the first. Aristotle was assuming a vital external force to direct the organization of living material. As observed earlier in this chapter, Aristotle would probably have been a preformationist if he had known about sperm cells. Epigenesis is also associated with the work of Harvey. It is evident, however, that many of Harvey's ideas and opinions were taken directly from Aristotle. Harvey spoke of the egg as a conception proceeding from the male and female and endowed with the virtue of both; hence it produces a foetus that resembles both parents.

Harvey did not believe in preformation which, he considered inconsistent with true generation, but he suggested that all parts of the embryo are present potentially in the egg. He attempted to explain generation by assuming the existence of a First Cause or Generative Principle, with the power of initiating growth. According to this view, the ovum is not itself a definite primordium exhibiting a common fundamental structure but a widely varying secondary product of the primordial principle. It is the principle, or the egg in a confused metaphysical sense, that is the common beginning, and not the morphological ovum. Although he did not interpret his dictum that all life proceeds from the egg, in the modern sense it was important in that it gave an impetus to a long series of researches on the subject. Those who followed, discovered in his dictum a profound truth of which he himself was only dimly aware. Harvey probably coined the word "epigenesis" to refer to the process that derives the embryo from an apparently undifferentiated and homogeneous egg by a gradual process of differentiation and growth.

Notwithstanding the powerful combination of Aristotle and Harvey, epigenesis found no immediate supporters. Freidrich Wolff, (1738-1794) a century after Harvey, became the most celebrated protagonist of epigenesis. Interestingly, he used the same chick material from which Malpighi had developed his view of preformation for the basis of his work on epigenesis. Wolff found Malpighi's account of the embryology of the chick to be well adapted for illustrating development by epigenesis. He was able to observe microscopically the building up of the chick embryo and found no evidence of an encapsuled chick in the egg. Hence he found no evidence for the enlargement of a pre-existing miniature, but rather a continuous growth accompanied by gradual development leading toward a more complex form. In spite of the great service that Wolff performed for embryology, he had no immediate followers. His thesis was not convincing because he was ahead of his time in methods of biological research. More importance was attached by his contemporaries to abstract reasoning than to observation. Wolff had already made excellent observations of the development of plants, particularly the flower parts. In his study of the chick he had demonstrated the precise development of the intestine and other structures. The primitive kidney or Wolffian body bears his name.

The history of embryology in the 18th century might have been different if John Hunter's work had been available. Much of his work was lost entirely. The detailed sketches of chick embryology prepared between 1773 and 1780, were not discovered until 1840. Hunter also made critical studies of the development of insects. In his discussion, 3 explanations for development were considered: preformation, metamorphosis, and a modified form of epigenesis, in which the parts were present at the beginning but were altered in form and function as development proceeded.

Theories of Generation

Several theories of generation were prevalent during the 17th century. Some of them influenced the biological thinking of the period but all are obsolete now and have only historical significance. Four of the more important theories, pangenesis, precipitation, seminism, and panspermy, will be identified.

The oldest theory of generation is called pangenesis. According to this theory, minute granules develop in particular areas of the body and represent the parts in which they originate. At the time of sexual maturity they come together in the reproductive organs and carry information that is transmitted in inheritance. The whole organism thus takes part in the generative act. Highmore, one of the first authors to produce a reasoned theory of pangenesis, published a work on generation, dated May 15, 1651, in which he speculated that the genital organs collect atoms corresponding to every part of the body. These undergo a concentration process in the gonad and develop into germs.

The theory of pangenesis also had an evolutionary aspect because it suggested a means by which animals become different from others of their kind and eventually give rise to new types. The theory was resuscitated by Charles Darwin in The Variation of Animals and Plants under Domestication, Volume 2 (1868), to account for the origin of variation. Darwin was unaware of Mendel's work and needed a theory of heredity. He theorized that body cells secrete minute corpuscles or "gemmules" that record growth patterns for the area they represent. These gemmules are carried by body fluids and the bloodstream to the reproductive organs where they are packed into the eggs or sperm. In the new individual they determine the characteristics and the growth pattern.

The theory of precipitation was based on the notion that the embryo is formed suddenly at the moment of fecundation, by precipitation of materials already present in the ovum. Seminism is based on the idea that the generative principle resides in the male and female "semen". The adherents of seminism, however, did not attempt to explain the origin of these primary substances. An early view of seminism was pronounced by Aristotle, who believed that the male semen represented the impulse or efficient cause, and the female "semen" was the substance upon which it operated in producing an embryo. According to the theory of panspermy, generation depends on a primordial, indestructible, and unorganized substance or principle comparable with air, water, and earth but endowed with life. A more modern statement of this theory is that a widespread distribution of germs accounts for apparent cases of spontaneous generation.

Fertilization and Developmental Mechanics

Fabricius (1600-1621) was the first author to propound a reasoned scheme for the mechanics of generation. He did not believe that the spermatic fluid reached the genital organs or formed any part of generation in the animal. Harvey was essentially in agreement with Fabricius on this point. Steno in 1667 first introduced the **term** ovary for the female reproductive gland. In 1672 De Graaf reported that he had succeeded in tracing the mammalian egg (which he maintained existed already in the ovary) down the Fallopian tube to the uterus. Although he saw the spaces left by eggs and not the eggs themselves, the spaces corresponded in number with the embryos in the uterus. The generative process was thus associated with changes occurring in the ovary.

Leeuwenhoek (1683), in stating his views on the nature of fecundation, maintained that the eggs are impregnated by seminal animalculae. He demonstrated that living spermatozoa can actually be seen with the microscope in samples taken from the uterus of a dog after coition. Hartsoeker (1649) believed that each spermatic worm of a bird enclosed a male or female bird of the same species, and in copulation a single worm enters an egg where it is nourished and grows. Andry (1700) believed that the function of the egg was to receive, enclose, and nourish the spermatic worm. Much confusion on the subject was prevalent during the 18th century mainly because the Graafian follicles were thought to be eggs and efforts to trace them led only to frustration and imagination. There was a difference of opinion as to when and where spermatozoa could be found in the female reproductive organs and how many spermatozoa were necessary to produce fecundation. This period was characterized by much speculation that tended to obscure simple truths with elaborate theories.

Spallanzani (1780) was first to demonstrate artificial fecundation. He showed that frog eggs fertilized artificially would develop like those naturally fertilized, whereas those left unfertilized would decompose. He successfully practiced artificial fecundation in various amphibia, insects, and dogs. When he came to explain the results, however, he maintained that semen deprived of animalculae still possesses fecundating properties.

The discovery of the true ovum of mammals by von Baer in 1827 had an important bearing on the history of embryology. It established the egg as the morphological unit that lies at the root of development of all animals. Lallamand published papers in 1840-41 in which he stated his belief that the egg and sperm play an equal and reciprocal part in the act of fecundation and each contributes an organized unit of living matter. The function of spermatozoa, he said, is intimately bound up with their origin, and the fact that they arise like the eggs, from a substance of the generative gland. He did not, however, believe that sperm penetrated the egg but that the sperm was grafted on the surface of the egg and formed the first rudiment of the cerebro-spinal system. Martin Barry in his <u>Researches in Embryology</u> (1840) suggested that the sperm passes into the substance of the egg but this theory was not favorably received at the time by the recognized biologists, Wagner, Leuckart, and Kölliker. In 1851, Nelson, working on the Ascaris of the cat, discovered the penetration of the egg by the sperm. Bischoff was probably first to discover that spermatozoa penetrate the ova by their own movement.

The assertion that fecundation is accomplished when one animalcule gets into one egg, was originally made by Leeuwenhoek in 1683, but verification did not come for a century and a half. The delay can be ascribed partly to the undeveloped condition of microscopic techniques. Pringsheim in 1855 first saw nuclear fusion in the plant <u>Vaucheria</u> and reported that numerous male and one female gamete were present. It is probable that he saw only insemination and not nuclear division. O. Hertwig (1875) suggested that such fusion would occur and would be followed by nuclear division. The phenomenon of penetration by a single sperm, the fate of the sperm within the egg, and the equal participation of the egg and sperm nuclei in fertilization were completely demonstrated in animals by the researches of O. Hertwig, A. Weismann, and H. Fol between the years 1875 and 1879.

Segmentation or cleavage of the ovum was first observed by Swammerdam in the 17th century and published in 1738. He saw the first furrow of the frog's egg in cleavage. Spallanzani (1780) described and figured the first 2 furrows in the egg of a toad. Other studies on cleavage followed but until the late forties and early fifties of the 19th century no one, except perhaps von Baer, suspected that the first cleavage plane of the frog's egg coincides with the medial plane of the adult body.

Sexual Reproduction and Hybridization in Plants

Sexual reproduction in animals was well understood in general terms before such a mechanism was described for plants. It is true that the Babylonians had practiced hand pollination of the date palm but the significance was not realized. During the latter part of the 17th century significant observations and experiments led to a basic understanding of sexual reproduction in plants. Since plants are more simple in some respects and more easily controlled than animals, they lend themselves more readily to experiments in hybridization. The discovery of sexual reproduction in plants, therefore, was a major factor in stimulating interest and experimentation in inheritance.

The first consistent studies which led to an understanding of the reproductive parts of plants were reported in 1682 by the English plant anatomist, Nehemiah Grew (Chapter 7). Twelve years later (1694) Rudolph Camerarius clearly described sexual reproduction in plants. This important contribution made possible the experimental approach to plant hybridization. Camerarius is also credited with the first artificially produced plant hybrid on record, from a cross between hemp and hop plants. Thomas Fairchild in 1717 was reported by his contemporaries to have pollinated a carnation by a pink (Dianthus). The hybrid, showing characteristics of both parents, was called Fairchild's sweet william and by some "Fairchild's mule." No record of this hybridization was left by Fairchild himself but there is good evidence that the reported results were actually obtained. Furthermore the experiment was designed and the results were not accidental. Following this beginning many artificial pollinations were performed between different related plants.

One of the most important researchers in the 18th century was the German botanist, Joseph Kölreuter (1733-1806), Figure 16-2, who found that hybrids between plant varieties might resemble one or the other parent or appear intermediate between them. One of his most valuable observations showed the equality of contributions from the two parents in reciprocal crosses. That is, the same results were obtained by mating a male from variety A with a female from variety B as by mating a female from A with a male from B.

Kölreuter had broad interests and sound judgment. His experiments were designed and carefully conducted. From one series of crosses between tall and dwarf varieties of tobacco, he obtained results that reflected the modern principle of quantitative inheritance. Progeny in the first generation were intermediate in height between the two parents. In the second generation the variation was continuous and a fairly normal distribution was observed. Some mature plants were as large as the tall parent and some were as small as the dwarf parent. The size of most of the hybrids, however, fell between the extremes of the two parents. Kölreuter could not explain these results; in fact, it was not until the early part of the present century that an adequate explanation was obtained in the multiple gene hypothesis.

19th Century Embryology

Karl von Baer (1792-1876) the "father of modern embryology" provided a great classic under the title, Development of Animals, that raised embryology to the status of a comparative science. He developed the theory of the primary germ layers: ectoderm, endoderm, and mesoderm, that had been suggested by Wolff. Von Baer was first to actually observe the mammalian egg. Von Baer also discovered the developing notochord and other embryological structures. In his comparative studies, von Baer observed corresponding stages in the development of

Fig. 16-2. J. G. Kölreuter, German experimental biologist

different animals.   He did not relate this observation to evolution but Ernest Haeckel (1834-1919) made that connection in his recapitulation theory that was stated concisely "Ontogeny recapitulates phylogeny" and became known as the biogenetic law.

On the surface, the evidence for recapitulation would seem to be convincing. Distinct pharyngeal clefts in early stages of vertebrate embryology bear a resemblance to the respiratory structures of fish.   The heart and central nervous system of higher vertebrates resemble, at least superficially, the structures of lower forms at succeeding stages of development. A cartilaginous endoskeleton and notochord in the early development of higher vertebrates have counterparts in lower forms.   Haeckel placed most emphasis on morphological characteristics of contemporary types and gave little attention to paleontological data.   When the history of animals is considered in time, many new variations seem to be superimposed on the old patterns.

More recent contributions in the field of developmental biology provide deep-seated reasons for treating Haeckel's recapitulation theory with caution.   For example, Child in 1915, showed that axial gradients can be followed in development. An organizer, described by Spemann in 1928, showed interdependencies of parts of living organisms in space and time. In amphibian material, the dorsal lip of the blastopore was found to induce differentiation in surrounding tissue.   The development of the gene theory has now provided the beginning of an explanation for a sequence of events as well as end products of ontogeny.   In perspective, the interpretation of von Baer that explained resemblances in terms of processes, fits modern concepts of embryology better than that of Haeckel which is based on precedents and recapitulation.

Francis Balfour (1851-1882) developed the best of Haeckel's work in his two volume Comparative Embryology that covers the development of vertebrates and invertebrates and makes critical comparisons.   The great mass of information that had been accumulated by the Haeckel school was sifted, digested, and molded by Balfour into an organized whole.

REFERENCES

Adelmann, H. B. *The Embryological Treatises of Hieronymus Fabricius of Aquapendente.*   Ithaca, N. Y.: Cornell Univ. Press, 1942.

Cole, F. J. *Early Theories of Sexual Generation.*   London: Oxford Univ. Press, 1931.

Meyer, A. W.   *The Rise of Embryology.*   Stanford: Stanford Univ. Press, 1939.

Meyer, A. W. *An Analysis of the De Generation Animalium of William Harvey.* Stanford: Stanford Univ. Press, 1938.

Needham, J. *A History of Embryology.*   Cambridge: The Univ. Press, 1934.

Radl, E. *The History of Biological Theories.*   trans. from German E. J. Hatfield.   London: Oxford Univ. Press, 1930.

Shumway, W.   The Recapitulation Theory, *Quarterly Rev. Biol.* 7:93-99, 1932.

The science of genetics developed in the 20th century. It was with the discovery, in 1900, of Mendel's work that the fundamental basis of genetics was established but the roots go back a long way in history. Practical accomplishments with some relation to genetics were made in remote periods of history. Tablets of stone prepared by the Babylonians 6,000 years ago have been interpreted to show pedigrees of several successive generations of horses, suggesting a conscious effort toward improvement. Other stone carvings of the same period illustrate artificial cross pollination of the date palm as practiced by the early Babylonians. The early Chinese, many years before the Christian era, improved varieties of rice. Cotton was grown and used

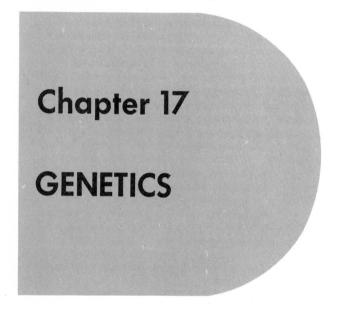

Chapter 17

GENETICS

by ancient peoples before the beginnings of the written record. Maize was cultivated and improved in the western hemisphere by the American Indians as early as the anthropologists have uncovered the history of American culture. In fact, all common domestic plants and animals were serving man before the first account of events that had occurred was made in writing. Methods of selection and hybridization were undoubtedly employed by early plant and animal breeders even though they were not aware of the principles of genetics. It is difficult to evaluate the actual information available to prehistoric man that might now be considered a part of the science of genetics.

Hippocrates, Aristotle, and other Greek philosophers made observations and speculations suggesting genetic prin-

ciples. The elements of truth, however, were vague and mixed with error. Stories of unusual hybrids were initiated by the Greeks and repeated with additional imaginative flourishes by Pliny, Gesner, and other popular writers of past centuries. The giraffe was supposed to be a hybrid between the camel and the leopard. The two-humped camel was thought to have resulted from a cross between a camel and a boar. When the camel mated with the sparrow an ostrich was imaged to appear. Plants were also considered capable of remarkable hybridizations. For example, the acacia tree crossed with the palm was said to produce the banana tree. Fantastic explanations of the mechanism of reproduction and sex determination were associated with these stories. Although many such tales have persisted, little information that could contribute to the science of genetics can be recognized before the 17th century.

Pre-Mendelian Concepts of Heredity

The Greek philosophers considered inherited characters of individuals to be acquired through direct contact with the environment. This idea, although not precisely stated until the 18th century, was widely accepted. The French scientist, Lamarck, formulated the common view of the 18th century biologists into a theory which bears his name and is known as the theory of inheritance of acquired characteristics. This theory emphasized use and disuse over long or short periods of time as the significant factor for determining the characteristics of the individual. The direct influence of the environment was considered to be represented in the germinal material (eggs and sperm) and therefore transmitted in inheritance.

The habits and manner of life of the ancestors were believed to fashion the bodily form and qualities of the individual. For example, fish living in deep, dark caves were blind, presumably because of disuse of their eyes. Flying birds, through use, acquired strong wings with well developed muscles. Wading birds developed long legs, long necks, and long beaks. Frogs were considered to have obtained their webbed feet from stretching their toes in swimming. Climate, geographical conditions, and food requirements were believed to cause new organs to appear and old ones to disappear. Lamarck considered an animal's needs to determine its desires. The animal's desires in turn would determine the use or disuse of parts of the body, that would bring about modifications. According to Lamarck, these modifications would eventually find their way into the hereditary material.

The mechanism proposed by Lamarck has never been demonstrated experimentally and present views concerning the nature of the germinal material make direct hereditary change by environmental modification most unlikely. The concepts of mutation and selection adequately explain most of the things that seemed to the last century biologists to require a Lamarckian explanation. In the western world, this theory has been relegated to the historical realm, but in Russia Lamarckism has been revived.

An alternative explanation was provided by August Weismann (1834-1915), a prominent German biologist, in the latter part of the 19th century. This theory emphasized the remarkable stability of the germ plasm. Little, if any, environmental influence was considered to affect the genes even though environmental modifications of external characters occurred. The germ plasm was distinguished from the somatoplasm and was described as the hereditary material carried from generation to generation. According to Weismann, reproduction was accomplished not by body cells, that is, somatoplasm, but by the germ plasm, that was transmitted essentially unchanged from generation to generation. Although some details of the germ plasm theory have been modified the fundamental premise is well established. Germ plasm is remarkably stable but it occasionally undergoes change by spontaneous mutation. The mutation rate can be increased experimentally by irradiation and by some chemicals supplied in the environment, but the changes occur at random. Only through selection does the environment provide a directing force in evolution.

Mendel

Gregor Mendel (1822-1884, Figure 17-1) is appropriately called the "father of genetics," because he made revolutionary contributions from his experiments on garden peas (<u>Pisum</u> <u>sativum</u>) and thus laid the foundation for the science of genetics. Throughout his life, Mendel showed great interest in living things. His home community was a gardening and fruit-growing area and he was raised on a small fruit farm. Mendel's father had great love for plants, especially fruit trees, and undoubtedly influenced his son greatly as they worked together in the orchard. A parish priest, Pater Johann Schreiber, also encouraged fruit-growing in the region and through his influence school children were instructed in methods of cultivation, grafting, and improving horticultural strains.

As Mendel grew older, he became intensely interested in plant hybridization and during his life he made crosses between varieties of many different plants, including the columbine, snap dragon, slipperwort, sedge, horse thistle, pumpkin, flax, stock, bean, pea, plum, pear, pepper, nasturtium, violet, maize, and hawkweed. Mendel also loved animals, both domesticated animals that he cared for on the farm, and wild animals that he observed with keen interest as he walked in the woods. For a time he kept a pet fox. He also maintained a colony of mice and made some attempts at breeding experiments with them.

Through the advice and assistance of his teacher, Professor Franz, he entered Altbrünn Monastery, an Augustinian religious community near Brünn, Austria. On his 25th birthday, he was ordained a monk. It was customary in the religious communities of that day for men to carry on creative work, either scientific or artistic, along with their religious duties.

Fig. 17-1. Gregor Mendel, German investigator who laid the foundation for the science of Genetics. "Reprinted with permission from Gardner, <u>Principles</u> of <u>Genetics</u>, 1960, John Wiley and Sons, Inc."

158

Mendel was thus encouraged to continue the work of his major interest dealing with living things. Later he became a substitute teacher in a preparatory school and held a position as a substitute teacher for some 14 years. These were the most pleasant and most productive years of his life during which he spent his summer vacations conducting experiments on garden peas.

Mendel's Experiments with Garden Peas

The experiments for which Mendel became famous involved garden peas that were chosen after several materials had been considered and discarded. Mendel was searching for an annual plant with well defined traits that could be grown easily and crossed readily. Garden peas fulfilled these requirements. Moreover the flower is so constructed that the female parts receive pollen readily from the anthers of the flower in fertilization. Pollen from other plants can be introduced but cross pollination does not occur to any appreciable extent in nature. Good fortune as well as wise judgment marked the selection of garden peas because they had other properties unknown to Mendel that were also valuable for the experiments. Through long-continued self-fertilization in nature, pure lines had developed and single alternations of genetic units were reflected in marked character changes. Furthermore, in all of the traits studied by Mendel, one expression was dominant over a contrasting, alternative trait.

Not only was Mendel's choice of materials wise and fortunate, but he demonstrated considerable insight in designing and conducting the experiments. Seven pairs of contrasting characteristics already available in different varieties of garden peas and familiar to Mendel were chosen for the study. The vines or stems were either tall or dwarf; the endosperms of the ripe seeds were green or yellow, the outer surface of the seeds was smooth or deeply wrinkled, and the seed coats were white or grey. Flower color was constantly correlated with this latter trait. Plants with white seed coats had white flowers and those with grey seed coats had violet flowers. The unripe pods were green or yellow, and inflated or constricted between the seeds; and the flowers were either distributed along the main stem (axial) or bunched at the top (terminal). The pairs of contrasting traits were recognized and studied separately in the progeny of different crosses. In contrast,

Mendel's predecessors had attempted to evaluate the hereditary mechanism from observations on the entire organism, making the problem hopelessly complex. Much of Mendel's success may thus be attributed to his good judgment in making crosses as far as possible between parents which differed in only one trait. When this was not feasible he considered only one trait at a time.

The crosses were made with great care when the peas were in blossom. Since in garden peas both male and female reproductive parts are located in the same flower, it was necessary to remove the anthers from the plants chosen as seed parents before the pollen was released. At the appropriate time when the female parts were fully mature the pollen was transferred from the plant chosen as the pollen parent to the stigma of the emasculated seed parent flower. Seeds were allowed to mature on the vines and in the next season they were planted. From observation of the seeds themselves or the progeny thus produced, appropriate classification was made. Results were recorded accurately and conclusions were drawn when sufficient classified data were available. The actual experiment and results were significant but the hypothesis Mendel developed to explain the mechanism of inheritance on the basis of physical elements was the most valuable contribution. Data and conclusion, drawn from the experimental results, were set forth in a paper entitled "Experiments in Plant Hybridization" that was read before the Brünn Natural History Society in 1865 and published in the proceedings of that society in 1866.

Analysis of Mendel's Experiments

In one experiment, Mendel raised two varieties of garden peas, tall and dwarf. When the flowers of the tall strain were allowed to be fertilized with their own pollen, the offspring were all tall. The other variety produced only dwarfs. Mendel observed that weather, soil, and moisture conditions had an effect on the growth of the peas, but the size of these two varieties was controlled largely by inheritance. At least heredity was the main limiting factor under the conditions of his experiments. Tall plants were 6 to 7 feet high whereas dwarfs raised in the same environment measured from 9 to 18 inches. No dwarfs ever turned into tall plants and no tall plants, even under unfavorable environmental conditions, turned into dwarfs.

Mendel proceeded with the hybridization by crossing tall with dwarf plants. From this cross all of the offspring in the first generation (F_1) were tall. The dwarf character had disappeared from F_1 progeny. When the tall hybrid plants were fertilized by their own pollen (selfed) and the progeny (second generation or F_2) were classified the missing trait turned up again. Some progeny were tall and some were dwarfs. Careful classification of the plants showed that on the average about three tall plants were produced to one dwarf. To be exact, from a total of 1,064 F_2 "grandchildren" from the original plants, 787 were tall and 277 were dwarfs. The actual results are compared with the calculated figures based on the 3:1 ratio (266 dwarfs and 798 tall).

In other crosses the remaining 6 of the 7 pairs of contrasting characters originally selected were studied. Mendel recognized from his studies of all 7 pairs of contrasting characters distinct inherited patterns. He observed, for example, only 3:1 ratios in the second generation (F_2) from all monohybrid crosses. One member of each pair of contrasting characters seemed to dominate the other. This member he identified as dominant in contrast to the other recessive member. Mendel's conclusions from the crosses were based on unit characters, dominance in inheritance which occurred in one member of each pair over the other, and segregation of the members of pairs.

Although Mendel conducted his experiment and reported his results with great care, the most significant part of his study was the penetrating explanation of the results that demonstrated imagination and ingenuity. He interpreted what he had observed by assuming that living organisms transmit hereditary traits in the reproductive mechanism by means of some kind of physical particles. Nothing was known about cells and chromosomes, but he visualized with remarkable clearness physical structures which were involved in inheritance. A German word, Anlage (pl. Anlagen), was used to identify the elements. Mendel considered the elements to be operating as independent units in some way through the reproductive process. Since a trait expressed by one parent could be hidden in the first generation and yet appear in the second generation, the elements, now called genes, must be paired. The contrasting expressions in seeds or plants were produced by different arrangements of the two members of a pair.

Evaluations of Mendel's Conclusions

When Mendel's conclusions are evaluated in terms of modern development in genetics, some modifications are necessary. Pioneers are seldom right in every detail. It is no reflection on the man and his work to show that re-evaluations are necessary to keep pace with a modern science. In fact, new interpretations are always necessary as data accumulate. Mendel considered a single gene to be responsible for a single trait. It is now known that many genes, perhaps all the genes present in an organism, have something to do with each characteristic. Certain differential genes, however, are known to influence basic reactions and thus to be responsible for particular end products or phenotypes. Furthermore, it is the genes and not the characters that are inherited. The genes segregate as independent units, whereas the characters result from complex interactions involving many genes.

Complete dominance was indicated in all 7 allelic pairs that Mendel studied. It was natural, therefore, for him to consider dominance as an inherent property of the genes and a universal principle. When sweet peas and snapdragons were studied shortly after the discovery of Mendel's paper, intermediate expressions were observed in the hybrids. For example, crosses between homozygous plants with red flowers and white flowers, respectively, resulted in pink F_1 progeny. The heterozygote could thus be distinguished phenotypically from either parent and was not obscured by dominance as in garden peas. Dominance has now been shown to be influenced by factors in the external, internal, and genetic environment. Therefore, Mendel's view that dominance was a fundamental inherent property of the gene itself is no longer tenable.

The most important conclusion that Mendel obtained from his first experiments was the principle of segregation that describes the separation of pairs of genes. The physical basis for segregation has been established in the process through which mature germ cells are developed. Since Mendel's time the principle of segregation has been found to apply not only to garden peas but to all groups of plants and animals in which sexual reproduction occurs and has become a basic principle of genetics. It is now known, however, that the chromosomes carrying groups of genes rather than the individual genes are the segre-

160

gating units. Further experiments in which two pairs of genes were involved in the same cross showed that one pair was independent with respect to the other. The principle of independent combinations was thus established to account for the independent assortment of genes that are located in different chromosomes.

Mendel's garden pea experiments, significant as they were, had no immediate influence on science or practical breeding. In fact, the results remained virtually unknown for 34 years after their publication in 1866. During that period only a few people knew of the experiments and it is safe to say that no one really understood them. Two biologists, W. O. Focke and Karl Nägeli, cited Mendel's experiments during this period in their own writings. Focke in 1881 made some 15 references to Mendel. Nägeli considered Mendel's work to be unfinished and in need of further verification. This indifference discredited the work and Nägeli's great prestige indirectly weighed against the recognition of Mendel's pea experiments. Various other explanations have been offered to account for this neglect. Most important was the fact that the conclusions were too new to find acceptance. The biological background had not been laid and the time was not ready for precise statistical work. In 1866, the knowledge of the structural and functional biological unit, the cell, was meager, indeed. Cell division was not understood and the sequence through which mature reproductive cells are developed was entirely unknown. Without such basic knowledge it was impossible to appreciate the significance of Mendel's results.

Another reason for the slow recognition was Mendel's own uncertainty and indifference concerning the significance of his results. After the experiments with garden peas he crossed other plants but was unable to confirm his earlier results. When he crossed varieties of hawkweeds, Hieracium, the progeny did not show evidence of segregation of genes from both parents but were like their mothers. These plants are now known to be apomictic, or capable of reproduction without fertilization. The plants that Mendel considered to be hybrids were thus not hybrids at all. He did not know whether his earlier results on garden peas reflected significant principles or merely peculiarities of garden peas. His uncertainty, along with his innate modesty, prevented him from advertising his own work.

The understanding and appreciation of Mendel's results may also have been retarded by the great interest in Darwin's work that was contemporary with Mendel's. The Origin of Species (1859), published while Mendel's pea experiments were in progress, became popular immediately and caused the temporary eclipse of other fields of biology. Darwin's later book Variation of Animals and Plants Under Domestication (1868) emphasized gradual changes and continuous variation in animals and plants and seemed to be in conflict with the abrupt discontinuous variation observed from Mendel's crosses.

Also there is reason to believe that Mendel used his data as a model demonstration of his theory. Perhaps he considered more data necessary to fully establish the mechanism. He must have had some idea as to how the chosen characteristics were inherited when the experiments were designed. Perhaps preliminary work gave him the necessary leads and he then conducted the classical experiments to test his theory. The paper might, therefore, be regarded as a report of a carefully planned demonstration rather than the report an originally designed experiment. It did not contain the complete raw data. The probability of selecting at random 7 characteristics of the pea (with 7 chromosome pairs) each on a different chromosome is low, indeed. Mendel was working with some 30 varieties of peas. He may have reported only on those crosses that fit the same pattern. Some of Mendel's "good fortune" in the choice of characteristics may have come from insight gained in preliminary work.

Many people have speculated on the reasons for Mendel's great success in discovering principles and the source of the brilliant idea that he developed. Unfortunately none of his contemporaries knew he would become famous and little was written about him at the time he lived. Brief sketches of his intimate life and thoughts have been found and compiled by his biographer, Hugo Iltis, and more has been learned from his letters to Nägeli that were published in 1950, but much remains unknown. He had a high level of native ability and curiosity. His early home life and his associations, particularly with his father and parish priest, stimulated his interest in living things and may have planted the seed of an idea that matured later. His training in the university gave him technical skill and a clear understanding of probability. The monastery and substitute teaching position provided a living and gave him time, a favorable intellectual atmosphere, and some incentive for experimental work. Whatever his background might have been, his contribution was revolutionary.

In 1900, Mendel's paper was discovered by 3 men simultaneously: Hugo de Vries, a Dutch botanist known for his mutation theory and studies on the evening primrose and maize; Carl Correns, a German botanist who studied maize, peas, and beans; and Erich von Tschermak-Seysenegg, an Austrian botanist who worked with several plants including garden peas. All 3 of these investigators approached Mendel's principles independently from their own studies, recognized their significance, and found and cited Mendel's work in their own publications.

DeVries and the Mutation Theory

The mutation theory provides an explanation for the source of variation. Mutations appear all at once, originating from the parent species without any visible preparation and without any observable series of transitional forms. The theory was set forth in modern form in the book entitled The Mutation Theory (1901) by the Dutch botanist, Hugo deVries (1848-1935 Figure 17-2). DeVries received

Fig. 17-2. Hugo de Vries who developed the mutation theory. "Reprinted with permission from Gardner, Principles of Genetics, 1960, John Wiley and Sons, Inc."

his university training at Leyden, Heidelberg, and finally Würzburg where he studied under Julius Sachs. After holding various academic posts in Germany, he became, in 1871, associated with the University of Amsterdam, first as lecturer and later as professor of botany and curator of the botanical gardens. He was particularly interested in variations and evolution.

The Swiss anatomist and physiologist, Rudolf Kölliker (1817-1905) had criticized Darwin's theory of evolution by natural selection and had presented an alternative hypothesis of evolution by sudden change. This idea appealed to deVries as superior to the slow method that Darwin had described and he searched for evidence to support the mutation theory in the evening primrose, Oenothera lamarckiana, that he was studying. The plant, originally introduced from America, had spread widely over Europe and grew in masses in the meadows near Amsterdam. It was observed that the seed of the recognized species usually perpetuated the species characteristics but occasionally a new type was produced with distinct new traits. One of these was a giant, another was a dwarf, and a latifoliate form was also observed. These were found to breed true and were considered at first to be new species. It has since been shown that the conspicuous changes observed were brought about by major chromosome changes and not by changes in single genes. It should be noted that this type of observational experimental work was introduced by deVries as a method of studying evolution, in contrast to inference, a method practiced by some of deVries contemporaries.

The mutation theory was subjected to much criticism when it first appeared, particularly from Darwinists. The possibility was pointed out that the experimental lines were not pure and that the new characters were the result of recombinations. Some biologists considered deVries' theory to be too different from the traditional ideas to be acceptable. The theory of mutations was not really in conflict with Darwin's natural selection and it later was shown to strengthen Darwin's case by providing a source of original variation different from the Lamarckian view that Darwin had reluctantly accepted. Darwin had no place in his theory for profound or sudden modifications. The mutation theory became more acceptable when it was shown that small variations as well as large ones may be

162

abrupt. It has been refined since it was first stated and now it represents a widely accepted explanation for the origin of original variation. Now that the theory of the gene has been established, a mutation is defined as a change in a gene. The definition is sometimes extended to include chromosome aberrations as well as gene changes.

The Birth of A Science

The Science of Genetics developed rapidly after 1900, and soon took its place among the biological sciences. At this time everything seemed to be in readiness and an explosive development occurred in which many investigators contributed. Five will be cited as conspicuous leaders during this early period. These include an Englishman, William Bateson, a Frenchman, Lucien Cuénot, an American, W. E. Castle, a Dane, W. L. Johannsen, and a German, Carl Correns.

William Bateson (1861-1926), an experimental biologist at Cambridge University, became immediately interested in Mendel's work following its discovery in 1900. According to R. C. Punnett, Bateson's student and close associate, Bateson, on May 8, 1900, was first to announce Mendel's work in England. He was on a train enroute to London to deliver a lecture entitled "The Problems of Heredity as a Subject for Horticultural Investigation" before the Royal Horticultural Society, when he read deVries' account of Mendel's work. He immediately revised his speech to include Mendel's discoveries and dramatically gave England the first news of Mendel. A full English translation of Mendel's paper was published at the beginning of the Royal Horticultural Society Proceedings for the year 1901.

Bateson was engaged in experimental breeding at the time Mendel's work was discovered and had already made significant contributions. In 1894, he published a book entitled Materials for the Study of Variation which suggested many problems. Bateson then designed and conducted experiments to answer the unsolved questions. These experiments were in progress at the time Mendel's work was discovered. Immediately following the discovery of Mendel's paper, new experiments were designed to determine whether Mendel's laws held for other plants and, particularly, whether they applied to animals as well. Bateson had been breeding poultry, and he along with C. C. Hurst immediately organized experiments to see if the Mendelian principles applied in poultry. These animals breed rapidly and large numbers of progeny can be obtained in a short time. It was soon observed that Mendel's principles did apply to poultry as well as peas. Hurst carried out experiments on rabbits and found that they, too, followed the Mendelian pattern.

Bateson and his associates, including Mrs. Bateson and R. C. Punnett, then set out in earnest to repeat and supplement Mendel's experiments. In the course of their work, 9 plant genera and 4 animal genera were studied; but sweet peas and poultry were investigated most intensively.

Viewing the events now in perspective, it seems possible that Bateson would have discovered Mendel's laws himself if Mendel's work had not come to light in 1900. In 1899, before the International Congress of Hybridization, Bateson had described his objectives and experiments that paralleled closely those of Mendel. Through Bateson's work, Mendel's Principles of Heredity--A Defense (1902) and Problems of Genetics (1913), the basic principles of genetics were confirmed and crystalized. In 1906, at a hybridization conference sponsored by the Royal Horticultural Society, Bateson presented the word Genetics that he had coined as the name for the new science. He also coined the terms homozygous and heterozygous, and described the two kinds of pairing of genes. The word, allelomorph, from which the abbreviation "allele" has been taken was also introduced by Bateson. A professorship of genetics was established at Cambridge in 1909 with Bateson as the first professor. The John Innes Horticultural Institute was established a year later and Bateson relinquished his professorship to Punnett and became the first director of that world famous research center for genetics and cytology.

Lucien Cuénot (1866-1951) who had distinguished himself as an invertebrate zoologist began genetic studies with mice immediately after the discovery of Mendel's work. In 1902 he announced a case of simple Mendelian inheritance in the mouse and in 1903 he published a more detailed analysis of fur patterns and colors. He not only discovered Mendelian ratios but followed the genetic investigations with chemical analyses designed to trace the steps between genes and characters. Basic and substantial contributions in rodent genetics were published in a series of papers completed in 1911. He then turned to studies of the genetics of cancer in mice and later published extensively in the broader field of evolution.

W. E. Castle in the United States began immediately to apply the Mendelian principles to mammals. In 1903 he published 5 papers dealing with such subjects as the heredity of the angora cat, albinism in man, the heredity of sex, and Mendel's law of heredity. This early exploration was followed by extensive investigations on coat characteristics in guinea pigs, rabbits, mice, rats, and other mammals. He later developed other aspects of mammalian genetics including body size and form and became a leading authority in this field. In his later years his interests led to studies on domesticated animals, particularly horses. Following his retirement from Harvard University in 1936 he continued his investigations for many years at the University of California in Berkeley.

The Danish geneticist and plant physiologist, Wilhelm J. Johannsen (1857-1927) was also closely identified with the development of genetics as a science. His early scientific work was in the field of plant physiology at the Carlsberg Laboratory and in 1905, he became director of the Institute of Plant Physiology at the University of Copenhagen. His first genetic paper "On Heredity and Variation" appeared in 1896. In 1898, he began the investigations on barley and beans that have become classics. From this time on his entire original work was in the field of genetics.

In the same year (1900) that Mendel's paper was discovered, Johannsen published a paper on "pure lines" that greatly stimulated interest in genetics. Through a series of ingenious investigations he showed a difference in the effects of selection when applied to populations of ordinary cross-fertilizing organisms as compared with self-fertilizing plants. Self-fertilization was found to produce homozygosity or pure lines. In cross-breeding populations, selection was found to be effective in altering the proportion of different types. When plants were self-fertilized over long periods, selection was no longer effective. The plants had become completely homozygous and no genetic variation was left for selection

to act upon. All variation in a pure line was thus environmental.

Following the investigations on pure lines Johannsen devoted his attention to the formulation of the principles of genetics and wrote one of the first books in the field Elements of Genetics published in 1905. This book represented a landmark in the development of the new science. The word "gene" was coined by Johannsen. He also coined the terms "genotype" and "phenotype" and stressed the importance of making a clear distinction between genes and characters.

Carl Correns (1864-1933), one of the 3 men to discover Mendel's work in 1900, made extensive hybridization experiments on maize, stocks, beans, peas, and lilies at the University of Tübingen during the 1890's. In 1900 he had data from 4 generations in a garden pea experiment and had arrived at conclusions similar to those of Mendel. Searching the literature for work on the subject he found Mendel's paper that was written 35 years before. In 1901, he published an extensive paper on maize hybrids and in the years that followed, he investigated many aspects of plant genetics including sex and the mechanics of reproduction, self-sterility, and leaf variegation dependent on cytoplasmic inheritance. This latter work on the four-o'clock plant of the genus Mirabilis has become a classic. In 1902, he moved to the University of Leipzig and in 1913 he became a Director of the Kaiser Wilhelm Institute for Biology at Berlin-Dahlem.

Chromosome Theory of Inheritance

Mendel's contribution to genetics was a precise mathematical pattern for the transmission of genes, but he had no conception of the biological mechanism involved. The next important problem was the location of the genes and the exploration of their relations with biological structures and functions. Transmission of genes from parents to offspring was obviously associated with the reproductive mechanism but curious biologists were interested in more specific reasons for inheritance. Which parts of the sex cells were involved and how were the dynamic living processes associated with inheritance? At the time Mendel's experiments were in progress, the general aspects of reproduction in animals and plants were known, but only crude notions of cells and their behavior in reproduction

164

were available.   Hence, Mendel could
not possibly have visualized his hereditary elements in their biological setting.
The basic principles of cytology were
established between 1865, when Mendel's
work was completed, and 1900, when it
was discovered.

Exciting discoveries of the last
quarter of the last century were the
mechanisms through which cells duplicate themselves and produce mature
gametes, mitosis and meiosis.   Complex organisms were found to arise from
single cells, develop to the adult stage,
and maintain themselves by cell division.
A human being, for example, arises from
a single fertilized cell or zygote that
develops eventually into an adult with a
million billion cells.   Biologists soon
became interested in structural parts and
later in the physiological and biochemical
properties of cells.   Although cells were
found to vary widely in structure and
function, they had some properties in
common and all represented units of living material.

All cells at some time during their
life cycle have a nucleus surrounded by
cytoplasm.   The nucleus is the most
constant part of the cell.   Its location
in the plant cell is determined to a large
extent by the position of the large central
vacuole.   Being more dense than the surrounding cytoplasm, the nucleus retains
its shape with comparative stability.   One
or more nucleoli may be present inside
the nucleus.   Other constituents, the
chromosomes, are visible during cell
division but cannot be seen as definitive
bodies while the cell is in the nondividing
or metabolic stage.   The cytoplasm and
its constituents are concerned with the
metabolic functions of the cell.   Food is
taken into the cell, some fractions are
released unused, some are converted into
energy, and some are assimilated into
the protoplasm of the cell itself.

Before Mendel's work was discovered interest had already developed in
locating the source of hereditary transmission.   Since sex cells, that is, eggs
and sperm, were known to be involved in
fertilization and both parents were known
ordinarily to transmit their characters to
their progeny, the first problem was to
determine which part of the cell was involved.   The German cytologist, Strasburger, observed that the egg carried
more cytoplasm than the sperm.   He
made reciprocal crosses (similar to
those made 100 years earlier by Kölreuter)

between different plant species that could
be crossed and found that the results of
the reciprocal crosses were similar.
Since the egg and sperm were unequal with
respect to size and amount of cytoplasm
carried, he suggested that the cytoplasm
was not responsible for hereditary differences between species.   Early experiments designed to explore this question in
animals were initiated by Boveri and continued by other cytologists.   It was shown
that the cytoplasm was not the carrier of
hereditary elements.

The Mendelian pattern of inheritance
requires that the genes be transmitted
from cell to cell in division.   How could
the genes behave in such a way that each
daughter cell receives all that is in the
parent cell, that is, becomes a complete
cell and not half a cell or only part of the
parent cell?   Wilhelm Roux (1850-1924)
speculated on this question and made
models to see how it could work.   The
only mechanism he could devise that
could accomplish the results was to line
up objects in a row and duplicate them
exactly.   He therefore suggested that the
significance of mitosis lies in the fact that
nuclei have strings of bead-like structures
which line up and duplicate themselves.
If nuclei really have such structures, he
reasoned, it might be possible to explain
the mechanics of gene transmission from
cell to cell.   The most likely constituents
of the nucleus to fill these requirements
were the chromosomes.   Boveri followed
this lead and was largely responsible for
developing the theory that genes are in
chromosomes.

Boveri and a young American, W. S.
Sutton (1876-1916), recognized a parallel-
ism between the behavior of chromosomes
and the Mendelian segregation of genes.
Genes, as judged by the end products, be-
haved as they would be expected to behave
in reproduction of the organism as well as
in cell division, if they were located in
chromosomes.   This led to a detailed
analysis of the process through which
higher organisms reproduce themselves.
Eggs and sperm in animals and comparable cells in plants that developed in the
sex glands and flower parts, respectively,
were known to be involved.   It was eventually shown beyond question that genes
are located in chromosomes.

Morgan and the Gene Theory

Thomas Hunt Morgan (1866-1945
Figure 17-3) made the next great contri-

bution to genetics through studies on the fruit fly of the genus Drosophila. His early investigations were in embryology and his first publication, The Development of the Frog's Egg, appeared in 1887.

Fig. 17-3. Thomas Hunt Morgan, American geneticist. "Reprinted with permission from Gardner, Principles of Genetics, 1960, John Wiley and Sons, Inc."

From this work along morphological lines he soon went over to the experimental attack on problems of development and became a leader in the rising school of experimental embryology. This led naturally into the field of regeneration with which he was occupied until 1901 when he published a book entitled Regeneration. Morgan next turned to a study of evolution from which he obtained empirical facts. He was an ardent believer in experimentation in whatever field he was working, and abhorred the term "speculation." In 1903, he published a book entitled, Evolution and Adaption.

Soon after the discovery of Mendelism, Morgan began genetic investigation, at first with mice and rats. In about 1909, he began his work on fruit flies of the genus, Drosophila. The adaptability of Drosophila to breeding experiments had been shown in the work of Castle, Moenkhaus, Lutz, and Payne, but it was Morgan's thorough investigation of this single species that provided much information in the field of genetics. At Columbia University, Morgan came in contact with E. B. Wilson another Professor of Experimental Zoology, who was interested in the cytological aspects of inheritance. The efforts of these two men were combined to make America the home of cytological-hereditary research.

Morgan gathered around him a group of students who have gone on to contribute extensively in the fields of cytology and genetics. Such men as C. B. Bridges, who has contributed much toward the mapping of the genes on the chromosomes of Drosophila, H. J. Muller, a leader in studies of mutations, A. H. Sturtevant who has carried on the work of Morgan in the analysis of the gene, and Curt Stern, who has contributed to the mechanics of heredity and variation. These men were greatly influenced by Morgan and they also influenced him.

The mutation theory initiated by de-Vries seemed, to Morgan, to provide a mechanism for the origin of species. Between the years 1909 and 1912, he and his associates discovered many mutations in Drosophila but found that mutations in themselves did not establish new species. Furthermore, mutations did not show a qualitative relation to the conditions under which they occurred, nor a tendency to be repeated.

In 1910, Morgan made 3 basic contributions: (1) he published an account of the first gene mutation observed in Drosophila (white eye); (2) through his studies on the inheritance of the white eye mutation, he proposed the explanation of sex-linked inheritance; and (3) he announced the gene theory of inheritance that included the principle of linkage and crossing over. Morgan was acquainted with advancements made in cytology up to that time and on the basis of the previous work done on chromosomes, he started, in 1910, to compile chromosome maps of Drosophila. This work was carried on by Bridges who located hundreds of genes on the 4 chromosomes of Drosophila, first from crossover data, and later from cytological data on the giant salivary gland chromosomes. In 1915, Morgan, Sturtevant, Bridges, and Muller published a book, The Mechanism of Mendelian Heredity, in which they summarized the progress that was made in 5 years of experimentation with Drosophila. This was an epoch making book in the field of genetics.

Morgan delivered a series of lectures at Princeton University in 1916 which was printed in book form under the title, Evolution and Genetics. In this book, Morgan summarized the evidence for evolution from the fields of comparative anatomy, embryology, paleontology, and genetics. He emphasized the genetic evidence that might explain the mechanism of heredity and variation. Smaller mutant variations were considered to be the small heritable variations that Darwin had visualized as furnishing the material basis for organic evolution. Morgan made it a point to distinguish these from non-inherited environmental variations which Darwin had not done. In reply to the objection that changes due to gene mutations are trivial and not significant in evolution, Morgan pointed out that minor superficial characters used by the geneticist and taxonomist may often be secondary results of changes that have invisible but more fundamental physiological effects on actual survival value. Also, genes for "useless" characteristics may be closely linked with those for "useful" ones. Systematists, of necessity, distinguish many species on the basis of characters that have played no part in the actual production of that species.

In 1928, Morgan brought the gene theory up to date in a book entitled: The Theory of the Gene. The characters of an individual were explained on the basis of paired elements (genes) in the germinal material. Genes were organized in a definite number of linkage groups corresponding with the number of chromosomes. Members of each pair of genes separate when the germ cells mature in accordance with Mendel's principle of segregation and in consequence each gamete (egg or sperm) contains one set (n) only. Members belonging to different linkage groups assort independently in accordance with Mendel's principle of independent assortment. An orderly interchange (crossing over) also takes place, between the elements in corresponding members of a linkage group. The frequencies of crossing over furnish evidence of the linear order of the genes in each linkage group and of the relative position of the elements with respect to each other.

Eugenics

Eugenics, the application of genetics to man, is concerned with the biological improvement of mankind. The eugenist is concerned with the problem of perpetuating the more desirable human qualities and improving the human germ plasm or at least maintaining the human stock at the present level. Such problems seem nebulous and insurmountable but the values of a program that would preserve the best human qualities for future generations are great enough to justify careful considera-

tion. Eugenics is a complex subject including along with its scientific aspects, fields outside science, such as social behavior and religion.

Sir Francis Galton (1822-1911 Figure 17-4) coined the word "eugenics" in 1883 to identify the science which deals with all influences that improve the inborn qualities of man and develop them to the upmost advantage. His early life was spent in a cultured home where the best possible opportunities for education and travel were provided. He was particularly gifted intellectually and was capable of independent thinking and original research. On the basis of his childhood development and later accomplishments, the psychologist Lewis M. Terman estimated his I.Q. at 200. His interests were broad, as indicated by the wide variety of scientific and cultural subjects covered in his 227 published works. Among his better known books on eugenics were Hereditary Genius (1869), Inquiries into Human Faculty (1883), Natural Inheritance (1889), and Essays on Eugenics (1909).

Perhaps Galton's greatest contribution to eugenics was the objective scientific treatment that he proposed and practiced. Eugenics was treated for the first time as a quantitative science. Mathematical tools were introduced for human studies and the new science of biometry was thus initiated. The concepts of probability, variability, frequency, mean, standard deviation, binomial series, and, correlation were used as tools to interpret data on mankind. Sampling techniques carried out with appropriate tests and measurements were devised to accumulate objective information. Such methods have made it possible to sift out the significant data from the hopeless jumble of old wives tales advanced over a period of many years. Human genetics thus became a quantitative science.

Some of Galton's specific contributions, however, have been discarded because they were based on unsound assumptions or concepts of heredity that are now obsolete. Galton did not distinguish clearly between genotype and phenotype. Furthermore, he assumed that desirable and undesirable phenotypes could be distinguished objectively. He also assumed that traits would always breed true and that infertility was largely a social consequence that could be mostly if not entirely overcome through enlightened

Fig. 17-4. Sir Francis Galton, English eugenist. "Reprinted with permission from Gardner, *Principles* of *Genetics*, 1960, John Wiley and Sons, Inc."

Unfortunately for the science of eugenics, ill founded plans for human betterment were promoted by some over-enthusiastic individuals and groups following the time of Galton, that were not based on adequate foundations of human genetics. Sterilization was proposed for sex offenders and habitual criminals on the assumption that these irregular forms of conduct were hereditary. This seems to have no scientific basis whatever. Unfortunately the term "eugenics" has been considered by many people to be synonomous with "sterilization." The Nazis in Germany killed and sterilized many who did not fit into the pattern of the master race that Hitler and his associates visualized. These and other premature developments caused, for a time, the whole eugenic movement to fall into disrepute. It is now emerging into better standing with the support of the Mendelian principles applied to man. There is still a long distance to be covered, however, before an objective basis for human improvement can be established. Eugenists recognize the inadequacies in the background of human genetics and make due allowance for them. Furthermore, they are contributing their share of the necessary objective data concerning the genetics of man.

public opinion. The more deep seated causes of infertility were unknown or at least unappreciated. Paradoxically, in spite of his persistent and energetic encouragement for the especially gifted members of the population to produce at least their share of children and thus perpetuate their genes in future generations, he died childless.

REFERENCES

Babcock, E. B. The Development of Fundamental Concepts in the Science of Genetics. *Portugaliae Acta Biologica Series.* 1949. Reprinted by American Genetics Association, Washington 5, D. C., 1950.

Bateson, W. *Mendel's Principles of Heredity.* Cambridge: The Univ. Press, 1909.

Dobzhansky, T. *Genetics and the Origin of Species.* 3rd ed. New York: Columbia Univ. Press, 1951.

Dunn, L. C. ed. *Genetics in the 20th Century.* (Chapter 3, The Knowledge of Heredity before 1900 by C. Zirkle; Chapter 4, The Beginnings of Mendelism in America by W. E. Castle.)

Coonen, L. P. Protogenetics from Adam to Athens. *Sci. Monthly.* 83:57-65, 1956.

Iltis, H. *Life of Mendel.* trans. Eden and C. Paul. New York: W. W. Norton and Co., 1932.

Iltis, H. A Visit to Mendel's Home. *J. Heredity* 38:163-166, 1947.

Jaffe, B. *Men of Science in America.* New York: Simon and Schuster, 1958. (Chapter 16 on Morgan.)

Mendel, G. *Experiments in Plant Hybridization.* Cambridge: Harvard Univ. Press, 1948. (Available in original German in Vol. 42, *J. of Heredity*.

Morgan, T. H. *The Theory of the Gene.* New Haven: Yale Univ. Press, 1926.

Muller, H. J. Genetic Principles in Human Populations. *Sci. Monthly* 83:277-286, 1956.

Peters, J. A. ed. *Classic Papers in Genetics.* Englewood Cliffs, N. J.: Prentice-Hall, Inc., 1959.

Punnett, R. C. Early Days of Genetics. *Heredity* 4:1-10, 1950.

Stern, C. ed. The Birth of Genetics. Suppl. *Genetics* 35, 1950. (English trans. of letters from Mendel to Nägeli and papers of de Vries, Correns, and Tschermak, the three men who discovered Mendel's paper in 1900.)

Stern, C. The Geneticist's Analysis of the Material and the Means of Evolution. *Sci. Monthly* 77:190-197, 1953.

Sturtevant, A. H. Thomas Hunt Morgan. *Amer. Nat.* 80:22-23, 1946.

Tschermak-Seysenegg, E. von The Rediscovery of Gregor Mendel's Work. *J. Heredity* 42:163-171, 1951.

Vries, H. de *The Mutation Theory.* Leipzig: Verlag von Veit and Corp., 1901.

Weismann, A. *The Germ-Plasm, A Theory of Heredity.* trans. W. N. Parker and H. Ronnfeldt. New York: Charles Scribner's Sons, 1893.

INDEX

174